Down the Wind

To: The friends I have made through sailing

DOWN THE WIND

A Yachtsman's Anthology
by Jack H Coote

Cover and Line Drawings by Trevor Ridley

Barnacle Marine Limited

First published 1966 by Hodder & Stoughton Ltd.

This edition published 1988 by Barnacle Marine Limited,
1 Crowhurst Road, Colchester, Essex, CO3 3JN

ISBN 0 948788 25 9

Printed and bound in Great Britain by
Richard Clay Ltd, Bungay, Suffolk

Introduction

M Y purpose in compiling an anthology for yachtsmen is easily explained. Sports such as cricket, football, golf and even motor-racing have anthologies galore, yet sailing has very few. Perhaps this difference is somehow related to the fact that sailing is not a sport for spectators. Whatever the reasons are, I think this may be a good time to offer a collection of material devoted to small-boat sailing.

I have made my selection with two groups of yachtsmen in mind. Firstly, and surely the more numerous, the thousands of newcomers to sailing who must be unaware of much of the literature on the subject that accumulated during the first half of the century. For them I have included excerpts from McMullen, Slocum, Belloc, Childers, and others of that remarkable group of early yachtsmen who could write as well as they could sail a boat.

Secondly, I was thinking of yachtsmen who read most of the many periodicals that nowadays are aimed at them and yet miss some of the good contemporary writing on sailing that can be found in sources that would normally escape their notice.

In between this old and new material, there is of course much good writing by yachtsmen such as Hammond Innes, Alfred Loomis, Weston Martyr, George Millar, Carleton Mitchell, Arthur Ransome, and others. From such abundance I have chosen largely to please myself, hoping that your taste and mine are not so very different; even gambling that you will laugh as readily as I do at Des Sleightholme's 'Old Harry'.

Since most people nowadays seem to agree with Alice in questioning the use of a book without pictures, I have included some specially drawn sketches by Trevor Ridley.

Jack H Coote

CONTENTS

Part I Sailing in fiction

Part II So much to learn

Part III Cruising in yachts

Part IV Racing in yachts

Part V Desperate moments

Part VI Boats sometimes leak

Part VII Short boards

Part I

SAILING IN FICTION

I yelled at Mike: 'The Aldis – quick!'
It was the starboard light of a big steamer, and it was bearing straight down
on us.

Hammond Innes: *The Mary Deare* 13

Gordon Rowbottom

THE ELAINE

THERE was quite a short paragraph about it in the paper: 'Yacht adrift in Channel. Search for crew abandoned.' It went on to say that a Dieppe fishing-boat had found the *Elaine*, a 10-ton gaff cutter, adrift off the French coast and had taken her into Le Havre. She had been sailing herself when found and there was no indication of what had happened. *Elaine*'s papers showed that she was on passage from the Beaulieu River to Le Havre with her owner, Leon Pavlides, and a Mr Frank Bretton on board. Two points of comment were the exceptionally fine spell of weather at the time and the fact that her small dinghy was lashed down as normal on deck. A footnote added that Leon Pavlides, a Greek subject, had served with the R.A.F. during the war and had been badly wounded and taken prisoner in 1943, and it mentioned the imposing string of decorations to his name. That was all. Fine weather of course suggests swimming, and they would not be the first two fools to take a dip together while their boat was becalmed and to see her sail away in a sudden puff of wind. It was not like Pavlides, but if no further trace was found of them that would probably remain the most likely explanation. But if it was . . . Eleven years is a long time, but . . . well, I wonder.

Eleven years ago, in the summer of the year after the end of the war, I was living at Burnham. One evening towards the end of September the telephone rang in my cottage and I got up to answer it in a very irritable frame of mind. It was the secretary of the club.

'Sorry to bother you,' he said, 'but I've got an Air Force fellow here wanting someone to help take his boat round to the Solent. Thought you might like a break.'

I chucked away my pencil, thanking providence for the interruption. My sister was away, staying with some friends in Cornwall, and without her the cottage seemed gloomy and lifeless. A three- or four-day spell was just what I wanted and I told the secretary so.

'That's fine, then. Come on down and meet him.'

My cottage was on the quayside only a few hundred yards from the club and I wandered down, looking at the boats in the river and wondering which one was his. As I turned up the steps the steward was just hauling down the northerly gale cone and I asked him what he thought of the weather.

'Blown itself out,' he said sourly. 'About time.'

The club was empty except for the few familiar figures in the smoke-room who did not bother to look up when I peered in on them. I found the secretary in the bar, sitting alongside a tall, dark-haired young man in a duffle coat.

'Wing Commander Pavlides,' he said. 'I think you two should get on well together.'

I hate that sort of introduction as a rule, but when Pavlides smilingly uncoiled himself from his stool to shake hands I soon forgot it in admiration for the man. I have always been susceptible to good looks of a certain rather effeminate kind in a man whom by no stretch of imagination could one think of as effeminate, and Pavlides was like that. His face was long and very fine, but it was his eyes that chiefly attracted me. They had a kind of olive warmth that seemed to suggest sun and soft brown earth and indolence. I felt at once that I would leave my work and sail with him to the corners of the world if he wanted me to, so that it was almost an anticlimax when he tossed back his drink and asked me to go with him as far as Cowes.

'There's nothing I should like better,' I told him truthfully, and felt like a small boy when he seemed pleased with my answer.

On the following morning he met me with the dinghy at the club hard. The wind had died during the night, and as we rowed out through the breaking dawn the water was still, and steaming with a ground haze that hid all but the tallest masts on the river. I put my gear below, and while Pavlides set about breakfast I had a good look round *Elaine*. There was no nonsense about her; gaff-rigged and straight-stemmed, she was built on solid, hardworking quay-punt lines and I was glad to see that her gear looked good and strong. Pavlides had told me that he had done most of the fitting out himself that summer when he came out of hospital. The mist was already beginning to clear when he called me below for breakfast, and an hour later, as *Elaine* swung to the first of the ebb, the sun came through with the promise of a perfect day.

There was no breeze yet on the water, but with the forecast of light north-easterly we decided to clear the Whittaker under power so as to get the full benefit of the wind when it came. The four-cylinder Ricardo started like a lamb, and it was without a thought beyond the usual pleasant sense of expectation that I cast off the mooring to begin what was to be, to say the least of it, a most disturbing cruise.

When all was clear below I came up to sit beside Pavlides in the cockpit. The sun was already strong in our faces as we cleared the Crouch and headed out north-east towards the Buxey buoy, and, with no wind but the breeze we made, it was hot enough to begin peeling off the outer layers of clothes. These first moments of a cruise with an unknown companion can so easily be spoilt by petty irritations at one another's ways, small things always, but indications of the troubles that so often lie ahead. I felt none of this and I do not think Pavlides did either. *Elaine* might have been mine for all the sense of ownership he showed and, for my part, I have seldom had such a feeling of easy contentment as during those first few hours while I sat lazing in the sunshine.

We drew the Buxey abeam and steered for the Whittaker light, just visible over the bowsprit. I asked Pavlides if he would go back to Greece one day.

'Probably,' he said, 'though I don't much care for what I hear of it now. I was born and brought up in Athens and my sister was there throughout the occupation. Perhaps you met her?'

I had not met his sister, but I knew Athens well and loved it more than any other city, so that I was happy to hear him talk of his childhood there.

We pushed on through the morning, revelling in the sun but longing for a breeze to break the monotony of the engine. Down through the Barrow Deep and the South Edinburgh channel, still under power. We ate a brief sandwich lunch in the cockpit, and through it all Pavlides talked, breaking off every now and then to identify the string of buoys that marked the channels. He had spent the last two years of the war in German hospitals after being shot down over France.

'It must have been the father and the mother of a crash from what they told me. I don't remember, but I know I owe a lot to those German surgeons.' As he spoke he pushed his cap to the back of his head in a way I had seen him do several times before. Then he took it off and ran his hand over his hair which was very long at the back. 'I got a bit of cockpit through my skull and they gave me a plate. It's a stupid thing,' he went on with a rather self-conscious laugh, 'but I always get the feeling that people can see it, though I know perfectly well they can't.'

He turned his head round for a moment and of course there was nothing to be seen, but I remembered that always up till then he had worn his cap. Even in the bar he had kept it on, and it was there I had first noticed the mannerism. I asked him if he was allowed to fly.

He shook his head. 'No, damn them, I'm not. You could get away with that sort of thing in the war, but not now — you know our medical boys. Nothing a German did was any good for them and they kept me nine whole months under observation with a bunch of lunatics, the theory being that no one could have a smack on the head like mine and remain completely sane. If you notice any eccentricity, put it down to them. We had every sort of crack-brain there and you've no idea how catching their ways can be.' His smile as he said that was the most natural thing in the world.

I knew of the place he had mentioned — a lovely old house in Dorset that was used as a rehabilitation centre for extreme cases of war neurosis — and the thought of him in such queer company made me laugh; for he looked the picture of normality as he sat there with a cigarette in his mouth and one leg crooked comfortably over the tiller.

Off the Knock John Tower a light breeze sprang up from the south-east and it was with an immense feeling of relief that we cut the motor and sailed peacefully on across the estuary towards the Foreland. At dusk we had the North Foreland abeam and, with the tide setting us down, we stood on close-hauled for Deal. Shortly after ten o'clock we dropped anchor off the remnants of the pier. A heavy swell made cooking an uncomfortable job, so that after only a hasty meal we turned in. I was tired, supremely contented with the day, and I slept well with the thought of at least two more days of good sailing before I had to return to my work.

The heavy day's motoring had eaten up most of the petrol and in the morning we took the dinghy ashore to fill up the cans. We breakfasted at the hotel to avoid losing any more time, but it was already mid-morning when we hove up our anchor and dropped down the coast to a light southerly breeze and the help of the tide. It was another glorious day, with a warm sun and a hint of wind in the sky. Pavlides was quieter, not talking much, and during my spells at the helm he lay stretched out on the cabin top, smoking and gazing up at the tranquil sky overhead. For the greater part of the day *Elaine* sailed herself with only an occasional touch on the tiller. It was slow progress, but the glare of the sun off the water brought a pleasant torpor and I was happy enough to keep her to myself for long spells.

Off Folkstone the breeze softened and we were held almost stationary by the flood until nightfall. We lit the navigation lamps and Pavlides took the helm while I knocked up a hot meal to warm us for the night. With the darkness came the breeze again, and at ten o'clock when I took over from Pavlides it was blowing fresh from the south-west. We went romping out to sea on the starboard tack with the coast lights growing dim behind us.

The wind freshened throughout the night and by six, when we changed watches, she was hard pressed under her full canvas. We took in the first reef before Pavlides went below, which eased her considerably, but the glass was falling and there was nothing attractive in the look of the dawn. It was depressing to find that the night's sailing and forty-five miles through the water had only brought us abeam of Fairlight. However, under her shortened canvas *Elaine* was sailing fast and easily, and I found that I could leave her to look after herself while I made everything movable below as secure as possible.

At half-past nine I called Pavlides on deck to have a look at the weather. The seas, which had increased greatly during the last three hours, were now showing signs of viciousness and we were getting a lot of water on board. The glass was still falling. We took the jib off her and set the storm jib; then, dropping the staysail, we close-reefed the main, leaving us ready for anything that might arise. For once there were no two ways to it. To run for shelter was out of the question; for Rye, the only harbour within reach, would be unnavigable until five o'clock. But with the wind steadied in the south-west we had sea room to ride out any normal gale and there was no great cause for anxiety.

At a quarter-past twelve the real force of the storm hit us and we hove-to about two miles to the south of the Royal Sovereign shoals. For an hour we stayed in the cockpit to see how she behaved, but with the jib a'weather and the helm lashed down *Elaine* lay-to steadily enough about four points off the wind. It was with a great sense of relief that I closed the hatch behind me and managed to drown some at least of the howling of the wind.

There is little comfort to be had below in a small boat riding out a gale of wind, but we lit the coal stove to dry our clothes and somehow managed to boil up some porridge, after which we both felt better. For all her smallness *Elaine's* saloon was roomy and cosy with the fire, and apart from frequent spells at the pump there was little that could be done during the rest of that day. We lay as best we could in our bunks, dozing, chatting, smoking. I had liked Pavlides before, but I liked him even better now. He was gentle and easy where so many men would have been irritable, and if he was ever anxious about the safety of his boat he kept it to himself. There was nothing we could do, but I wondered then if I would have taken it so calmly if *Elaine* had been mine.

At dusk we lit the navigation lights and set them in the boards.

The night was long and cold and evil. The seas, magnified no doubt by the darkness, reached mountainous proportions, and there were times during a lonely watch when I swore she could not live through it. The shriek of the wind was nerve-racking. It was impossible to sit in the small protection of the cockpit without being thrown constantly from one hard object to another, and yet with it all, the discomfort, the cold, the drenching spray, there was something stirring beyond words in the battle that was being fought out in the darkness. Each time the little boat rose to a towering wave I gripped the coaming, and held my breath as I slid with her down the crest into the appalling blackness of the trough. Nor was there much comfort in the watch below. Lashed into a heaving, straining bunk, infuriated by the ceaseless clanking of the galley pans, I tried to sleep, but for the most part lay awake interpreting the battle by the sounds it sent below.

Once I did fall into a restless doze, to be woken by the sense of something wrong. Pavlides was standing beside me, looking down, the top of his gleaming sou'wester illuminated by a sudden shaft of moonlight. He looked unreal and beastly as I saw him then, like some part of a dream, but he had moved before I came back to real consciousness and I closed my eyes again.

At last the night ended, as all nights must, and the watery dawn brought promise of relief.

Pavlides had the last watch. Now he came below to wake me. 'I've got a very rough fix on a couple of French lights,' he said. 'Let's have some coffee and I'll see if I can find them on the chart.'

I lit the primus while we pored over the chart.

'Here we are, about forty miles from Rye if I got the flashes right. Now what would you rather do, run for Rye, or carry on?'

'How's the weather?' I asked.

'The sea's gone down a bit and the glass is rising.' He grinned then and that decided me.

'Run for Rye,' I said. I wanted some sleep.

By eight o'clock, after a sketchy meal, we were under way, with a big cross sea that called for careful steering. At noon we sighted Beachy Head on our weather bow and, shortly after, the familiar line of Fairlight cliffs hove into view. The seas were dropping as quickly as they had risen, while the wind, shifting into the north, constantly threatened to head us, but we stuck to our course for Rye. At half-past seven in the half light, we slid between the breakwaters under power to tie up to the piles along the wooden pier on the eastern bank.

'To hell with everything!' Pavlides said. 'We're going ashore.'

There is a pleasant restfulness about Rye harbour that makes it a perfect haven from a storm. The warm hospitality of the fishermen ashore was in keeping with this atmosphere, and it was with an agreeable sense of happiness that we said our last good-nights and rowed back to *Elaine*. With our warps made fast to the vertical piles and the mast-head secured by a double block on the pole halyards we felt that we could safely leave her to ride the rise and fall of the tide while we slept the clock round. I stretched out my tired limbs, and fell instantly asleep.

It seemed only a moment later that I was roused to semi-consciousness by a violent lurch that threw me against the side of the ship. With my mind still wandering at sea I grabbed for an imaginary tiller with one hand, and with the other reached forward to fend off Pavlides who had fallen in a heap across my bunk. Possibly I was still half asleep, I do not know, but there was a sound coming from him, like the snapping of a dog's teeth, that made my flesh creep. When I pushed at his face he caught my arm and the next moment his hands on my throat shook off the last faint spell of unreality and I was fully awake, fighting to throw off the grip that roared in my ears like breaking seas. With my fingers tearing for a hold in his hair I threw his head hard against the planking at my side and the grip on my throat relaxed. The effort of it had exhausted me and I could do no more than lie back helplessly while our strangled breathing seemed to fill the small cabin with noise. The ship lurched again, fully on to her side, flinging him down on me again, but he recovered quickly and shrank back into his corner.

There was no sleep for me that night. *Elaine* was lying over on her beam ends down the bank with water rippling along the side of the coach-roof. There were many things we could have done to ensure her floating to the flood tide but nothing was done. Pavlides was evidently exhausted past caring, and I was watchful and quite sick with fright. Not for one moment during that cold, cramped night did I take my eyes from him. We lay as we had fallen, crouched on opposite sides of the bunk, our backs soaked by the bilge water covering the planking on which we sat.

By five o'clock the water was lapping once more around the deck. She bumped an inch or two and then began to rise unaided. At dawn we were back on an even keel.

For the last hour or so Pavlides had slept. The movement of the boat against the piles woke him now and he yawned and stretched himself before sinking back on to the untidy heap of his own bunk. His voice when he spoke was low but it sounded natural enough. 'Something happened in the night; that masthead rope must have snapped.' I did not say anything and he went on, 'I had a horrible dream. I'm afraid I might have frightened you.'

'Frightened me!' I exclaimed. 'You damned nearly killed me!' And for the life of me I could not keep a tremor from my voice.

He looked at me in an odd sort of way and went over to the galley. The floor was in an unholy mess with bilge water and smashed crockery and he began to tidy it up. Presently I saw the methylated flare in the primus cup. 'I'll get you some breakfast first,' he said quietly, 'and then we'll see about a train.'

He was standing in the cabin door as he said that and in the unflattering early morning light his face looked ghastly.

'Are you going to leave her here?' I asked.

'No, I've got to get round to Cowes. For one thing I've arranged to meet some friends there, and for another . . . well, I think I'd prefer to push on.'

'You'll take her by yourself?'

'Yes.'

Somehow it all seemed so far away then. There was the shambles of the cabin to remind me of the night, but against that was the sight of this apparently normal and very likeable young man in trouble that, God knows, was not of his own making. He had been shot down, as my own brother had been, and only a miracle of surgery had kept him alive. He was a sick man, not a lunatic.

'Look,' I said, 'tell me really what happened in that place of yours. Why did they keep you under observation all that time?'

He did not say anything for a long time. I watched him get the primus alight and put a saucepan on for coffee. When the cabin floor was clear of all the debris he sat down on the bunk and pushed his cap to the back of his head in that nervous way of his. 'I don't know exactly, except that it's this damned plate. I got a knock on it and had a sort of blackout. They never told me what happened. I think I must have hit it again last night when we went over.'

What was more likely than that? I grinned, and he tossed me over a cigarette.

'Do you mean you'll stay?'

'Yes,' I said.

We were tired, but I doubt if either of us could have slept that day. Instead we breakfasted and then set to repair the other ravages of the night. By nine o'clock we were clear of Rye harbour and heading across Fairlight on the final leg to the Solent. The wind at last was fair for us, a good sailing breeze from the north-east, with the sun hot enough to warm bare arms and legs.

Off Newhaven the breeze dropped to a whisper and we lay becalmed in a glassy sea for the three hours until dusk, when a light offshore breeze sped us on our course once more for Nab Tower. The twinkling lights of Newhaven dropped astern and in the distance we could see the reflection of the glare that was Brighton. We altered course off Brighton, and with the wind again in the north-east *Elaine* swam through the water at a steady six knots, rolling easily to the small following sea.

There was magic in that night. A full moon and a bright canopy of stars lit us on our way. From her bows came shimmering lines of phosphorescence that fanned out and died astern like the twinkle of falling tracer. Pavlides went out of his way to be an entertaining companion and it was from no sense of uneasiness that I gave up my watch below to enjoy the perfection of such a night. We talked for hours of his Athens. He had a fine tenor voice and together we sang her haunting melodies that I had come to love so much. The time passed all too quickly, and for once there was little pleasure in the dawn that revealed the beauty of the Solent shores. It was with a feeling of regret that I watched the Forts slide by us as we took the inshore channel up to Cowes. At half-past seven we picked up a mooring in the Medina River, off the Island Sailing Club.

If the trip had ended there, on that sunny morning at Cowes, the memories of pleasant sailing hours would have remained for ever and I could soon have laughed away the horror of the night. But Pavlides persuaded me to stay on for another day. We had finished breakfast and I was throwing my things into a bag when he came below.

'Don't do that,' he said. 'You've had a rotten trip. It's much too good a day for a train journey and there are some people I'd like you to meet.'

'I must get back in case Anne arrives.' Anne is my sister.

'Please,' he smiled. 'You can send her a wire.'

I hesitated, and was lost. Of course I wanted to stay. The sun was pouring through the open hatch and there was no pleasure in the thought of the long journey home.

He laughed when he saw my indecision. 'Write out the wire and I'll telephone it through from the club.'

For a while after he had come back we worked lazily on deck at the hundred and one things that wanted seeing to – washing down, coiling warps, drying and stowing sails still wet from the night dew. Then we took our mattresses and lay dozing in the sun until late afternoon when it was time to shave and dress for going ashore.

Cowes in the off-season can be a melancholy spot, and at first when we left the dinghy to make our way up through the empty streets I began to wish I had not been so indecisive in the morning. I felt liverish and sour from sleeping in the sun and the thought of dragging round the town all night appalled me. I need not have worried. Pavlides was well known there, and within an hour of going ashore he had laid the foundations of a most memorable evening.

Hitherto I had only seen him on his own and had fallen an easy enough victim to his charm of manner. Now, when I saw him in a crowd, my admiration for him knew no bounds. There was a curious magnetism about the man that seemed to make him at once the centre of attraction in any room; he was the hub round which the spirits of a party revolved. I have seen a Greek woman change the atmosphere of a room in a moment from the deepest depression to a pinnacle of laughter and high spirits by her mere presence, and Pavlides had the same gift. For some reason that night he wore uniform. Looking at him across the room, the double row of ribbons on his chest, his hair dark and glistening at the back where he put his hand repeatedly to smooth it down, one would have been hard put to it to think that under that plate was anything but the most normal, active brain; and if some memory of that other night returned I have no doubt I was able to thrust it quickly away.

Most of the people we met that night were his close friends and many of them knew Greece, but he seemed to single me out from the crowd around him as if I was the only one who mattered. Under his skilful guidance I crept for the first time in two years from the shell beneath which I had been hiding and, swept on by the intoxication of this blessed release, my memories of the latter half of the night are dim.

I can remember brightly-lit rooms and laughter and music; a piano, and Pavlides singing us his native songs which rise to one's head more startlingly than any wine; rowing back across the moonlit harbour; slumping fully dressed into my bunk aboard *Elaine*, and my last glimpse of Pavlides, smoothing his hair back in a mirror while he hummed to himself another of those lovely songs.

The habits of wartime are not easily cast off, and I woke suddenly to an instinctive sense of being watched. Soft bands of moonlight were playing through the open hatch and in their eerie light I saw Pavlides. He looked as he had looked that night at sea, ill and old and evil, and as I stared at him my mouth grew dry and hot with fright. His hands were locked behind his head as if like that he could hold back the horror that he knew was there. There was a conflict in his face so awful that I swung my legs down from the bunk and tried to speak to him, though no sound came. His face was close enough to mine to feel his breath.

'Get out,' he said.

I backed away from him, feeling for the hatchway steps, and he came after me. His mouth was trembling with the effort of control and I saw his lips trying to form words. They were hard, those hatchway steps; for he was always there below me, but suddenly I felt the cool night air and, for a moment, hesitated.

'Get out!' he said again. 'GET OUT!'

As I stumbled through the cockpit he was behind me. In his hands, now pushing and now pulling at my throat, I seemed to feel the struggle of all the horror that was in him and the fear of it was like ice. The dinghy was there on its long painter, but before I could reach down for it I felt myself lifted and the next moment the water closed mercifully about my head. When I came to the surface the tide had drifted me against the dinghy. The moon was high above *Elaine*. As I hung there for a moment in a daze of water and spent breath I saw Pavlides leaning out over the counter and I think he saw me too, for the dinghy tore from my fingers as he grabbed at the painter. The spell of that evil, watching figure was so great that I let the current take me far down from *Elaine* before turning my back on him and swimming for the shore.

For the rest of the night I walked the streets of Cowes in my sodden clothes. I knew I could have found a bed at the club, but I had no coherent story to tell and I wanted time to think out the nightmare of the last few days. Dawn came and brought no answer. At last, I went into the deserted Fountain Hotel and told some rambling story to the porter. I took a room and bathed while my clothes were dried, and then caught the early train to Ryde for the ferry over to the mainland.

On the next day I had a letter from Pavlides saying that he was sending off my case. He made no reference to the night at

Cowes, but at the foot of the page he had written in green ink: 'I'm going down to Dorset to stay with some old friends whom you said you knew. I'm sure everything is going to be all right.' It was a perfectly normal letter and in answer to it I did what I think most people would have done in my place—nothing. I never saw or heard of him again until today.

The paper was still there, open on my desk to show the paragraph, and I read it carefully again. Almost without thinking I turned out the light and went over to the window and looked out. The moon made a clear path across the water and in its light I saw the cold, dark surface of the water. I shivered then, and quickly drew the blind.

Hammond Innes

THE WRECK

In this passage from his book Harvest of Journeys, *Hammond Innes relates how he came to the idea that led to his writing 'The Mary Deare'.*

'But at night a fog at sea is different. It can creep up on you unawares. I remember lying-to one night off Cherbourg, waiting for dawn in order to get into the little fishing port of Omonville-la-Rogue. It was around two in the morning. It was dark and cold, not much wind and a lumpy sea. I was at the helm when suddenly my companion gripped my arm. "What's that?" he cried, pointing astern. I looked over my shoulder and all behind us was a green translucence as though some phosphorous-coated monster were emerging from the depths.

'And then it seemed to gather itself together, hardening abruptly into a point of light, and I yelled to him to get the signalling lamp. It was the starboard navigation light of a steamer seen through thick fog, and it was very close. I put the boat about, and when I looked again, there was a big passenger ship lying stopped, with all her lights blazing, not a hundred yards astern of us. The sequel proved more satisfactory than the experience, for the fact that I had so nearly been run down gave me the opening for a book about the sea that I had been wanting to write for a long time.'

I WAS tired and very cold; a little scared, too. The red and green navigation lights cast a weird glow over the sails. Beyond was nothing, a void of utter darkness in which the sea made little rushing noises. I eased my cramped legs, sucking on a piece of barley sugar. Above me the sails swung in a ghostly arc, slatting back and forth as *Sea Witch* rolled and plunged. There was scarcely wind enough to move the boat through the water, yet the swell kicked up by the March gales ran as strong as ever and my numbed brain was conscious all the time that this was only a lull. The weather forecast at six o'clock had been ominous. Winds of gale force were reported imminent in sea areas Rock-all, Shannon, Sole and Finisterre. Beyond the binnacle light the shadowy outline of the boat stretched ahead of me, merging into the clammy blackness of the night. I had dreamed of this moment so often. But it was March and now, after fifteen hours at sea in the Channel, the excitement of owning our own boat was gone, eaten up by the cold. The glimmer of a breaking wave appeared out of the darkness and slapped against the counter, flinging spray in my face and sidling off into the blackness astern with a hiss of white water. God! It was cold! Cold and clammy —and not a star anywhere.

The door of the charthouse slammed back to give me a glimpse of the lit saloon and against it loomed Mike Duncan's oilskin-padded bulk, holding a steaming mug in either hand. The door slammed to again, shutting out the lit world below, and the darkness and the sea crowded in again. 'Soup?' Mike's cheerful, freckled face appeared abruptly out of the night, hanging disembodied in the light from the binnacle. He smiled at me from the folds of his balaclava as he handed me a mug. 'Nice and fresh up here after the galley,' he said. And then the smile was wiped from his face. 'What the hell's that?' He was staring past my left shoulder, staring at something astern of us on the port quarter. 'Can't be the moon, can it?'

I swung round. A cold, green translucence showed at the edge of visibility, a sort of spectral light that made me catch my breath in sudden panic with all the old seamen's tales of weird and frightful things seen at sea rushing through my mind.

The light grew steadily brighter, phosphorescent and unearthly —a ghastly brilliance like a bloated glow-worm. And then suddenly it condensed and hardened into a green pin-point and I yelled at Mike: 'The Aldis —quick!' It was the starboard navigation light of a big steamer, and it was bearing straight down on us. Her deck lights were appearing now, misted and yellow; and gently, like the muffled beat of a tom-tom, the sound of her engines reached out to us in a low, pulsating throb.

The beam of the Aldis lamp stabbed the night, blinding us with the reflected glare from a thick blanket of mist that engulfed us. It was a sea mist that had crept up on me in the dark without my knowing it. The white of a bow wave showed dimly in the brilliance, and then the shadowy outline of the bows themselves took shape. In an instant I could see the whole forward half of the ship. It was like a ghost ship emerging out of the mist, and the blunt bows were already towering over us as I swung the wheel.

It seemed an age that I watched *Sea Witch* turn, waiting for the jib to fill on the other tack and bring her head round, and all the time I could hear the surge of that bow wave coming nearer. 'She's going to hit us! Christ! She's going to hit us!' I can still hear Mike's cry, high and strident in the night. He was blinking the Aldis, directing the beam straight at her bridge. The whole superstructure was lit up, the light reflecting back in flashes from the glass windows. And the towering mass of the steamer kept on coming, thundering down on us at a good eight knots without a check, without any alteration of course.

The main and mizzen booms swung over with a crash. The

jib was aback now. I left it like that for a moment, watching her head pay off. Every detail of *Sea Witch*, from the tip of her long bowsprit to the top of her mainmast, was lit by the green glow of the steamer's starboard light now high above us. I let go the port jib sheet, hauling in on the starboard sheet, saw the sail fill, and then Mike screamed, 'Look out! Hold on!' There was a great roaring sound and a wall of white water hit us. It swept over the cockpit, lifting me out of my seat, tugging at my grip on the wheel. The sails swung in a crazy arc; they swung so far that the boom and part of the mainsail were buried for a moment in the back of a wave whilst tons of water spilled across our decks; and close alongside the steamer slid by like a cliff.

Slowly *Sea Witch* righted herself as the water poured off her in a white foam. I still had hold of the wheel and Mike was clutching the backstay runner, shouting obscenities at the top of his voice. His words came to me as a frail sound against the solid thumping of the ship's engines. And then another sound emerged out of the night — the steady thrashing of a propeller partly clear of the water.

I shouted to Mike, but he had already realised the danger and had switched the Aldis on again. Its brilliant light showed us plates pitted deep with rust and a weed-grown Plimsoll mark high above the water. Then the plates curved up to the stern and we could see the propeller blades slashing at the waves, thumping the water into a swirling froth. *Sea Witch* trembled, sails slack. Then she slid off the back of a wave into that mill race and the blades were whirling close along our port side, churning white water over the cabin top, flinging it up into the mainsail.

It was like that for a moment and then they flailed off into the darkness beyond the bowsprit and we were left pitching in the broken water of the ship's wake. The Aldis beam picked out her name — *Mary Deare* — Southampton. We stared dazedly at her rust-streaked lettering while the stern became shadowy and then vanished abruptly. Only the beat of her engines remained then, throbbing gently and gradually dying away into the night. A faint smell of burning lingered on for a while in the damp air. 'Bastards!' Mike shouted, suddenly finding his voice. 'Bastards!' He kept on repeating the word.

The door of the charthouse slid back, and a figure emerged. It was Hal. 'Are you boys all right?' His voice — a little too calm, a little too cheerful — shook slightly.

'Didn't you see what happened?' Mike cried.

'Yes, I saw,' he replied.

'They must have seen us. I was shining the Aldis straight at the bridge. If they'd been keeping a lookout —'

'I don't think they were keeping a lookout. In fact, I don't think there was anybody on the bridge.' It was said so quietly that for a moment I didn't realise the implication.

'How do you mean—nobody on the bridge?' I asked.

He came out on to the deck then. 'It was just before the bow wave hit us. I knew something was wrong and I'd got as far as the charthouse. I found myself looking out through the window along the beam of the Aldis lamp. It was shining right on to the bridge. I don't think there was anybody there. I couldn't see anybody.'

'But good God!' I said. 'Do you realise what you're saying?'

'Yes, of course, I do.' His tone was peremptory, a little military. 'It's odd, isn't it?'

He wasn't the sort of man to make up a thing like that. H. A. Lowden—Hal to all his friends—was an ex-Gunner, a Colonel retired, who spent most of the summer months ocean racing. He had a lot of experience of the sea.

'Do you mean to say you think there was nobody in control of that ship?' Mike's tone was incredulous.

'I don't know,' Hal answered. 'It seems incredible. But all I can say is that I had a clear view of the interior of the bridge for an instant and, as far as I could see, there was nobody there.'

We didn't say anything for a moment. I think we were all too astonished. The idea of a big ship ploughing her way through the rock-infested seas so close to the French coast without anybody at the helm . . . It was absurd.

Mike's voice, suddenly practical, broke the silence. 'What happened to those mugs of soup?' The beam of the Aldis lamp clicked on, revealing the mugs lying in a foot of water at the bottom of the cockpit. 'I'd better go and make another brew.' And then to Hal who was standing, half-dressed, his body braced against the charthouse: 'What about you, Colonel? You'd like some soup, wouldn't you?'

Hal nodded. 'I never refuse an offer of soup.' He watched Mike until he had gone below and then he turned to me. 'I don't mind admitting it now that we're alone,' he said, 'but that was a very unpleasant moment. How did we come to be right across her bows like that?'

I explained that the ship had been down-wind from us and we hadn't heard the beat of her engines. 'The first we saw of her was the green of her starboard navigation light coming at us out of the mist.'

'No fog signal?'

'We didn't hear it, anyway.'

'Odd!' He stood for a moment, his long body outlined against the port light, and then he came aft and seated himself beside me on the cockpit coaming. 'Had a look at the barometer during your watch?' he asked.

'No,' I said. 'What's it doing?'

'Going down.' He had his long arms wrapped round his body, hugging his seaman's jersey. 'Dropped quite a bit since I went below.' He hesitated and then said, 'You know, this gale could come up on us pretty quickly.' I didn't say anything and he pulled his pipe out and began to suck on it. 'I tell you frankly, John, I don't like it.' The quietness of his voice added strength to his opinion. 'If the forecast turns out right and the wind backs north-westerly, then we'll be on a lee shore. I don't like gales and I don't like lee shores, particularly when the lee shore is the Channel Islands.'

I thought he wanted me to put back to the French coast and I didn't say anything; just sat there staring at the compass card, feeling obstinate and a little scared.

'It's a pity about the kicker,' he murmured. 'If the kicker hadn't packed up —'

'Why bring that up?' It was the only thing that had gone wrong with the boat. 'You've always said you despise engines.'

His blue eyes, caught in the light of the binnacle, stared at me fixedly. 'I was only going to say,' he put in mildly, 'that if the kicker hadn't packed up we'd be halfway across the Channel by now and the situation would be entirely different.'

'Well, I'm not putting back.'

He took his pipe out of his mouth as though to say something and then put it back and sat there, staring at me with those unwinking blue eyes of his.

'The real trouble is that you're not used to sailing in a boat that hasn't been kept up to ocean racing pitch.' I hadn't meant to say that, but I was angry and my nerves were still tense from the steamer incident.

An awkward silence fell between us. At length he stopped sucking on his pipe. 'It's only that I like to arrive,' he said quietly. 'The rigging is rusty, the ropes rotten and the sails —'

'We went over all that in Morlaix,' I said tersely. 'Plenty of yachts cross the Channel in worse shape than *Sea Witch*.'

'Not in March with a gale warning. And not without an engine.' He got up and went for'ard as far as the mast, bending down and hauling at something. There was the sound of splintering wood and then he came back and tossed a section of the bulwarks into the cockpit at my feet. 'The bow wave did that.' He sat down beside me again. 'It isn't good enough, John. The boat hasn't been surveyed and for all you know the hull may be as rotten as the gear after lying for two years on a French mud bank.'

'The hull's all right,' I told him. I was calmer now. 'There are a couple of planks to be replaced and she needs restopping. But that's all. I went over every inch of her with a knife before I bought her. The wood is absolutely sound.'

'And what about the fastenings?' His right eyebrow lifted slightly. 'Only a surveyor could tell you whether the fastenings —'

'I told you, I'm having her surveyed as soon as we reach Lymington.'

'Yes, but that doesn't help us now. If this gale comes up on us suddenly . . . I'm a prudent mariner,' he added. 'I like the sea, but it's not a creature I want to take liberties with.'

'Well, I can't afford to be prudent,' I said. 'Not right now.' Mike and I had just formed a small salvage company and every day we delayed getting the boat to England for conversion was a day lost out of our diving season. He knew that.

'I'm only suggesting you steer a point off your direct course,' he said. 'Close-hauled we can just about lay for Hanois on Guernsey Island. We'll then be in a position to take advantage of the wind when it backs and run for shelter to Peter Port.'

Of course . . . I rubbed my hand over my eyes. I should have known what he was driving at. But I was tired and the steamer incident had left me badly shaken. It was queer the way the vessel had sailed right through us like that.

'It won't help your salvage venture if you smash the boat up.' Hal's voice cut across my thoughts. He had taken my silence for refusal. 'Apart from the gear, we're not very strongly crewed.'

That was true enough. There were only the three of us. The fourth member of the crew, Ian Baird, had been sea-sick from the time we had left Morlaix. And she was a biggish boat for three to handle—a forty-tonner. 'Very well,' I said. 'We'll head for Guernsey.'

He nodded as though he'd known it all along. 'You'll need to steer North 65° East then.'

I turned the wheel, giving her starboard helm, and watched the compass card swing to the new course. He must have been working out the course in the charthouse just before the steamer came up on us. 'I take it you worked out the distance, too?'

'Fifty-four miles. And at this rate,' he added, 'it'll be daylight long before we get there.'

An uneasy silence settled between us. I could hear him sucking at his empty pipe, but I kept my eyes on the compass and didn't look at him. Damn it, I should have thought of Peter Port for myself! But there'd been so much to do at Morlaix getting the boat ready . . . I'd just about worked myself to a standstill before ever we put to sea.

'That ship.' His voice came out of the darkness at my side, a little hesitant, bridging the gap of my silence. 'Damned queer,' he murmured. 'You know, if there really was nobody on board . . .' He checked and then added, half-jokingly, 'That would have been a piece of salvage that would have set you up for life.' I thought I sensed a serious note underlying his words, but when I glanced at him he shrugged his shoulders and laughed. 'Well, I think I'll turn in again now.' He got up and his 'good-night' floated back to me from the dark gap of the charthouse.

Shortly afterwards Mike brought me a mug of hot soup. He stayed and talked to me whilst I drank it, speculating wildly about the *Mary Deare*. Then he, too, turned in and the blackness of the night closed round me. Could there really have been nobody on the bridge? It was too fantastic—an empty ship driving pell-mell up the Channel. And yet, cold and alone, with the pale glimmer of the sails swooping above me and the dismal dripping of mist condensed on the canvas, anything seemed possible.

At three Hal relieved me and for two hours I slept, dreaming of blunt, rusted bows hanging over us, toppling slowly, everlastingly. I woke in a panic, cold with sweat, and lay for a moment thinking about what Hal had said. It would be queer if we salvaged a ship, just like that, before we'd even . . . But I was asleep again before the idea had more than flickered through my mind. And in an instant I was being shaken and was stumbling out to the helm in the brain-numbing hour before the dawn, all recollection of the *Mary Deare* blurred and hazed by the bitter cold.

Daylight came slowly, a reluctant dawn that showed a drab, sullen sea heaving gently, the steepness flattened out of the swell. The wind was northerly now, but still light; and some time during the night we had gone over on to the other tack.

At ten to seven Hal and I were in the charthouse for the weather report. It started with gale warnings for the western approaches of the Channel; the forecast for our own area of Portland was: *Wind light, northerly at first, backing north-westerly later and increasing strong to gale.* Hal glanced at me, but said nothing. There was no need. I checked our position and then gave Mike the course to steer for Peter Port.

It was a queer morning. There was a lot of scud about and by the time we had finished breakfast it was moving across the sky quite fast. Yet at sea level there was scarcely any wind so that, with full main and mizzen set and the big yankee jib, we were creeping through the water at a bare three knots, rolling sluggishly. There was still a mist of sorts and visibility wasn't much more than two miles.

We didn't talk much. I think we were all three of us too conscious of the sea's menace. Peter Port was still thirty miles away. The silence and the lack of wind was oppressive. 'I'll go and check our position again,' I said. Hal nodded as though the thought had been in his mind, too.

But pouring over the chart didn't help. As far as I could tell we were six miles north-north-west of the Roches Douvres, that huddle of rocks and submerged reefs that is the western outpost of the Channel Islands. But I couldn't be certain; my dead reckoning depended too much on tide and leeway.

And then Mike knocked the bottom out of my calculations. 'There's a rock about two points on the starboard bow,' he called to me. 'A big one sticking up out of the water.'

I grabbed the glasses and flung out of the charthouse. 'Where?' My mouth was suddenly harsh and dry. If it were the Roches Douvres, then we must have been set down a good deal farther than I thought. And it couldn't be anything else; it was all open sea between Roches Douvres and Guernsey. 'Where?' I repeated.

'Over there!' Mike was pointing.

I screwed up my eyes. But I couldn't see anything. The clouds had thinned momentarily and a queer sun-glow was reflected on the oily surface of the sea, merging it with the moisture-laden atmosphere. There was no horizon; at the edge of visibility sea and air became one. I searched through the glasses. 'I can't see it,' I said. 'How far away?'

'I don't know. I've lost it now. But it wasn't more than a mile.'

'You're sure it was a rock?'

'Yes, I think so. What else could it be?' He was staring into the distance, his eyes narrowed against the luminous glare of the haze. 'It was a big rock with some sort of tower or pinnacle in the middle of it.'

The Roches Douvres light! I glanced at Hal seated behind the wheel. 'We'd better alter course,' I said. 'The tide is setting us down at about two knots.' My voice sounded tense. If it was the Roches Douvres and the wind fell any lighter, we could be swept right down on to the reef.

He nodded and swung the wheel. 'That would put you out by five miles in your dead reckoning.'

'Yes.'

He frowned. He had taken his sou'wester off and his grey hair, standing on end, gave his face a surprised, puckish look. 'I think you're underrating yourself as a navigator, but you're the boss. How much do you want me to bear up?'

'Two points at least.'

'There's an old saying,' he murmured: 'The prudent mariner, when in doubt, should assume his dead reckoning to be correct.' He looked at me with a quizzical lift to his bushy eyebrows. 'We don't want to miss Guernsey, you know.'

A mood of indecision took hold of me. Maybe it was just the strain of the long night, but I wasn't sure what to do for the best. 'Did you see it?' I asked him.

'No.'

I turned to Mike and asked him again whether he was sure it was rock he'd seen.

'You can't be sure of anything in this light.'

'But you definitely saw something?'

'Yes. I'm certain of that. And I think it had some sort of a tower on it.'

A gleam of watery sunlight filtered through the damp atmosphere, giving a furtive brightness to the cockpit. 'Then it must be the Roches Douvres,' I murmured.

'Look!' Mike cried. 'There it is—over there.'

I followed the line of his outstretched arm. On the edge of visibility, lit by the sun's pale gleam, was the outline of a flattish rock with a light tower in the middle. I had the glasses on it immediately, but it was no more than a vague, misty shape — a redish tint glimmering through the golden haze. I dived into the charthouse and snatched up the chart, staring at the shape of the Roches Douvres reef. It marked drying rock outcrops for a full mile north-west of the ninety-two-foot light tower. We must be right on the fringe of those outcrops. 'Steer north,' I shouted to Hal, 'and sail her clear just as fast as you can.'

'Aye, aye, skipper.' He swung the wheel, calling to Mike to trim the sheets. He was looking over his shoulder at the Roches Douvres light as I came out of the charthouse. 'You know,' he said, 'there's something odd here. I've never actually seen the Roches Douvres, but I know the Channel Islands pretty well and I've never seen any rock that showed up red like that.'

I steadied myself against the charthouse and focused the glasses on it again. The gleam of sunlight had become more positive. Visibility was improving all the time. I saw it clearly then and I was almost laughing with relief. 'It's not a rock,' I said. 'It's a ship.' There was no doubt about it now. The rusty hull was no longer blurred, but stood out clear and sharp, and what I had taken to be a light tower was its single funnel.

We were all of us laughing with the sense of relief as we turned back on to the course. 'Hove-to by the look of it,' Mike said as he stopped hauling in on the main-sheet and began to coil it down.

It certainly looked like it, for now that we were back on course her position didn't seem to have altered at all. She was lying broadside on to us as though held there by the wind and, as we closed with her and her outline became clearer, I could see that she was stationary, wallowing in the swell. Our course would leave her about half a mile to starboard. I reached for the glasses. There was something about the ship . . . something about her shape and her rusty hull and the way she seemed a little down at the bows.

'Probably pumping out her bilges,' Hal said, his voice hesitant as though he, too, were puzzled.

I focused the glasses and the outline of the vessel leaped towards me. She was an old boat with straight bows and a clean sweep to her sheer. She had an old-fashioned counter stern, an untidy clutter of derricks round her masts, and too much superstructure. Her single smoke stack, like her masts, was almost vertical. At one time she had been painted black, but now she had a rusty, uncared-for look. There was a sort of lifelessness about her that held me with the glasses to my eyes. And then I saw the lifeboat. 'Steer straight for her, will you, Hal,' I said.

'Anything wrong?' he asked, reacting immediately to the note of urgency in my voice.

'Yes. One of the lifeboats is hanging vertically from its davits.' It was more than that. The other davits were empty.

I passed him the glasses. 'Take a look at the for'ard davits,' I told him and my voice trembled slightly, the birth of a strange feeling of excitement.

Soon we could see the empty davits with the naked eye and the single lifeboat hanging from the falls. 'Looks deserted,' Mike said. 'And she's quite a bit down by the bows. Do you think —' He left the sentence unfinished. The same thought was in all our minds.

We came down on her amidships. The name at her bows was so broke up with rust streaks that we couldn't read it. Close-to she looked in wretched shape. Her rusty bow plates were out of true, her superstructure was damaged and she was definitely down by the bows, her stern standing high so that we could see the top of her screw. A festoon of wires hung from her mast derricks. She was a cargo ship and she looked as though she'd taken a hell of a hammering.

We went about within a cable's length of her and I hailed her through our megaphone. My voice lost itself in the silence of the sea. There was no answer. The only sound was the sloshing of the swell against her sides. We ran down on her quickly then, Hal steering to pass close under her stern. I think we were all of us watching for her name. And then suddenly there it was in rust-streaked lettering high above our heads, just as it had been during the night: '*Mary Deare* —Southampton'.

She was quite a big boat, at least 6,000 tons. Abandoned like that she should have had a salvage tug in attendance, ships standing by. But there wasn't another vessel in sight. She was alone and lifeless within twenty miles of the French coast. I glanced up along her starboard side as we came out from under her stern. Both davits were empty, the lifeboats gone.

'You were right then,' Mike said, turning to Hal, his voice tense. 'There wasn't anybody on the bridge last night.'

We stared up at her in silence as we slipped away from her, awed by the sense of mystery. The rope falls hung forlornly from the empty davits. A thin trailer of smoke emerged incongruously from her funnel. That was the only sign of life. 'They must have abandoned ship just before they nearly ran us down,' I said.

'But she was steaming at full ahead,' Hal said, speaking more to himself than to us. 'You don't abandon ship with the engines going full ahead. And why didn't she radio for help?'

I was thinking of what Hal had said half-jokingly last night. If there was really nobody on board . . . I stood there, my hands braced on the guardrail, my body tense as I stared at her, searching for some sign of life. But there was nothing; nothing but that thin wisp of smoke trailing from the funnel. Salvage! A ship of 6,000 tons, drifting and abandoned. It was unbelievable. And if we could bring her into port under her own steam. . . . I turned to Hal. 'Do you think you could lay *Sea Witch* alongside her, close enough for me to get hold of one of those falls?'

'Don't be a fool,' he said. 'There's still quite a swell running. You may damage the boat, and if this gale—'

But I was in no mood for caution now. 'Ready about!' I called. And then, 'Lee ho!' We came about on to the other tack and I sent Mike below to get Ian out of his bunk. 'We'll jog up to her close-hauled,' I told Hal. 'I'll jump for the ropes as you go about.'

'It's crazy,' he said. 'You've a hell of a height to climb to the deck. And supposing the wind pipes up. I may not be able to get you—'

'Oh, to hell with the wind!' I cried. 'Do you think I'm going to pass up a chance like this? Whatever happened to the poor devils who abandoned her, this is the chance of a lifetime for Mike and myself.'

He stared at me for a moment, and then he nodded. 'Okay. It's your boat.' We were headed back for the ship now. 'When we get under her lee,' Hal said, 'we'll be pretty well blanketed. I may have some difficulty—' He stopped there and glanced up at the burgee.

I had done the same, for there was a different feel about the boat now. She was surging along with a noise of water from her bows and spray wetting the foredeck. The burgee was streamed out to starboard. I checked with the compass. 'You'll have no difficulty standing off from her,' I said. 'The wind's north-westerly now.'

He nodded, his eyes lifting to the sails. 'You're still determined to go on board?'

'Yes.'

'Well, you'd better not stay long. There's some weight in the wind now.'

'I'll be as quick as I can,' I said. 'If you want to recall me in a hurry signal on the fog-horn.' We were doing all of four knots now and the ship was coming up fast. I went to the charthouse door and yelled to Mike. He came almost immediately. Ian was behind him, white-faced and still sweaty-looking from his bunk. I gave him the boat-hook and told him to stand by in the bows ready to shove off. 'We'll go about just before we get to her. That'll take the way off her and you'll be all set to stand-off again.' I was stripping off my oilskins. Already the rusty sides of the *Mary Deare* were towering above us. It looked a hell of a height to climb. 'Ready about?' I asked.

'Ready about,' Hal said. And then he swung the wheel. *Sea Witch* began to pay off, slowly, very slowly. For a moment it looked as though she was going to poke her long bowsprit through the steamer's rusty plates. Then she was round and I made up the starboard runner as the boom swung over. There was little wind now that we were close under the *Mary Deare,*

The sails flapped lazily. The cross-trees were almost scraping the steamer's sides as we rolled in the swell. I grabbed a torch and ran to the mast, climbed the starboard rail and stood there, poised, my feet on the bulwarks, my hands gripping the shrouds. Her way carried me past the for'ard davit falls. There was still a gap of several yards between me and the ship's side. Hal closed it slowly. Leaning out I watched the after davit falls slide towards me. There was a jar as the tip of our cross-trees rammed the plates above my head. The first of the falls came abreast of me. I leaned right out, but they were a good foot beyond my reach. 'This time!' Hal shouted. The cross-trees jarred again. I felt the jolt of it through the shroud I was clinging to. And then my hand closed on the ropes and I let go, falling heavily against the ship's side, the lift of a swell wetting me to my knees. 'Okay!' I yelled.

Hal was shouting to Ian to shove off. I could see him thrusting wildly with the boat-hook. Then the end of the boom hit me between the shoulder-blades, the jar of it almost making me lose my hold. I hauled myself upwards with desperate urgency, afraid that the stern might swing and crush my legs against the ship's side. There was the slam of wood just below my feet and then I saw *Sea Witch* was clear and standing out away from the ship. 'Don't be long,' Hal shouted.

Arthur Ransome

OUT TO SEA

'BUT we promised not to go to sea at all. . . .' Susan moaned and turned her head away. Titty and Roger were both looking at her, and she could not bear to see their questioning faces.

'We didn't do it on purpose,' said John. 'We're at sea now, and we can't get back in the fog. If we tried we'd be bound to wreck the *Goblin* on something. Like trying to get through a narrow door in pitch dark. The door's wide open if we go the other way. You can see it yourself. If we go a bit east of south-east we'll get through. There's nothing for us to hit for miles. It's no good thinking of doing anything else. We've got to do it. South-east and a little bit east . . . and we'll be all right. But we've got to do it now or it'll be too late. That lightship's awfully near. . . .'

'Beu . . . eueueueueueu. . . .'

The *Cork* lightship, sending its bleat out into the fog once every fifteen seconds, was like the ticking of an enormous clock telling them they could not put things off for ever.

'We can't keep a promise when it's already broken,' said Titty.

'Is that another buoy?' said John. 'Over there. Do keep a look out. I've got to watch the compass and the sail. . . .'

'Can I sound the foghorn again?' said Roger.

'No. . . . Wait half a minute. We've got to make up our minds.'

'Let's do what John says,' said Titty. 'Daddy'd say the same. . . . You know. . . . When it's Life and Death all rules go by the board. Of course, it isn't Life and Death yet, but it easily might be if we bumped the *Goblin* on a shoal.'

'How shall we ever get back?' said Susan.

'If we keep her going about south-east till the fog clears, we'll be able to get her back by turning round and coming north-west. . . . And anyway, when it clears we'll be able to see things. . . .'

'Beu . . . eueueueueueueu.'

The lightship bleated again and John's decision was made. There was not a moment to lose.

'I'm going to take her right out,' he said. 'Come on, Susan. We'll have to jibe. It'll be easier steering too. Come on. Will you take the tiller or shall I? You'd better. Bring her round when I say. Got to get the mainsheet in first. And there'll be the backstay to set up and the other one to cast off before the boom comes over. Titty. . . . You be ready to let it go. . . . Come on, Susan. . . .'

'What about the jib?' said Roger. 'Shall I? . . .'

'Never mind about the jib till afterwards. . . . So long as we get the boom over all right. . . . Ready, Susan?'

Susan found herself at the tiller . . . found herself watching the burgee away up there in the fog as she had often watched the flag at the mast-head of the tiny *Swallow* away on the lake in the north. John was hauling in the mainsheet, hand over hand, as fast as he could.

'Not yet, Susan. . . . Not yet. . . . Don't let her come yet. . . . Help her, Roger. . . . Just while I make fast.' He took a turn with the sheet and made ready to set up the backstay. The cockpit seemed full of ropes.

'Now then. Let go, Titty. Go on, Susan. Bring her round. Put your weight on the tiller, Roger. Good. She's coming. . . . Now. . . .'

The boom swung suddenly over their heads, but John had hauled it so far in that it had not far to go. It brought up with a jerk not half as bad as he had expected. The *Goblin* heeled over to port. John had his backstay fast and was letting out the mainsheet a good deal quicker than he had been able to haul it in.

'Steady her,' he shouted. 'Don't let her come right round.'

Susan and Roger wrestled with the tiller.

'Oh look out. . . . Don't let her jibe back again.'

'You take her,' begged Susan.

John, out of breath, took the tiller once more.

'We can let the jib come across now. Yes. Let go the sheet.'

The jib blew across the moment it was free. It hardly had time to flap before Susan had hauled in the port jibsheet and tamed it to quiet.

John, with two hands on the tiller, peered through the port-hole at the swinging compass card. South, south-east . . . south-east . . . south-east by east. . . . He must keep her heading like that. Easier now, with the wind on her quarter. No need to be afraid of a jibe, with all its dangers of breaking boom or backstay or even bringing down the mast in ruin. And even if the sails were not set as well as Jim would have set them, the *Goblin* was going beautifully. The chart, in the turmoil of jibing and changing course, had slipped to the floor of the cockpit. He picked it up from under his feet and looked at it, and then at the compass again. Gosh! Already pointing too far south. He pressed on the tiller and the compass card swung back to its old position and a little beyond it. Back again. He leaned on the tiller and tried to see both chart and compass at once. Yes, it must be all right. Clear water all the way till you came to the *Sunk* lightship right on the edge of the chart. Out there they would be all right. Jim had waited out there himself. This was what Jim would do. This was what Daddy would do. John, in spite of being able to see nothing but fog, in spite of the broken promise, in spite of the awful mess they were in, was surprised to find that a lot of his worry had left him. The decision had been made. He was dead sure it was the right decision. Sooner or later the fog would clear and he would have to think about getting back. Now the only thing to do was to steer a straight course, not to hit anything, to go on and on till he was clear of those awful shoals that were waiting to catch his blindfold little ship. John, in spite of his troubles, was for the moment almost happy.

He nodded to Roger, who was waiting with the foghorn handle pulled out.

'All right. Three blasts. Wind's still aft. But keep a look out at the same time. Keep a look out for all you're worth. We mustn't run into a buoy. . . . You, too, Titty. . . . I say, what's the matter?'

Titty was holding her forehead with both hands.

'I'm awfully sorry,' she whispered. 'I . . . I think I'm going to be sick.'

'Nobody's going to be sick,' said John, and tried to say it as if he thought it, though he found that difficult when he saw the greenness of Titty's face. There certainly was much more wind and the *Goblin* was bucketing along. He looked from Titty to Susan. Susan was hunched up in a corner of the cockpit, with her head in her arms, leaning against the cabin top. Her shoulders heaved.

'Susan,' said John. 'Susan. I know it's all right.'

There was no answer. Susan had helped in bringing the *Goblin* on her new course. She had been the mate, as of old in the little *Swallow*, taking the Captain's orders and doing what she was told. But now that all that hurried business was over and she had time to think again, all her doubts had come back. It was all very well for Titty and Roger. They could not help themselves. They were in her charge and John's. 'Not to go outside the harbour.' . . . And where were they? Outside the harbour, and sailing, and going faster every minute with the rising wind. With every minute they were further out at sea, further from Pin Mill where Mother and Bridget were waiting to see them come sailing up the river, further from Felixstowe dock where Jim Brading must be straining his eyes to get a glimpse of his ship in the fog. The wind was getting up. The night would be coming down on them. And there they were in this thick blanket of fog, sailing, sailing. And on the top of all that, there was this horrible feeling in her inside, and she had to keep swallowing, and no matter how deep she breathed she did not seem able to get enough air.

'Susan,' said John again.

She turned, and he saw that tears were streaming down her face.

'It's all wrong,' she cried. 'We must go back. We oughtn't to do it. I didn't want to, and I can't bear it.'

'We can't go back,' said John. 'It isn't safe to try.'

'We must,' said Susan.

Roger, who had just been going to give another three hoots on the foghorn, stared at her. This was a Susan he had never seen.

And then Titty suddenly clutched the coaming of the cockpit and leant over it.

'She's being sick,' said Roger.

John stretched out a hand to hold her shoulder.

'Leave me alone,' said Titty. 'I'm not. I can't be. It's only one of my heads. I'll be all right if I lie down just for a bit.'

She scrambled to the companion-way, got down one step, slipped on the next, and fell in a heap on the cabin floor.

'Titty, are you all right?' cried John. 'Look here, Roger. You go and help her. I can't let go of the tiller.'

This was too much.

'I'm going,' said Susan furiously. She took a long breath and struggled down into the cabin, leaving John and Roger looking at each other with horrified eyes. Neither of them said a word. John attended to his steering. Roger waited a moment and then went on staring into the fog.

Down in the fore-cabin Titty scrambled into her bunk. Something was hammering in her head as if to burst it. Susan, once more the mate, with a job to do, wedged her in with rugs. It was all she could do to keep her footing. One moment she was leaning over Titty, and the next moment had to grab at the side of her bunk so as not to fall. Somehow or other she managed to spread a blanket over her.

'Try to go to sleep,' she said.

'It's all right now I'm lying down,' said Titty.

And then the thing Susan had dreaded happened. Could she get out of the cabin in time? Spots danced before her eyes. She swallowed, though there was nothing in her mouth. She flung herself at the companion-steps. She scrambled up them, fell into the cockpit, grabbed the coaming, just as Titty had done. 'Oh. . . . Oh. . . . Oh . . .' she groaned, and was sick over the side. She was sick again and again. When it was over she remembered that she was in the way so that John could not see the compass. She dragged herself across the cockpit and sat in the opposite corner, holding the coaming, ready to be sick once more.

'Susan,' said John at last. 'Poor old chap.'

There was no answer.

'Susan,' said John again. 'We've simply got to sound the foghorn.'

Susan leaned her head against the cabin and sobbed.

John's lip trembled. He bit it. There was a hotness behind his eyes. For one moment he thought of giving in and going back. He looked astern into the grey fog. No. He must go on. The only hope of safety was outside. He wedged himself firmly with a foot against the opposite seat. He had the tiller with both hands. He peered at the compass card with eyes that were somehow not as good as usual. South-east. . . . East-south-east. . . . East by south. . . . South-east by east. . . . He nodded to Roger.

Roger drove in the handle of the foghorn, once, twice and again. If John said it was all right, it must be. He patted Susan's cold hand.

The bleat of the *Cork* lightship sounded already far astern.

Before them was the grey curtain of the fog. And beyond it was the open sea.

Alfred F Loomis

PROFESSIONAL AID

THE eighth day of a transoceanic yacht race frowned on a sea rising in long, crest-tortured rollers, sinking in foam-flecked hollows. The sky, a grey ceiling of nimbus, darkened here and there over falling showers of rain, and the sea, reflecting the hue of the clouds, ineffectually attempted independence with its flashing white-caps. The wind ever the tormentor of sky and sea, pressed heavily from the west, ironically belying its force by the delicate tracery of its invisible fingers on the breasts of the waves.

At about the forty-fifth meridian of longitude and the fortieth parallel of latitude—an intersection discernible only to the human imagination—a small schooner of low freeboard drove across the tumbling confusion of the waves. There were men aboard her, and by that token the schooner was superior to the chaotic triune of wind, sky and sea—she alone having definite form and pursuing a definite course. And these were men indeed, as could be told from the sail the schooner carried. It was not in the reefed main-sail that they asserted superiority. The two tucks in that expanse of canvas, bellying outboard to starboard, were, in fact, a concession to the pressure of the wind. But the number three spinnaker, its four-inch pole flexing like a willow wand, its thin canvas straining at the seams! That impertinent kite showed invincibility of mind.

And yet the men aboard the fifty-four-foot over-all schooner, half of them sitting in the cockpit while the other half slept below, saw nothing magnificent in their audacious defiance. Those on watch—except the captain-helmsman, who occupied himself otherwise—looked steadily at the whipping spinnaker pole, at the frail triangle of cotton interposed before the rushing strength of the hard westerly. They would have said—had said, in fact—that if the Lord objected, He could easily blow it away. Failing divine interference, if the spinnaker drove the schooner so fast that the sea sucked aboard her stern, the sail could easily be handed and passed below. While it preserved its integrity against the wind it added three knots to the schooner's speed and steadied her helm in the lifting, overtaking seas.

There was appreciation in the eyes of the three idlers of the watch on deck, an amused quirking of the lips as they regarded the spinnaker and reflected that in ordinary circumstances a yacht like theirs would have been hove to. But they were racing.

The captain, who was also the owner and at the moment the helmsman of the schooner *Thetis*, looked only occasionally at the racing sail, and then only when the heave of a swell rolled the little ship to port and he wanted visual assurance that the spinnaker pole would not jab the wave crests. He steered with an automatic co-ordination of muscle and sense, a co-ordination so perfect that it almost defies division into its separate elements.

The helmsman's hands on the wheel, for instance, now lax and now suddenly white-knuckled, kept the schooner as true as might be on her easterly course—and it was the touch of the wheel which largely told him when to apply strength to right or left. So swift, so instinctive, was the reaction that the sensory impulses short-circuited direct to the muscles and even transcended instantaneity, to the end that for long periods of time the schooner hung immovable on her course, no more than a finger's strength sufficing on one spoke or another to keep her so.

Yet the little black-hulled schooner, presenting her stern to the onward drive of the rolling seas, was potentially able to outdo the strength of two men if more than an instant's inattention gave her charge. She could broach—that is the word of awful significance—and bury her nose and be pressed down by the weight of the wind in her sails while the sea threw high her stern and rolled her over. And then what of the men in her cockpit and those four below who had done their trick and had reposed their lives in the keeping of the helmsman?

But it was not by the delicacy of his strong hands alone that the captain steered. His eyes, clear, now snapping with enjoyment, now soft with content, watched intermittently the compass needle in the binnacle before him. That noiselessly oscillating magic of immovability gave the base course, the steering ideal. The hands, deceived by a groove in the sea when the yacht rode even-keeled and true, might have departed from the ideal by a point or more. But the needle, transmitting its immutability to the eyes and thence to the hands, brought her back again. Nor did the eyes linger in self-hypnosis on the compass card. They looked out ahead to see that the course was clear; they sought every minute the telltale whipping forward from the mainmast-head. They watched the tumble of the seas near and far, and ranged often the sails and rigging. Each glance of the clear blue eye conveyed to the captain's brain a message of reassurance, each constituted an addition to his overflowing cup of timely knowledge.

With all going well, the sense of hearing was not called upon to aid the steersman's other senses. His ears picked up but let go the spasmodic conversation of his watchmates, and the overtone of the wind in the rigging. They were attuned only to the sibilant susurrus of the schooner's rush through the water, the rhythm of the waves overtaking.

In this art which the captain practised, the sense of touch informed him by another means. The wind, ruffling the short hairs of his neck, was a truer guide even than the mast-head telltale. The eyes must impart many messages to the brain, but the skin has only to feel the direction of the wind. If the skin of the cheek as well as that at the back of the neck feels the draught, then the wind has shifted and some change must be made in steering. If, however, the cheek warms again, then it was only a temporary flaw and the course may remain the same.

Blending with all these sense impressions which made steering possible in that hard-pressed sea was the authority given by still another sense — the captain's sense of balance. At intervals the ship rose to a wave and for an instant hung. Then occurred a transition so light as to be indefinable — so slight that not the compass card could detect it, not even the trained responsiveness of the hands on the wheel. But the helmsman's body as a whole felt the infinitesimal change in balance, and the anticipatory message was telegraphed to the wheel. Sliding off the crest of the wave, the yacht drove fast and true.

All this complicated human mechanism of steering was accomplished without fettering the imagination of the helmsman. His conscious brain forged ahead to possible eventualities, reflected back to past experiences on such stormy days at sea. His judgement hovered in a state of delicate equilibrium, ready to interpret an unusual sound in the schooner's rigging or to seize a portent from the sea. On a moment when the *Thetis* lifted high on a greedy, disappointed wave, he looked ahead and saw a patch of weeds in the course. Instantly a ferment started in his cup of knowledge.

The schooner had cruised for days the axis of the Stream, where Gulf weed floats in long brown disrupted banners. She had ploughed through it, and her men, leaning over the side, had scooped up handfuls of the growth to examine it for crustacean life. Gulf weed had been a commonplace of the voyage. But, the Stream curving north-east while the yacht continued east, its distinctive weed had thinned. This patch ahead lacked the suggestion of buoyancy and mobility. Better, then, not to sail through it, but to give it a berth and watch it as it went by. At the next wave crest the patch was dead ahead and a hundred yards away. Tenderly the helmsman altered course to starboard and prepared to look overboard to port. The weed flashed by, and a wave in the schooner's wake broke over it.

The helmsman spoke: 'Boys, did you see that? The stump of a spar with moss growing on it. Three feet in diameter and twenty feet long — end on.'

The three in the cockpit jumped up and looked astern. They

sat down. One of them spoke: 'Hmph. Good thing you saw it. Charley. It would have gone clean through us.'

'Good thing it wasn't night,' said another. 'Bye-bye, *Thetis*.'

The spell of silence having been broken, the captain, shifting slightly on the wheel box, asked one of his shipmates for a cigarette. When it had been thrust, ready lighted, between his lips, he puffed and offered comment.

'Good going, this. Wonder how the boys on the sloop *Alcazar* are making it?'

'I dare say they're carrying on,' said the first speaker in the cockpit but added admiringly. 'I never saw a boat pushed like this one, Charley.'

The captain shifted position again.

'A grand rag, that small spinnaker. I don't see why it stays with us.' Thus he disclaimed personal merit. Of his skill as a helmsman, no thought entered his consciousness. A clock struck in the cabin, its quick double notes faintly covering the rush of wind and water. 'Read the log, somebody,' continued Charley. 'We're making knots.'

One of the three rose and half climbed, half walked, around the helm to the low taffrail. He leaned over, his bare toes hooked over the mainsheet traveller, supporting and steadying himself on knees and elbows. Astern the white cotton log line spun dizzily and whipped the water in long, serpentine billows. The revolving wheel of the log stopped reluctantly as the sailor bent his hands from the wrists and brought the moisture-beaded dial into range of his vision. 'Twelve point eight,' said he. 'That's — let me see — ten and a half miles since five. A tenth less than the previous hour. I wonder if the wind's letting up, Skipper.'

The captain stole a second from his employment and cast a glance around the heavens.

'Maybe,' he conceded. 'But as long as we're doing better than ten we'll carry on with this short rig. No use running risks.'

'Oh, I wasn't criticising!' exclaimed the sailor, steadying himself with a hand on the captain's shoulder as he stepped back into the cockpit. 'If I were in command I'd have been hove to all night.'

'Yes you would,' jeered one of his watchmates. 'You'd be blowing away topsails, ten every hour.'

The first sailor and the captain grinned. 'You're a sail-carrying crew,' observed the latter happily. 'And look at the smile on Chris's face.'

The paid cook had emerged from the galley hatch and stood by the fore shrouds, re-acquainting himself with the appearance of a stormy sky and sea. He looked aft and caught his employer's eye. 'Where we go now?' he shouted. 'To hell maybe?'

'Speak for yourself, Chris,' returned the captain. 'We're all pure aft here. How do you like ocean racing, Chris?'

The cook nodded his head in enjoyment and admiration.

'You fellers sure know how to sail!' he exclaimed. 'I'll get you a good hot breakfast.'

A murmur of appreciation rose from the cockpit. 'Good man that,' said one. 'The first pro I've ever seen that wasn't sick or scared in an ocean race. But he positively likes it.'

Chris, with one foot down his hatchway, took a look around. He pointed suddenly to northward. 'Look!' he shouted. 'Schooner in distress!'

'The *Alcazar*, I hope,' said the captain, sceptically.

'No. Honest. A coal hooker or something. Main-mast gone and sails carried away. See the shirt in the fore rigging?'

Everybody jumped up, and one sprang to the weather main shrouds.

'Yes,' he confirmed. 'Her hull's practically awash, and I see men waving from her quarter-deck. What do we do. Charley?'

'Get that spinnaker in quick. We'll have a look.'

There was instant concerted action. The man in the rigging jumped down and ran to the lee pinrail from which he upset the spinnaker halliard to the deck. Another jumped to the foremast, and the third, at the word of command, cast off the after spinnaker guy. The outer end of the spinnaker pole swept forward, spilling the wind out of the sail. The man by the foremast jumped the jaw of the pole clear and staggered aft with it. The man at the halliard cast off, but kept the line within the circle of his arm as he hauled down the shaking spinnaker and smothered it. As the racing sail came in, Chris, acting spontaneously, shot the staysail up.

'Snappy work, boys!' called the skipper. 'Set the jib too, cast off the boom tackle, and then come aft on the main sheet.'

For the moment interest in the discovered wreck was in abeyance, and even when *Thetis* on her new course plunged towards it the crew were concerned with their own change of circumstance. Instead of flying smoothly (however dangerously) before the wind, they were now jammed hard upon it. Two men from the watch below, finding themselves thrown from their weather bunks to the cabin floor, came up, rubbing sleepy eyes. A vicious burst of spray doused them from head to waist, and they descended with howls of protest. *Thetis* became a leaning, labouring thing, her decks and booms dripped and her bow rising and falling with a force that jarred. Instead of slipping quietly by, waves now broke against her port side, and the wind which whined evilly in the rigging threw the crests high.

'There's weight behind this breeze,' exclaimed Charley, whose helmsmanship was now concerned only with meeting the onrushing waves to best advantage. 'Glad we haven't had this for the last eight days.'

A shout from below preceded the eruption of four men from the cabin. They were all clad for heavy weather, and they scrambled to places in the crowded cockpit with expectancy in their faces.

'What's the big idea?' asked their leader, amateur mate of the amateur crew. He was large, his bulk accentuated by the close fit of the borrowed oilskin jacket into which he had thrust himself. The straining sleeves stopped short of his wrists and the button and buttonhole at the throat came not within three inches of meeting. With the first dash of spray his bare head glistened, while drops streamed from his rugged face and coursed unregarded down the strong column of his throat.

Charley glanced at this tower of strength affectionately. 'Glad you came up, Hank,' said he. 'We've sighted a shipwrecked schooner, and we'll need your moral support.'

'Not one of our compet—No, I see her. Golly, she is wrecked. Say, Charley, it's been blowing out here.'

'And still is. We've got all we can stand under this rig, but I need both headsails for manoeuvring.'

'Right. What'll you do? Come up under the schooner's lee?'

'Yes, but they'll have to jump. We can't go alongside.'

'We-ll', the mate drawled in disagreement, and then changed his mind.

'I guess you're right. We've still got the race to think of. Hope they can swim.'

Each corkscrew heave of *Thetis* brought her nearer to the wreck, which was now seen to be heeled to an appalling angle. Five men clung to the weather rail of the slanting poop deck and their calls for help came thinly down the wind. Charley, on his feet now, sized up the situation. He knew little of merchant schooners and could not guess the life expectancy of this one. She might float for an hour or a month. His problem was how to approach her. There might be—there was—wreckage to leeward. He must not go too close. And yet he must not expect her crew to swim far. Perhaps they were on the edge of exhaustion. Nor could he throw his own vessel into the wind and let her lie there indefinitely, her sails spilling. Slatting about, they would blow to pieces.

'Boys,' he suddenly said, 'her stern's pretty much up in the wind, and we'll pass under the bow and come about to weather. I'll luff past as close as I dare, and we'll tell 'em what to do as we go by. Then we'll have to work fast. As soon as I get room I'll run off, gybe over.'

'Gybe, in this?' someone asked incredulously.

'The boom will be hauled flat. She'll stand it. We'll gybe, shoot up, and lose headway abreast her stern. Hank, you tend jib sheets; Chris, stand by to back the jumbo and the rest of you heave lines and haul the men aboard. Somebody fetch the megaphone now, and stand by to come about.'

They passed close to leeward of the wreck. Her mainmast with its smaller spars and shreds of sail trailed in the water, still held by the starboard shrouds, which on the instant snatched the sticks back to punch hollowly against her. Of her decks all but the poop and forecastle were under water, and the sea tumbled over her weather bulwark to resurge convulsively over her waist. The foremast and the bowsprit, still upthrust, seemed to lean despairingly from the wind's blast. A sound of the groaning of tortured wood and wire came to *Thetis* as she plunged by.

Now *Thetis* tacked to weather of the wreck, and the crew saw how her main chain plates had been torn away, opening up her port side and letting the mast go by the board. This side was high out of water — at least, as the breaking waves fell away from it — and all the opened seams of its black planks wept rivulets.

A leaping sea threw *Thetis* bodily so that scarce twenty feet of open water kept her from the sullen hulk, and a voice which carried upwind arose from her poop. 'Sheer off, you fools! You can't do anything to weather of us!'

Charley smiled as his crew watched him anxiously. He raised his megaphone. 'Pipe down and take instructions. Can you all swim?'

'All but one. What's the matter with your dory?'

'It won't live in this sea. I'll round up to loo'ard. Jump as you see your chance. We can handle you all at once.'

Hank added a postscript. 'Here's a lifebuoy with a rope. Give it to the one that can't swim.' He swung his powerful arm and a white ring bounced over the ship's rail. A grasping hand caught the attached rope and Hank let go its end. *Thetis* passed astern.

Instantly Charley brought up his helm and paid her head off. Her jibs, from curved, straining boards, became gently shaking cloth. The spray dropped and the motion eased, but now the mainsail, feeling the wind on its leech, began jumping and pulling intermittently at its taut sheet. 'Gybe oh!' cried the captain. 'Weather jib sheet! Hold on!' With a sudden shift from port to starboard the main boom swept rebelliously through its narrow arc, and for the instant that *Thetis* swung broadside to the wind she lay over on her starboard beam ends. Then, rudder and pressure of wind assisting her, she whisked around, presented her bowsprit to the eye of the wind, righted, and lost headway. She lay where her captain wanted her, no more than a long jump from the bulk, smooth water between.

'Your only chance, men!' he shouted through his megaphone. 'I might crock up next time.'

They slid, scrambled, and fell down the sloping deck and plunged, heads thrown back, into the water. Three swam independently and reached *Thetis*'s side in ten strokes and were hauled aboard. The fourth wore the white life ring beneath his arms, and the fifth paddled with the end of the rope in his fist. He passed it up to reaching hands, and turned back to his helpless comrade. But impatient voices restrained him. 'We've got him, all right. Come within reach. We can't lie here all day.'

To these persuasions Charley added his. 'We're gathering

sternway, boys. If we get meshed in those spars and rigging we'll never get out. Now! I've got to let her fill away. Back that jumbo, Chris.'

'Heave ho!' cried Hank, hauling in the port jib sheet, but watching the rescue operations over his shoulder. 'There are five aboard us, Charley. Is that all, Cap?'

'That's all—and damn glad to be here. Where are you bound?'

'Never mind that now,' answered Charley. 'I'm gybing again.' His heart thumped with the exultation of a dangerous job well done. His eyes shone. 'Somebody write up the log and get their names and facts. Oh, and the patent log. Did that foul anything?'

'No. It was taken in.'

'Fine. Stream it, and—gybe oh!'

Again the close-hauled mainsail thundered over, and now, as its sheet was slacked out, *Thetis* resumed the long rushing roar of her former gait. The derelict dwindled rapidly over her port quarter.

'I guess you can set that spinnaker again. No. Wind's moderated a lot. Make it the size larger . . . Well, men, you're welcome to what hospitality we have.'

To the crew of *Thetis* these five shipwrecked mariners who lay exhausted on the schooner's deck were Titans of the sea. They belonged to that unfathomable, almost mythical order of beings who keep to the sea in all seasons to wrest a scanty living from it; who, with inadequate equipment and in insufficient numbers, drive ponderous schooners through winter gales, and arrive, overdue, unconscious of their heroism. These five, who had suffered shipwreck and stared death in the face, who had accepted rescue without visible emotion, were objects of special admiration. Under their eyes, and particularly under the eyes of their captain, who had shown his contempt of amateurs in the moment before his rescue, the Thetans must sail with every ounce of smartness at their command.

As was to be expected, the story of the mariners' privations was simply told. In a hard blow seven days previous the schooner *Maribella*'s cargo had shifted. To top that, the main chain plates had pulled out of timbers which had long been rotting, and the mast had given way. A week of pumping had been in vain. The stores were wet and the fresh water was gone. The end had been in sight when *Thetis* came up. Luck had been with them, and now where were they bound?

Hank brought brandy, and Chris fresh water and biscuits, and promised hot food within the hour. Feeling the stimulant, the shipwrecked ones sat up and looked about them in amazement.

Their captain, who gave his name as Duggan, voiced their wonder.

'What the hell is this little peanut shell doing here with no harbour to run to? Racing? Where? To England from New York? What for? For the sport of it? Could anybody be so crazy as to look for sport in midocean, in a thing like this?'

These questions prodded the pride of the Thetans. Their schooner was a staunch little ship, designed especially for ocean cruising. They raced her because there was no sport like it — no other sport in which man pitted his wits against the elements while in competition with his fellows.

It was Duggan's opinion, candidly expressed, that if they wanted to live to race another day they'd better be jogging along under foresail and swung-out jumbo.

'But what about the other birds?' asked Charley, who had been relieved of the wheel. 'There are four of them back there who won't be jogging along. They'll be carrying on.'

'What! More of them doing the same?' asked Duggan, his wonderment increasing. 'Well, if there were any professional seamen in the lot they'd be riding easy under square sails.'

Professionals. The Thetans had small opinion of such as ship aboard yachts, looking for soft berths and generally finding them and these shipwrecked mariners had been excluded from that category. But here was the classification out of Duggan's own mouth —if they had the wisdom of professionals they'd be playing safe under square sails.

'If any of our adversaries are carrying square sails,' said Charley, 'you don't have to ask why they're behind us. This number two spinnaker of ours makes us know we're racing.'

'So that's what you call that balloon, eh? I was wondering what it was. Looks to me like a man-killer.' Duggan cast his glance aloft. 'Look at your spars buckling. And look at that damn slender preventer stay. It isn't heavy enough to seize a clew to a boom, and if that let's go you'll be like we were a week ago.'

'That's a chance we have to take,' said Charley, 'and I hope you won't feel you've jumped out of the frying pan into the fire.'

'Who, me? Race your fool heads off for all of me. But suppose the ship does break up beneath your feet and you have to take to the small boats. Where'd you be in that dory, even without the five of us?'

The crew of *Thetis*, attending to this conversation with interest and a sense of disillusionment, glanced at the dory lashed bottom up on deck and grinned. It was intended for ferrying men to shore in quiet harbours. Five was its maximum capacity in still water. There were now fourteen souls aboard. The dory situation was one of the inherent humours of ocean racing. It never had seemed more laughable than at the present moment.

'We'd have to swim ashore,' said Charley and the conversation lapsed.

Around midday, by which time the rescued mariners had fed and had fallen into a heavy sleep below decks, the wind moderated still more, and changes were made in the schooner's sail spread. The reefs in the main were shaken out and the whole sail hoisted. The spinnaker was taken in. The balloon jib and the balloon staysail were set, and the course was slightly altered so that these swollen acres of canvas would fill and draw to top advantage. By these changes the schooner's speed was maintained despite the softened wind.

As Duggan came topside in the afternoon his eyes lifted to see blue between the scurrying wefts of cloud. But his square, unshaven jaw dropped as he looked forward and observed the schooner's mountain of canvas. Speechless, he walked gingerly to the foremast and with his tough fingers felt the texture of the balloon staysail. It was thin, like the cloth of a much-laundered shirt. He returned aft and sat down. Like a man in the zoo he inspected one by one those of the Thetans who were on deck, seeming to see rare specimens in which indications of rampant madness were all too evident. But he remained silent, neither displaying interest in the badinage which flashed back and forth between the lighthearted watchmates nor offering to help them in the minor details of ship's work which engaged their hands.

Three of Duggan's shipmates dribbled up, refreshed, and grouped themselves compactly near him. They were clad in an odd assortment of flannel trousers and varsity sweaters with the initials turned in. In response to questions they declared that they had never felt better but they too seemed disinclined to talk or mingle with their rescuers. They exchanged words among themselves, but these were monosyllabic. They touched cleats and rope ends and such other small objects as lay within their reach—touched them wonderingly, as one will a baby's hand, or a tiny bird's egg.

At supper time the commander of this incomprehensible craft came up from a berth which he had fashioned for himself on the cabin floor. He inspected carefully the stand and trim of the sails and climbed aloft to look for signs of chafe. Satisfied, he came down and for some minutes watched in silence the run of the sea and the appearance of clouds and westering sun. At length he gave the result of his deliberations.

'I think we'll have a good night, eh, Hank? Certainly no reason for shortening before sundown.'

'Everything's as slick as hair oil. We batted off 240 between afternoon sights, yesterday and today. And that's going.'

Captain Duggan stirred and spoke. ' 'Scuse me, Cap'n, but you ain't thinking of carrying this light stuff all night are you?'

'Why, yes. Every mile we make in this westerly weather is good for two miles at the other end. Play your luck while it lasts, or it won't last.'

'I was just wondering. S'pose there was some other derelict like the *Maribella* on your course at night. What then?'

Charley shrugged his shoulders. 'I've also heard,' said he, 'of icebergs, and ships struck by meteors. We take those chances.'

'At least you keep a proper lookout?'

'I've been thinking of that. You noticed, I suppose, that we have places in the two cabins for only six to sleep at one time. Your cook has gone forward to help Chris, and there's a spare berth for him in the fo'c'sle. So that leaves just a dozen of us aft. Now, I don't want to make you work, as we have a full crew without you; but I'm afraid you'll have to stand watches with the rest of us, so there'll be room to sleep. If you and your men care to do lookout duty, it would be a first-rate solution of the difficulty.'

'That's fine. Men, we'll keep the regular watch order, and I'll stand with the captain here. And, Cap, don't think we don't want to work. Anything we can do, or any advice my mate and I can give, we'll be glad to.'

No doubt it was the memory of his almost fatal shipwreck which warped Duggan's weather judgement in the continuing days of fine westerly weather. This, and his deep-rooted conviction that a yacht less than sixty feet long was a rich man's toy, fit only for harbour sailing. The advice which he contributed with less and less reserve was always on the side of caution. Fair-weather clouds when robbed of the lingering luminosity of the setting sun, became the forerunners of black squalls. Minor fluctuations of the barometer aroused his concern.

Once, calling upon his years of experience to back up his dicta, Duggan persuaded Charley to take in his kites on the advent of a midnight squall. But his acceptability as a weather prophet terminated when with the lapse of two hours of expectant waiting nothing happened.

Duggan's men, ever suspicious of the amateur's sailing ability but faithful to their duties as lookouts, met their Waterloo on the day when, the fine weather ending, *Thetis* crashed into an easterly. This was in the Chops of the Channel, where the ocean shoals and the waves are steep. The Thetans could and did make allowances, for they had been unmercifully shaken up the day after the start. They knew, too, that a man who is immune in big ships or even in ships of moderate size may succumb to the violence of a small yacht lying on her ear in a short head sea.

So on this revealing occasion the Thetans said nothing, and did not even exchange meaning glances among themselves. But the distressed mariners, more distressed now than they had been in a lifetime of sailing, dropped their heads in mortification. Lookout duty might have seemed to them a supererogation when each tortured, sea-whipped lurch of the frail *Thetis* promised to be her last. They huddled wet and miserable during their tours on deck, and one of them expressed the sentiments of all when he said, 'We knew we were going to drown on the *Maribella* schooner, but this damn being half-drowned and half-bounced to death is what gets me.'

When the strong clear easterly gave way to a thick south-westerly and *Thetis* once more laid her course, her captain showed first signs of worriment. He was now, after more than two weeks of unlimited sea room, running fast on a lee shore, and a reliable fix was as important as the need for making every minute count. But here luck intervened. At noon the sun showed itself long enough for an accurate shot for latitude, and two hours later two coasters crossed *Thetis*'s bow — one bound north and the other south.

At sight of them the worried frown left Charley's face. 'Boys,' said he, bringing a folded chart up on deck, 'here's where we are. Latitude by observation, forty-nine, fifty-two; longitude, a line drawn close to westward of Wolf Rock. See? That's where those coasters are going — one south out of the Irish Sea, having rounded the Longships and given the Wolf a berth, and the other on the reverse course.' He gave the helmsman a steering order that, allowing for tides, would take them close past the Lizard.

But Duggan interposed his last objection. 'I want to say, Cap, that in the last nine days I've changed my mind about yachts and gentlemen sailors. I take off my hat to you for making a schooner go. But going it blind on a day as thick as this ain't seamanship.'

'How do you mean, "going it blind"?' asked Charley. 'My latitude was good; and what could be better than longitude gained from those two coasters? Don't they know their way?'

'Yes, they know it; but you don't. They might be going anywhere but where you say.'

'But where?' Would they be running on to the rocks of the Scillies? Or full bore into Mount's Bay? And we can't be as far east as Plymouth. You'll find I'm right, Duggan, I've cruised this region.'

'That's all right, but if this were my ship coming on to a foreign coast I'd feel my way. You'll pile her up, and then what will the underwriters say? Were you taking it easy? Did you run a line of soundings?'

'I'm not insured. So what do you say, boys?' And Charley put it up to his men.

'I say I'm with you until the keel rises up through the deck,' said Hank.

'That bad spell of easterly weather let the sloop *Alcazar* and probably a couple other windward workers slip through us. At least we don't want to finish last.'

So the final hundred miles were run in an atmosphere brittle as icicles. The Thetans felt intuitively that if ever they had held the ascendancy over their rivals they had lost it in the head winds. The Maribellans knew that they would yet have to swim for their lives, holding to the gunwales of that ridiculous dory. And the quartering sea roared, and invisible steamers bound down Channel shaved them as darkness came in, and every man jack stayed up to see the finish.

The siren of the Lizard boomed too close as they flashed by it in a thin fog. But it sounded when and where the captain of the *Thetis* wanted it. And four hours later—but it seemed like fifteen minutes—they clocked their time of rounding Plymouth breakwater and brought up in the anchorage. No committee came to greet them, and until morning there was no way of telling whether they were first boat in or last. This gave to the trans-oceanic race its final fillip of excitement.

There were people at home fully as anxious for news of the finish of the race as the crew of *Thetis*, and they had only another day to wait for it. It ran, from the facile pen of a shore correspondent:

'At 12.15 Monday morning the yacht *Thetis* won the trans-oceanic race in the remarkable time of seventeen days and seven hours, setting up a record for small yachts that may stand for many years. She defeated her nearest competitor, the sloop *Alcazar* by twenty-three hours and forty minutes. On the harrowing voyage the *Thetis* figured in the thrilling rescue of the captain and four men of the merchant schooner *Maribella*, abandoned in mid-Atlantic. While there is no inclination here to belittle the sterling performance of the amateur crew of the *Thetis*, it is believed in shipping circles that they could not have won such an overwhelming victory without the superior ability of the professional seamen from the *Maribella*. If this is true, the race must take its place among the stirring romances of the sea. In return for their lives, Captain Thomas Duggan and his men from the *Maribella* showed the amateur sailors the way to the winning post. . . .'

There was more in this vein, but a little should suffice.

E Arnot Robertson

THE REGATTA

MEANWHILE there was the Under-Five Tons race in which
Ronald, in a bold moment on a calm day, had entered his own
nailsick craft *Hedgehog*, given to him years ago by father to save
the bother of scrapping her. *Hedgehog* was about the only
floating object which even father could not sell. There was a
family legend, started by father, that whenever one of our linen-
backed charts disappeared, the odds were that Ronald had
found another spot between wind and water where daylight
shone through her hull, and needed something for patching.

'Hullo,' Lester greeted him icily in passing. 'Indulging in
any of your merry pranks today?'

Ronald did not answer: he was standing by me trying to get
father's ear, but father was deep again in conversation with the
American chemist, whose brother, it appeared, had been on a
scientific expedition up the Amazon many years before, but
still vividly remembered meeting father—and no wonder.
Listening distractedly, with my eyes on the tumultuous water,
I could picture that encounter from what was being said   the
once-trim little American steamer stuck in a floating morass of
flowering weed, her paint blistered off, her crew appalled by
their growing suspicion that the stream up which they had
been forcing their way for weeks was only a tributary of the
giant river, into which they had turned by error; and the
impenetrable wall of tropical forest on either side, broken by no
sign of human habitation for hundreds of miles. And then the
canoe with the half-naked man in it, skimming through openings in the damnably scented vegetation that blocked their
passage: their excited attempts to hail this gold-skinned god
in Brazilian-Spanish and the local Indian dialect. And his
answering, 'Where are you from? . . . No, this is the Parana
. . . you'll have to go back two hundred miles. . . . My name's
Rush . . . did you hear before you left who won the America
Cup last year?'

Genuinely, I knew, the fate of the America Cup contest of
the previous year would have been one of father's first interests
on meeting white men again after months in the Chaco. But

what satisfaction he must have derived, immediately afterwards, from realising just how odd this interest really was! I could imagine, too, without the American's halting efforts to convey his brother's lasting stupefaction, what father must have looked like in those days. He was still the handsomest man I had met. It was not surprising that hearing the name Rush and seeing him standing on the sunlit Hard with his light, wild hair ruffled by the wind, the American had known without hesitation that this man with the figure of a boy must be the apparition seen long ago by someone else on the other side of the world.

The firing of the first gun for the five-tonners brought him back to Pin Mill. Ronald got his word in at last.

'I'll have to scratch my old *Pig*,' he said regretfully, 'she couldn't stand such a bucketing.'

'Too late,' said father curtly. 'First gun's gone. If you wanted to get out of the race you should have given notice before. Off you go.'

Ronald stiffened and the slight change in his face and bearing was reflected in father's.

'It's nothing to do with getting out of the race,' he said hotly. 'I know the state of the hull. So ought you. She'd sink.'

'That's your lookout.' Father was angry, half-smiling in a way I had not seen before. He said slowly, dropping the words one or two at a time into a cold pause, 'And personally, I'd rather my family didn't do their funking in public, Ronald.' I do not think the American heard: even if he did, no outsider would have guessed the slow-kindled enmity that flamed up between father and son. The two looked at one another for a few seconds while I dug my nails into my hands, wishing furiously I did not know what: that father had not just this splendid air which always brought me to his side in any argument; that I did not feel such intense sympathy with Ronald.

He stood quite still for a minute, with the blood draining out of his face, 'All right, I'll go,' he said. Turning he ran down the Hard. Margaret and I, who were to have been his crew, shouted after him; he took no notice, and I at least was relieved. 'You'll come. And you. And you. To bale,' he said high-handedly to three of the village boys of his own age. They had already withdrawn their own boat from the race. He was curiously like father at the moment, though much more vehement than they had ever known father: somehow he made them go with him. All through the race they passed a bucket at top speed from hand to hand—cabin to step, step to well, contents shot overside in one movement, and then back to the cabin, where the water rose in spite of their efforts, rushing in through the rotten hull while Ronald drove her with 'all plain sail' on her. Each of his five competitors (four others had scratched on account of the weather) had three reefs in the mainsail and only a rag of a jib. As she sank lower in the water the over-'tender' *Hedgehog* seemed stiffer. Ronald chanced the water gaining on them too much to be fought back later, and we saw him signal to the balers to come out for a second and get her spinnaker ready as she approached the last buoy, only a length or so ahead of Basil Quest's taut little boat, to which Ronald had to give five minutes on time, through a whim of father's. From here on he had a straight run home.

To the spectators it was the most exciting race of the day. No one who knew the state of the *Hedgehog*'s planking expected her to stand, from one minute to the next, the constant burying of her bow by the weight of the canvas to which Ronald clung stubbornly even when, yawing perilously, *Hedgehog* was running goose-winged and by the lee on the last lap.

Father was fairly dancing about the committee boat towards the finish. 'She'll do it—Christ! Did you see her boom lift then?—If he gybes all standing she's a gonner—About three minutes ahead— No, she can't possibly do it now. . . .'

Ronald won, beaching the sinking boat on Cathouse Point before he left her. Father walked over to welcome him, but mother was there first. Ronald looked worn out and still rather pale when he waded ashore. 'Done the old *Pig* in,' he said to her. 'Well, it doesn't matter, she wouldn't have lasted another season anyway.'

'Well done, Ronnie!' father said, standing behind mother. 'Awfully good show.'

'I say, there's at least three inches of mud over some of this shingle, mother,' Ronald said quickly. 'You'll get it over the top of your goloshes. I'll give you a lift across the worst bit, because I'm soaked anyway.' He picked her up in spite of protests, holding her small body like a shield between himself and father, whose congratulations he did not acknowledge.

'Got a welt over the eye from the foresail cringle,' he told her. 'You know how that makes it stream. Could hardly see for weeping on one side.' But there was no mark on his forehead that I could see and both eyes looked equally shiny beyond the normal, and slightly red, I thought. *Hedgehog* had been his first command, and father his closest friend. I do not know if father realised, as he hurried back to the Hard to resume his duties, that because his son was so like him, he had lost the boy for ever by that one insult, an aspersion, absurdly enough, on the one quality, physical courage, which was really beyond question in both of them.

Charles Rawlings

BLUE DUSTER

SIR JAMES STILTON came into Halifax that year from those few exclusive square leagues of British water, the Solent. He sailed in thirty days across the Atlantic in his fifteen-ton Brixham ketch; a Cornwall fishing crew at the running rigging, gentlemen's cabins below, a royal burgee at his main top. The Halifax matrons made the most of him. It was an easy thing to do, for he was moderately young and delightfully simple and conscious of his responsibilities. But in the wardroom of the Royal Haligonian Yacht Squadron he set down his glass one morning and said:

'You have such delightful girls here. Why can't I meet them? I go about to a stuffy shindy here and another there, but vainly. I see them striding to work, all rosy from badminton and hockey and dancing and things.'

He said it across a wardroom table to MacGregor Mac-Glashen. MacGlashen was large and freckled and Canadian. He had a sandy texture and in his eye a clean, scrubbed look that made the utmost ribaldry glow with gentility. Two remote activities gave him his livelihood and his pleasure. He was a toilet-goods salesman. He sighed and tossed square black cases into his automobile and departed for far reaches of the Maritime Provinces, selling tiny opalescent vials of perfume, scented soaps in modernistic cartons, and vast gallonages of what he called 'Winchell Juice'. He returned and consumed every possible moment driving a black-hulled, oversparred racing cutter like a madman.

He surveyed Sir James with a quick appreciative glance.

'You have,' he asked, 'no teas on this afternoon?'

'None, thank heaven.'

'There's no hurry,' MacGregor said. 'We'll drink another Collins. I'll show you presently.'

They drove slowly down the street in MacGregor's car. It was scented heavily with lavender and soap. A blonde girl, tailored and brisk, strode ahead. MacGregor regarded her, then slowed beside her.

'Hi, Toots!' he said.

He made a slight gesture of accompaniment—a short flick of his large hairy right hand, a little wipe across the air, palm outward. It was at once a salute, a wave, an expression of the utmost friendliness. It was as if, with its slight wipe, all the frosts of formality, of aloofness and distrust that make opaque the windows before mankind's inner heart were swept away. The blonde girl smiled and stopped.

'Good morning,' MacGregor said and stood politely beside his car. 'We're having a dance tonight. This is my friend Jim Stilton.' Sir James doffed his hat and bowed. 'He's sailed in from England, and'—he cast a twinkling eye at Sir James—'he's dying to give an open-house dance aboard his ketch. We need a few good-looking girls.' MacGregor wrinkled his freckled nose, grinning as she sized him up. 'This is,' he said, 'a trifle informal. Don't make up your mind yet. If it grows on you, just take a cab to the squadron at eight o'clock. My name's MacGlashen. Tell the taxi-driver to charge the fare to me. We'll be there to meet you.'

'At the squadron?' she said. 'I'd love to come. You're not spoofing?'

'Oh, perish the thought!' said Sir James.

As they drove on, 'The lady's name is—ah—Toots?' he asked.

'The eternal Toots,' MacGregor said. 'All the girls' names are Toots. Here's a brunette.'

'By Jove!' softly said Sir James.

'Do you,' he asked, after the party had a working nucleus of four girls, 'suppose I could do it? It is a most amazing power you have. An open sesame, isn't it? Hi, Toots.' He said the magic phrase and attempted the gesture. He did it stiffly, self-consciously.

'No! No!' MacGregor said. 'Like this: Hi, Toots! You have to feel it. Bold! Carefree! A little impudent. Not too dashing. On the level. Nothing snide about it. Not one thing in your eyes but fun, friendliness. Try it again.'

Sir James practised very seriously: 'Hi, Toots. Hi, Toots! Better, don't you think? Here, watch me.'

She was a small girl in blue. She stopped in her tracks, startled, and stared wide-eyed at Sir James. Then she tossed her head and walked rapidly away.

'Missed, by Jove!' he said. 'Don't laugh, you scoundrel. You are laughing. I'll get one yet.'

He fished in his pocket. 'Now,' he said, polishing a monocle and screwing it into his youthful eye, ' "Hi, Toots," it is. Put me on game, fellow.'

What followed was good, but we have no room for it. MacGlashen, at the right moment, stuck his tongue out at a stern-faced Halifax policeman whose murderous glare made Sir James gasp with terror and hiss hoarsely, 'The bobby! The bobby!' Other events occurred, and Sir James finally met with success. She was not a beautiful girl, but jolly, and Sir James was very proud of her.

'Like your first partridge, you know,' he told MacGregor as they prepared for the evening, 'or your first antelope. I feel I should hardly call the lady a tiger.'

They had the dance in the ketch's big oak-floored saloon, accompanied by an accordion and two mouth harps. It was an immense success, especially after the girls finally became convinced that Sir James was Sir James.

At the farewell dinner tendered him in Halifax he made his address. It was a boyish, charming speech. Salutes, gestured symbols, were becoming increasingly fashionable in the changing Europe, he pointed out. He threw his arm aloft in the proud *saluto* of Italy, gave the reaching thrust that expresses the haughty *Heil* of Germany. But greater, dearer, he said, was the one he had discovered in Canada. It knew no boundaries, no loyalties, save those surrounding and imbuing the simple human heart.

'I give you,' he told the flanked rows of tables, 'not "hands across the sea" — that is, possibly, growing a bit thin — but from Ottawa to London, from Halifax to Cowes, I give you what I shall take back: "Hi, Toots!" '

He sailed away and left the memory of his charm behind him. Some weeks afterwards MacGlashen received a bulky envelope from England. It contained bills of lading for a thirty-foot yacht ferry. It had been loaded as deck cargo on a freight vessel arriving, MacGlashen discovered, that very morning. There was a note saying, 'Hello, old chap!' for MacGlashen; and another formal one, addressed to the yacht squadron itself. The little ferry, it said, was a bread-and-butter token of the happy time its sender had had in Halifax.

The squadron's commodore read the note, cleared an ex-navy throat with an ex-navy 'Hurr-rumph,' and peered up over his glasses at MacGlashen.

'A ferry, and coming from Cowes, by Jove! From Sir James Stilton! For our fleet, of course. Damned thoughtful of his lordship. I will go at once and receive her.'

They stood on the dock as the freighter's crane lifted a mysterious crate some thirty feet long and sat it softly on the concrete at their feet. The stevedores' prize bars ripped away the covering, and as their knives cut into a sacking swathing, she emerged. She was spotlessly white, a chubby, shallow-craft, beamy, perky little vessel. She was decked over with a small storm hood in the bows, painted dandelion yellow, sheltering a small copper-jacketed engine and a driver's seat. Aft of that she was all open cockpit. There was a grey floor, smooth as glass, where bags of racing canvas could be tossed. A continuous oak bench ringed the cockpit sides where the owners of the canvas could sit. Her top-sides were a white which only those ancient, old-country yacht hands, hoary and slow as gardeners planting basil, can spread on perfect planking. On each of the bows was a small Haligonian Squadron burgee, done in blue enamel with the crown in red and gold, and very fine. The commodore, the squadron secretary, who had come to take charge of the unloading, and MacGregor MacGlashen walked slowly about her and stopped at her stern.

It was a stern that perfectly became the rest of her lines. They were the contours and the bulges of a white-haired, round-spectacled, plump aunt. Of the sort of woman who can move all abustle, who bakes cookies and keeps them in stone jars for nephews. Even perched up on the pierhead, her stern was a chuckle, something to slap gently, lovingly. A mallard drake, if he had a spark of gallantry in him, could not possibly have swum by it and remained unmoved. The three men, the three quite different men, stared at it in amazement. Across its rounded, buxom whiteness, in gold letters bordered with black, merrily gleamed, '*Hi, Toots!*'

'The—*Hi, Toots!*?' The commodore broke the silence. He broke it the way an ex-navy commander wearing a black derby, cholered by a Mediterranean-station liver, and saying, '*Hi, Toots!*' could break it. 'MacGlashen, you're responsible for this.'

The sudden merriment welling inside MacGlashen, that he battened down with all his will, escaped through his eyes.

'Yes, sir,' he said, making it an abashed admission.

'I'll not stand for it,' the commodore said, 'Sir James Stilton or no Sir James Stilton. We may be the provinces, but we'll not forget dignity while I'm top flat. *Hi, Toots!*'

'The commodore could write a letter,' MacGlashen said quickly ,helpfully. ' "Dear Sir James: The name '*Hi, Toots!*' is, we feel, we beg your lordship, without a dignity befitting . . ." '

The commodore's neck, very like a dreadnought's bow turret, swelled out over his spotless white collar.

'With every man jack on Cowes roadstead waiting for me to do just such a thing?' he roared. 'Me write a schoolgirl letter?'

'It could not, begging your pardon, sir,' the secretary said, 'be done save on a personal basis. After all, it is Sir James Stilton. The squadron could not formally, in my opinion, question his taste.'

'Quite,' MacGlashen agreed. 'You will remember, sir, Sir James placed a strangely noble connotation on the phrase.'

'On Hi, Toots?' roared the commodore. 'A noble connotation? God bless me, are you laughing at me, MacGlashen?'

'After all, sir, it is a good hailing name. She will be hailed, you know, constantly by men out in the anchorage. It is a name that will carry. *Hi*—ah!—*Toots!*' He cupped his hands and sang it out.

The commodore flinched and his fury mounted as the sound echoed impudently down the long rows of grim dock warehouses.

'Damn the hailing! If a vessel's to be hailed, she should have a name, not a thing like that! It sounds like a squeal at a shop-girls' picnic. *Hi, Toots!*'

He stuttered, then burst into a fit of coughing that turned the turret neck a livid red and filled his eyes with tears. He waved his hand. 'Put the damn thing in,' he gasped.

'Have you anyone in mind'—the secretary straightened his tie knot—'to man her, sir? I would advise someone small and limber who knows engines.'

'That little Newfoundlander. That one who looks like a seal. He'll *Hi, Toots!* her.'

'Jarge, sir?'

'Yes, Jarge. Give her to him. Buy him a jacket. Brass buttons! A hat!' He glared down his nose at the gold letters and straightened his black bowler. He had quite recovered his composure and was once more calmly on the quarter-deck. 'A red ensign. That's it, by Jove! Give her the red duster and keep her outside the pale. That will show that I'm not taking her seriously. We'll send in no warrant for the Admiralty to snicker at asking the blue for her. The *Hi, Toots!*'

British bunting afloat, like British society ashore, is happily cleft into classes. Exalted is the royal standard, flown only by the king. Next is the white ensign, the symbol of the navy. Then, signifying the king's service, ranking buff to fly with the official navy white, is the blue. 'The blue ensign of His Majesty's fleet,' is the correct phrase. The royal clubs of the British Empire are entitled to fly it, and their individual boats, through royal warrant, proudly unbend it. At the foot of the social—we use the word advisedly—scale is the red ensign. It is the common flag of England afloat; the red duster, 'old blood and guts'. It is the work flag; the freighter, scow, lorry, trawler, barge ensign of Britannia, rich in its simple nobility but without social exaltation. It requires no official sanction. All it asks is that what it flies over be honestly British.

Jarge—Newfie Jarge—rowed a skiff across the harbour as he had been ordered. He rowed with short deep strokes, his wrists held high from habit. He had been a doryman, a Conception Bay doryman. Drifting down into Nova Scotia to fish with the Lunenburg cod bankers, he found the job as one of the fleet boys with the yachts. He was a little, bleach-browed, sad-mugged Newfoundlander with a mixture of Belfast Irish, Channel Island, God-knows-what blood in him. His eyes were the watered blue of his sun-faded denim shirt. He wore his boots Conception Bay style. They were short, half-way up the calf, made of oxhide, and red topped. He held his oars and regarded the *Hi, Toots!* She was afloat by that time.

'Ben't ye,' he said softly to her, 'the pretty now?'

She was, he saw as he said it, gently rubbing a row of dock piling with her white rub rail. He hurried to draw her free and shinnied up the dockside to borrow a rag from the freighter's mess boy and wipe the piling smear away. Her little copper-jacketed motor purred to him as he slowly crossed the harbour. He entered the fleet, her perfect run leaving the water as smooth as a floor, swung alongside the landing float, dropped her into reverse and snugged her home so softly that she would not have cracked an eggshell, threw the clover in her painter, and was aft to catch the towed skiff before it could nuzzle. A doryman has a sense of the action of a boat as a man who has ridden for his livelihood has of the action of a horse.

The secretary nodded to himself from the club-house veranda and sent a page boy down to the float. Jarge followed him and stood, silent and frightened, while the tailor's tape recorded the circumference of his small hard chest, the span of his narrow corded shoulders, how far it was from his armpit to just past the tattooed blue anchor and the green serpent.

'None of your snide shoddy now,' the secretary told the tailor. 'Pilot serge, brass buttons with the insignia, silk sewed.... And now for you.' He glared at Jarge. 'You're to take charge of that ferry. Anchorage to shore, shore to anchorage. Members only. Answer all hails any time of day or night. Carry dunnage, sails. I want some style to you. I want you to handle that boat with style. She's Bristol fashion every minute if she's going to suit me.'

'Ye means, sor-r, I'm masterin' her? That new *Toots*, sor-r-r? She's mine to command?'

'If you're good enough. It's commodore's orders. Can you do it?'

'Yes, sor-r-r.'

He clapped his tattered cap back on his head, forgetting his manners in his excitement, and bowed backwards out on to the thick grass matting of the clubhouse porch. He turned, and there she was waiting, her white like a swan, her yellow like a dandelion. He walked towards her, a man in a trance. It was a trance that continued while all the new undreamed-of things happened. The brass-buttoned coat. The peaked official hat. The new clean gear from the chandler's. The new hemp lines to splice. The buckets, the great new chamois, the sponges. The new burgee and the ensign as red as blood, fresh out of their wrapping paper from England, and smelling of dye. How brave she looked with her colours was all that occurred to him. Their propriety he never questioned, no more than a devotee would question the propriety of a miracle, or a waif the colour of the paint on a bag of undreamed-of toys. It is quite possible that he would have looked in amazement if anyone had pointed at his bunting. He had never been anything but a red-ensign sailor. The codbankers all flew the red duster; the boats about the Newfoundland harbours, the liners that ran the Grand Banks. There were other flags, he knew, far above, just as there were great robes of state and names like 'lord' and 'earl'. They were not in his world.

But the *Toots* was not only in his world, she became all of it. Would he care for her? If she had been the *Endeavour* and she had won the America's Cup instead of losing it, he could not have cared more intently. His pride in her was a passion. She exalted him, like a man lifted up by love of a woman. With her he found what was for months a happiness that he had never dreamed of. There was occasionally, at first, a flare-up inside him when someone chuckled about her stern, or her name, or her cosy lines. Everything about her, to him, was perfect. But he soon learned to understand that the chuckles were not derision, and soon even they stopped, for, in her way, she was perfect, and the men whom she served, good boatmen all of them, soon found it out.

She was a born servant. She had her even four knots, no more, no less, steady chugging knots up sea or down. She could take a whole string of the six metres—they were racing them hard that year—trailing astern of her and tow them, upwind, out to the line, as gracefully as she would tow a skiff. Born in her was a perfect understanding of her position and her caste that in itself is a peculiar charm. A sense of proportion that entitles servants, perfect ones, to almost as much quiet esteem as those they serve. The *Toots* had it, and she gave it to Jarge. They became a fixture. Jarge and the *Toots*! One spoke of them always like that, two entities but really one, like 'Scotch and soda' or 'man and wife'.

Because she had Jarge to bring the best out of her, she was the admiration of the fleet.

'Watch that ferry come up to that stage with a beam sea working at her,' a skipper would proudly suggest to a guest. Or, 'Just notice, please, how this ferry comes alongside us here in this bobble. She is the most beautiful handling thing.'

And because Jarge had her, it was 'Jarge, b'y' from the pages all race morning long. 'Wanted on the telephone, Jarge.' And there, his hat in one hand, the receiver squeezed until it creaked in the other, it was, 'Oh, Jarge, could you get my number-two mainsail aboard, like a good fellow?' Or, 'Will you hunt up my working jib, Jarge, and have a look at the club? It's blowing up a bit here in town.' Or, 'Will you jump aboard when you are out with the *Toots* and have a look under the floors? She seemed to be leaking a sly drop, Jarge.' There would be a pint of good Scotch, or a fat tip for a reward, or a pleasant 'Thank you, Jarge, very much. What would we do without you?' from the smart wife of a racing owner who was a power afloat and ashore. Jarge knew the racing secrets. The new jib smuggled aboard after dark. The new back-stay runners or the imported thin wire rigging carried out in a sail bag.

MacGlashen had been right about her name. It was a perfect hail. A still night, with the anchorage breathless and the white hulls like silent ghosts and a thin, high-pitched wail from far out, '*Hi-i-i-ah, Toots!*' and the quiet men, smoking on the veranda, would chuckle silently and listen for the starting chortle of her motor and its steady beat softening with distance.

On race days she would fill to overflowing with canvas and men. Sometimes she could hardly be seen for them sprawled atop the piled-up canvas or sitting in the laps of those lucky enough to find a place on her bench — a rick of men, of blazing coloured jerseys, of blond heads, black heads, bald heads, shouting and caterwauling like schoolboys because they were happy to be bound out to the hard racing over the open-sea courses. Then, when they sailed in and made up, Jarge picked them off their boats again — the silent, spray-soaked, doubly bedraggled losers, the wild-eyed, jubilant winners. They all mixed together in the good nature of the *Toots*.

It was well along in mid-season when the serpent entered the garden of Jarge's bliss. It came, not very successfully disguised, in the form of the bos'n off a rich steam-yacht just in from England. He was a loud-mouthed Liverpool man, and he came ashore with a list of grocery stores.

' 'Ow,' he asked, as he settled on the bench close up to Jarge and stretched out his legs, 'comes hit ye ain't as ratin' over 'ere in the sticks as ye would be at the other side?'

'What ails Oi?' Jarge asked, all innocence.

'Ye're flyin' the red.' He nodded at the ensign billowing over the smooth wake. 'They're two of ye hover there at the Royal Thames. The syme as you, runnin' the gentlemen about. Like as two peas out of the syme pod to ye. They flies the blue. 'Ere you are flyin' the bloody red, like a chartered wherry.'

'Oi t'inks all is proper.' Jarge turned and bristled. ' 'Tis the commodore's orders. De *Toots* is all proper, I'll thank ye.'

'Proper!' scoffed the bos'n. 'Hignorance! What flies at the bow? Your burgee, man. Hit bears the crown. Look at the staff before your bloomin' club-'ouse. Hit flies the blue. Are ye somethin' less than a flagstaff? Me own skipper noticed hit. "Hit's a bloody chartered wherry, flyin' the red," he says to me. "This plice is thick with hice ten months. They charters a wherry to save the odd pound".'

Jarge landed the man at the float and watched him swagger off up the dock. Slowly he stepped ashore and stared up at the club flagstaff. It was a noble stick, rigged with a topmast, a yard and a gaff. At the gaff, on the honour halyard, flew the blue ensign. He had seen it a thousand times, watched it being dipped by the head steward in answer to the salute of important vessels passing down the fairway. It was the proudest flag afloat he knew, but.... He sat slowly on a spile top and stared up at it, preening and rippling its royal blue in the light harbour breeze. He turned and surveyed the *Toots*.

'A bloody chartered wherry, be-damn,' he repeated.

He looked up the path where the swaggering bos'n had disappeared. 'Gawan, ye big bully lad,' he growled.

MacGregor MacGlashen walked down the stairway to the

boathouse dock and sat on a bench in the sun and filled his pipe. He was in that morning from the road and had soaked in a shower for an hour to wash away the perfumes of the Indies that, from weeks of living with his toilet-goods samples, clung cloyingly to his tough freckled hide. The dank smell of the tidal flats under the cocks and the reek of oakum and paint smelled good to him. He had never felt better. He surveyed Jarge through a cloud of tobacco smoke.

'Please sor-r-r,' —Jarge held his hat in his hand —'would ye be knowin' anything about de blue duster?'

A shadow crossed MacGregor's face. 'Put on your hat,' he said. 'Somebody's been telling you about the *Toots*, eh? I'm sorry about it, Jarge.'

'Dere was a big bully lad from de steam-packet not ten minutes ago, sor-r-r. He is fresh in from across de sea. "Ye looks unproper," he says. "What ails Oi?" Oi says, "Ye should fly the blue. Ye look like a chartered club wherry," he says.'

MacGregor nodded slowly.

'Dat wouldn't be right, sor-r-r?'

MacGregor looked away over Jarge's head, studying diplomacy.

'Yes!' he said decisively, looking down again. 'That is right.'

'De *Toots* rates the blue, sor-r-r? On de schooners and such where ships de likes of Oi is always de red duster, sor-r-r. "Are ye somethin' less than a flagstaff?" de bully lad says. And dat's roight, whin ye t'ink on it.'

'Yes. The *Toots* rates the blue. But you see, Jarge, there has to be permission.' MacGregor talked very seriously. 'A letter must be written. You get a warrant. The commodore sends a letter away. He —oh —he just hasn't done it yet.'

'Dere's a writin', sor-r-r? To who, sor-r-r?'

'To the king —the king's lords.'

'Where would de likes of de writin' be, sor-r-r?'

'In the little brown book. The little brown club book.'

'It's under de name of a warrant, ye say, sor-r-r? A warrant about de blue duster?'

'Ensign! The blue ensign. "Duster" is a sailor's word.'

'And it's not Oi keepin' it from her, sor-r-r? De loikes of Oi?'

'No.' MacGregor stood up and walked past Jarge. As he passed, he made two quick pats on Jarge's arm. 'No, Jarge, you're perfect. . . . Ah-h-h! There's somebody wants you out there.'

Jarge, when he had time after lunch, looked through the book. He read very poorly, but he found what MacGregor MacGlashen had mentioned. 'Warrant,' it said in big letters. 'By the commission for executing the Office of Lord High Admiral of the United Kingdom of Great Britain and Ireland,' and so on. Down in the body he found 'hereby warrant and authorise the Blue Ensign of His Majesty's fleet to be worn on board the respective vessels . . .' It meant very little to him. On the next page it told more about the warrant. It told what should be on the 'writin''. 'To their lordships,' it began. It listed what had to be known, words he knew: 'Name of vessel . . .' it said. 'Rig . . . Length . . .' He closed the book hurriedly, shoved it in his pocket and ran to answer a hail.

That night, hidden away in the far corner of the sailroom, he lit a lantern, and, on a large piece of wrapping paper, with a stub of a pencil squeezed in his weathered, salt-cracked fingers, like a child laboriously writing a primer text, he toiled. Most of it was copying. 'To their lordships,' he began in the far upper corner. Phrases as meaningless to him as Greek went down letter by letter. The lines drifted away from him and went downhill like the back of a slow ground swell, but he took a fresh start and calmed them down. Finally he came to 'Name of Vessel.'

'Dere ye be!' he said softly, and the pencil stub made '*Hi, Toots*' boldly.

The commodore's bags arrived by cab. Jarge stowed them on the floor of the *Hi, Toots!*, and carried them out.

'Where's the old walrus think 'e's goin'?' said the hand at the flagship gangway who helped him unload. The flagship was a big ketch. *Intrepid IV* was her name. She had tall yellow spars rigged with aluminium spreaders. She was a palace of mahogany and ivory below, with shower-baths and fire-places. Jarge always liked to make her gangway and squint his eyes at the *Toots*, set off by such grandeur.

'There's enough bloomin' luggage to take him to Bombay,' the deck-hand said. 'Women's duffel, too, Lord help us! A cruise! Another bloody cruise.'

'Did he be sayin', now, when he would be castin' off?' Jarge asked.

'On the tide, dearie on the tide. Did ye ever see a navy bloke 'oo would cast off when his grandmother was dyin' if the bloomin' tide was wrong?'

Jarge had to hurry. He opened the office door slowly and stepped inside. He had his hat in one hand and the warrant carefully folded in the other. He stood waiting. The commodore sat at his big mahogany desk. There was a clock with a steering-wheel around the face, and a bowl of roses. The commodore's back was turned and he was talking to the secretary. The secretary looked up and his eyebrows lifted as he saw Jarge, but he turned and closed a side door behind him.

'Please, sor-r-r, ye goin' away and all, sor-r-r. I'll be gettin' a hail, the first minute, sor-r-r.'

The commodore swung about and glared over his nose glasses.

'Who gave you permission to come aft?' he asked.

'No one, sor-r-r. It's about de *Toots*, sor-r-r.'

He opened the brown paper. It made a loud noise.

'Oi heared she should be havin' the blue, sor-rr-r-r, to be proper, sor-r-r. Could ye send to the king, sor-r-r?'

'Who,' roared the commodore, 'put you up to this? Let me see that paper! Here, by—'

He bored into the pathetic scrawling. '*Hi, Toots!*' stood out confidently as Jarge had written it. The letters were an inch high. Intently the commodore looked at each line, seeking some trace of fraud. Then quickly he folded the document and shoved it into a drawer.

'Back to duty,' he commanded, without looking at Jarge. 'When I want you I'll pipe you to the mast.' His red neck swelled and he swung about. 'Have you been stealing paint?'

'Paint, sor-r-r? No, sor-r-r. Stealin', sor-r-r?'

'That ferry looks too white for issue paint to me. Mind you don't.' He swung back to his desk. 'I've a party going aboard the flagship. There will be ladies. Mind you swab down those benches. Mind you look smart.'

The whole Atlantic seaboard had been fogbound for three days. The big headland's horn on Sambro Head and the smaller lighter-throated harbour horn inside the great shoal Thrum Cap called back and forth like stupid, lovelorn dinosaurs. The ocean hulls crept blindly, helplessly, filled with dread, down the fairway. Terrorised bellows came from their own deep throats. Only the gulls and the terns were fearless. They flew in over the land, sporting in the thick vapour. Their high cries came, 'Ee-eek, ee-eek,' to Jarge.

The yacht anchorage was a dreary place. It was deserted, save for the regular hands, who moved silently about, grumpy and glum. The yachts were buried in fog. Only the small boats moored close inshore were visible, and they seemed forlorn and lonely with the rest of the world blotted out. Jarge was as desolate as the fog, as the 'Ee-eek, ee-eek' of the gulls. The weather had settled down over his Celtic soul to complete his unhappiness.

He had had three weeks to brood. Living with the *Toots* as an underling hostler sleeps with the horses in the stable, he had not had a single moment when the strange unfairness of the slight she was suffering had not burned into his mind. It had grown until it obsessed him. It was probably as deep an unhappiness as he was capable of suffering. It was completely unselfish. That the commodore had suspected him of stealing paint, he had forgotten. All that mattered was that the *Toots*, his beloved *Toots*, was being forced to go about 'unproper' and shamed.

He had tried at first to take matters into his own hands. If the red ensign were improper, he would fly none at all. He hid it the first day after the commodore and his party had departed. He had been smartly scolded for that and then he had destroyed the bunting. It had dropped overboard and the propeller had caught it, he explained. He was 'makin' a bit of a back-about', he told the secretary. The secretary listened, biting his lip, wise in the knowledge that wool bunting bent to a mahogany staff will float away from a backing boat's stern.

'My fine fellow,' he had said, 'just one more peep out of you and I'll set you down without waiting for the commodore to return. You fly what we tell you to fly.'

Yesterday, when the foghorns had made him more and more disconsolate, he drank some rum. Today the black sou'wester which was too big for his head drooped its earlaps down beside his jowls and framed a face that mirrored both his aching skull and his unhappy heart. Squatting on his hunkers, wiping off the *Toots*, he looked with unseeing eyes out into the fog.

It was driving a bit on a new onshore wind and the sounds were coming crazy, now loud, now far away. There was a break in the smother. He could see slantwise out the harbour; see Lighthouse Bank with its squat tower and one big dead sea exploding against its rocky foundation. He looked up the alley in the fog and saw, leaning at a sick angle, the two yellow masts of the commodore's flagship. He could see the aluminium spreaders. She was inside of Thrum Cap shoal. Inside of it. The big flagship was on 'de sunkers'! He had not stopped swabbing with the chamois. He was still squatted on his hunkers.

'Oi tinks—Oi tinks dere has been some mistake,' he said.

He straightened and looked about for someone. There was no one to be seen. He ran up the steps from the float. At the top he stopped and looked back up the fog. It had closed in again. He closed his eyes, and in his mind he saw again the one big dead sea bursting on the rocky lighthouse base. He pointed with his hand where he had seen the spars past that. Back of Thrum Cap was where she was. She had come over the top of Thrum Cap. That meant the bottom was out of her. Out of her like a kicked melon. She'd be breakin' up with the sea hammerin' her cruel.

'Oh, sor-r-r-r!' he said in pity. 'Oh, sor-r-r-r!'

He trotted down the stairs again. What could get to her? The tide—he looked at the white-faced tide gauge—the tide was full ebb. What could get in there over the back of the shoal? He moved up and down the float, rubbing his palms on his buttocks as if his hands were wet. Then he stood still, ran to the *Toots*'s painter and threw it off.

He stumbled as he jumped in over her rail, and fell on his hands and knees, but he came up again, his eyes wide, staring as if he had the place marked. He fumbled for the starter button and swung the *Toots* away automatically. She cleared the anchorage obstructions. She chugged her same unfailing pace with its smooth, untroubled wake, carrying him, a little atom of a man, with the sou'wester's earpieces trailing down his jowls and a wide-eyed fixity on his face, staring speechless out into the face of all immensity.

The fog swallowed him. There were only sounds about him: the 'ooo . . . ooo . . . ooo' of Lighthouse Bank horn every thirty seconds, the 'su-u-ush' of the *Toots*'s bows easing into the back of the dead long swells, the wet whip of the burgee on the bow before him, the purr of the little warm motor. He waited until he could hear the clucking of the air-compressor engine that blows the horn on Lighthouse Bank, then he slowly swung the wheel in his hands towards it. The 'ooo . . . ooo . . . ooo' roared at him full blast and, as if it had blown the fog away with its force, he saw the squat tower. He took his departure from that and headed the *Toots* for the inside of the shoal. He did not know just where to cross. It would not matter if he did know, for there would be no hunting for any channel in the fog. His mind began to have quick, outside thoughts. The doubt that he had really seen anything began again. Wid a rum head, now, would it be a fancy? 'Oi widout orders. Oi widout orders.' He stared and stared, trying to pry the fog apart to see again. The shoal was ahead of him. A long-backed swell as big as a hill of land began to turn ahead. It broke off his port hand in a hissing roar of white water. He shot scared, quick looks at it, away from it, at it again. It was still smooth ahead. Off to starboard there was a hiss and a boil of white water. A swell came at him, dead at him.

'Oi! Oi!' he whimpered. 'Give us a schwim by! No sunkers, de grace o' Mary!'

The swell lifted them and stayed whole, and 'No sunkers! No sunkers!' he screamed as they dropped into the trough, into the blessed, green, floating water. He heard a shout.

'A motor, sir!' it said. 'I hear it! Off to starboard!'

Then he heard the commodore's great 'Be still, all hands!' and then a moment's silence while he swallowed and tried to shout from his dry throat. And then out of the fog, ' 'Tis the *Toots*'s motor, I believe, sir! She's still off to starboard!' Then the whole air was full of cries. He was steering up the sound of them. Over them all was the commodore's quarter-deck bellow: '*Toots*! Ahoy! Ahoy! Here, *Toots*! Here, God bless you!'

'Oi's comin', sor-r-r,' he said in a whisper, and the flagship jumped out of the fog at him as big as a liner. She was far up on the hard, stern to him. Her bow was hiked up crazily and she was gone, finished. As Jarge closed with her, a swell drove at her and she lifted sullenly, then slammed down with a crash of tearing planking and groaning frames. All her people were huddled on the stern. The swell shot into the air like a geyser and they buried their heads in their arms as it showered down atop them.

The *Toots* moved in as evenly as if she were making the club float. The same little curl of wave at her bow, the same smooth, unperturbable wake, her same quiet, unhurried, lady-servant pace. Jarge placed her alongside, dropped her into reverse, made his landing.

The commodore gave the orders. His soaked moustache bristled up out of its bedragglement with the first barked word, snapping off its spray. Four hands aboard to fend off. Easy now; wait for the rise. Now the ladies. They came, poor things, lifted down with their helpless white faces and sad soaked furs about their necks. One of them, a grey-haired lady with her hair in wisps down her cheek, stroked Jarge's rubber-coated arm and cried, saying 'You! You! You!' over and over again.

' 'Tis Oi, Jarge, mum,' he said to her, trying to make her see. 'Jarge of de *Toots*. 'Tis de *Toots*, mum.'

He eased her down to the bench and then ran aft.

'No gear!' the commodore shouted. 'The spars will come out of her the next sea! Aboard, everyone!'

Jarge leaped and caught the flagship's rail and swung inboard on to her deck. In two leaps he had it. It was hanging down over the flagship's stern. It was soaked and sodden, and its staff had broken, but it still hung by its lanyards. He ripped the lanyards off their cleat, and in two more leaps he was at the rail again.

'You!' the commodore roared. 'Aboard! No gear!'

Jarge leaped, and its blue folds wrapped around his face, and he staggered as he landed on the *Toots*'s floor; but hands caught him, and he held the bunched blue bunting in his arms. Then he was at his wheel and the blue folds fell, together with the splintered staff, into a puddle in the corner beside him.

Up in the other corner the commodore stood. He had his arm about the lady with the grey hair wet against her cheek.

'Joe,' she said to the commodore, 'I prayed and he came.'

'Yes,' he said. 'We're all right now.'

'We steers on the horn, sor-r-r,' Jarge said softly. 'Pray Jesus de sunkers stays hid.'

The commodore sucked in his breath and shut his eyes and stroked the lady's head as a wave broke over the shoal beside them.

Jarge steered silently. There was another wave with its white reaching crest, then another, and then:

'All's well, sor-r-r,' Jarge said. 'I sees Lighthouse Bank, sor-r-r.' Then he went on rapidly: 'Would ye please, sor-r-r, give a bit of an order for me, sor-r-r? Aboard me vessel, sor-r-r? Would ye say now over your shoulder to one of your lads aft, sor-r-r?' He reached down and picked up the wet blue bunting and held it out to the commodore without turning his head, looking straight up his course. 'Would ye say, "Put me blue duster where it should be. We'll go in proud, wid the king's blue at me taffrail. She's me flagship now, de *Toots* is"?'

'Oh, Joe,' the lady with the grey hair wet on her cheek said to the commodore. She leaned forward and looked into Jarge's face.

'I think you are one of the bravest men I have ever known,' she said softly. 'I thank you very much for saving my life.

Would you' —she took the blue bundle—'let me put the king's blue at your taffrail? I feel sure he would be glad to put it there himself if he could see.'

Jarge looked at her as if he did not sense what she was saying, but the commodore took her arm and nodded. Jarge let the bunting slide from his hand.

After a moment he stole a quick glance aft. The people were all in the way. He looked back into the fog out over his course, then he turned again and squatted, trying to see. There was one small opening between legs. It was there. He could see just a tip of the blue whipping out over the wake. He turned back to his wheel and stood very straight, so straight and stiff that the sou'wester's earpieces hung as if plumbed down beside his stubbled, weathered jowls.

Erskine Childers

THE PORTMANTEAU

'It's awfully good of you to come.'

'Not at all; it's very good of you to ask me.'

We were both of us ill at ease. Even in the dim gaslight he clashed on my notions of a yachtsman—no cool white ducks or neat blue serge; and where was the snowy-crowned yachting cap, that precious charm that so easily converts a landsman into a dashing mariner? Conscious that this impressive uniform, in high perfection, was lying ready in my portmanteau, I felt oddly guilty. He wore an old Norfolk jacket, muddy brown shoes, grey flannel trousers (or had they been white?) and an ordinary tweed cap. The hand he gave me was horny, and appeared to be stained with paint; the other one, which carried a parcel, had a bandage on it which would have borne renewal. There was an instant of mutual inspection. I thought he gave me a shy, hurried scrutiny as though to test past conjectures, with something of anxiety in it, and perhaps (save the mark!) a tinge of admiration. The face was familiar and yet not familiar; the pleasant blue eyes, open, clean-cut features, unintellectual forehead were the same; so were the brisk and impulsive movements; there was some change; but the moment of awkward hesitation was over and the light was bad; and, while strolling down the platform for my luggage, we chatted with constraint about trivial things.

'By the way,' he suddenly said, laughing, 'I'm afraid I'm not fit to be seen; but it's so late it doesn't matter. I've been painting hard all day, and just got it finished. I only hope we shall have some wind tomorrow—it's been hopelessly calm lately. I say, you've brought a good deal of stuff,' he concluded, as my belongings began to collect.

'You gave me a good many commissions!'

'Oh, I didn't mean those things,' he said absently. 'Thanks for bringing them, by the way. That's the stove, I suppose; cartridges this one, by the weight. You got the rigging-screws all right, I hope? They're not really necessary, of course' (I nodded vacantly, and felt a little hurt); 'but they're simpler than lanyards, and you can't get them here. It's that portmanteau,' he said slowly, measuring it with a doubtful eye. 'Never mind! we'll try. You couldn't do with the Gladstone only, I suppose? You see, the dinghy—h'm, and there's the hatchway too!' —he was lost in thought. 'Anyhow, let's try. I'm afraid there are no cabs, but it's quite near, and the porter'll help.'

Sickening forebodings crept over me, while Davies shouldered my Gladstone and clutched at the parcels.

'Aren't your men here?' I asked faintly.

'Men?'—he looked confused. 'Oh, perhaps I ought to have told you, I never have any paid hands; it's quite a small boat, you know—I hope you didn't expect luxury. I've managed her single-handed for some time. A man would be no use, and a horrible nuisance.' He revealed these appalling truths with a cheerful assurance, which did nothing to hide a naïve apprehension of their effect on me. There was a check in our mobilisation.

'It's rather late to go on board, isn't it?' I said, in a wooden voice. Someone was turning out the gaslights; and the porter yawned ostentatiously. 'I think I'd rather sleep at an hotel tonight.'

A strained pause.

'Oh, of course you can do that, if you like,' said Davies, in transparent distress of mind. 'But it seems hardly worth while to cart this stuff all the way to an hotel (I believe they're all on the other side of the harbour), and back again to the boat tomorrow. She's quite comfortable, and you're sure to sleep well, as you're tired.'

'We can leave the things here,' I argued feebly, 'and walk over with my bag.'

'Oh, I shall have to go aboard anyhow,' he rejoined; 'I *never* sleep on shore.'

He seemed to be clinging timidly, but desperately, to some diplomatic end. A stony despair was invading me and paralysing resistance. Better face the worst and be done with it.

'Come on,' I said grimly.

Heavily loaded, we stumbled over railway lines and rubble heaps, and came on the harbour. Davies led the way to a stairway whose weedy steps disappeared below in gloom.

'If you'll get into the dinghy,' he said, all briskness now, 'I'll pass the things down.'

I descended gingerly, holding as a guide a sodden painter which ended in a small boat, and conscious that I was collecting slime on cuffs and trousers.

'Hold up!' shouted Davies cheerfully, as I sat down suddenly, near the bottom, with one foot in the water.

I climbed wretchedly into the dinghy and waited events.

'Now float her up close under the quay wall, and make fast to the ring down there,' came down from above, followed by the slack of the sodden painter, which knocked my cap off as it fell. 'All fast? Any knot'll do,' I heard, as I grappled with this loathsome task, and then a big dark object loomed overhead and was lowered into the dinghy. It was my portmanteau, and, placed athwart, exactly filled all the space amidships. 'Does it fit?' was the anxious inquiry from aloft.

'Beautifully.'

'Capital!'

Scratching at the greasy wall to keep the dinghy close to it, I received in succession our stores, and stowed the cargo as best I could while the dinghy sank lower and lower in the water, and its precarious superstructure grew higher.

'Catch!' was the final direction from above, and a damp soft parcel hit me in the chest. 'Be careful of that, it's meat. Now back to the stairs!'

I painfully acquiesced, and Davies appeared.

'It's a bit of a load, and she's rather deep: but I *think* we shall manage,' he reflected. 'You sit right aft and I'll row.'

I was too far gone for curiosity as to how this monstrous pyramid was to be rowed, or even for surmises as to its foundering by the way. I crawled to my appointed seat, and Davies extricated the buried sculls by a series of tugs, which shook the whole structure, and made us roll alarmingly. How he stowed himself into rowing posture I have not the least idea, but eventually we were moving sluggishly out into the open water, his head just visible in the bows. We had started from what appeared to be the head of a narrow loch, and were leaving behind us the lights of a big town. A long frontage of lamp-lit quays was on our left, with here and there the vague hull of a steamer alongside. We passed the last of the lights and came out into a broader stretch of water, where a light breeze was blowing and dark hills could be seen on either shore.

'I'm lying a little way down the fiord, you see,' said Davies. 'I hate to be too near a town, and I found a carpenter handy here — There she is! I wonder how you'll like her!'

I roused myself. We were entering a little cove encircled by trees, and approaching a light which flickered in the rigging of a small vessel whose outline gradually defined itself.

'Keep her off,' said Davies, as we drew alongside.

In a moment he had jumped on deck, tied the painter, and was round at my end.

'You hand them up,' he ordered, 'and I'll take them.'

It was a laborious task, with the one relief that it was not far to hand them—a doubtful compensation, for other reasons distantly shaping themselves. When the stack was transferred to the deck, I followed it, tripping over the flabby meat parcel, which was already showing ghastly signs of disintegration under the dew. Hazily there floated through my mind my last embarkation on a yacht: my faultless attire, the trim gig and obsequious sailors, the accommodation ladder flashing with varnish and brass in the August sun, the orderly snowy decks and basket chairs under the awning aft. What a contrast with this sordid midnight scramble, over damp meat and littered packing-cases! The bitterest touch of all was a growing sense of inferiority and ignorance, which I had never before been allowed to feel in my experience of yachts.

Davies awoke from another reverie over my portmanteau to say cheerily: 'I'll just show you round down below first, and then we'll stow things away and get to bed.'

He dived down a companion-ladder, and I followed cautiously. A complex odour of paraffin, past cookery, tobacco, and tar saluted my nostrils.

'Mind your head,' said Davies, striking a match and lighting a candle, while I groped into the cabin. 'You'd better sit down; it's easier to look round.'

There might well have been sarcasm in this piece of advice, for I must have cut a ridiculous figure, peering awkwardly and suspiciously round, with shoulders and head bent to avoid the ceiling, which seemed in the half-light to be even nearer the floor than it was.

'You see,' were Davies's reassuring words, 'there's plenty of room to *sit* upright' (which was strictly true; but I am not very tall, and he is short). 'Some people make a point of head-room, but I never mind much about it. That's the centre-board case,' he explained, as, in stretching my legs out, my knee came into contact with a sharp edge.

I had not seen this devilish obstruction, as it was hidden beneath the table, which indeed rested on it at one end. It appeared to be a long low triangle, running lengthways with the boat and dividing the naturally limited space into two.

'You see she's a flat-bottomed boat, drawing very little water without the plate; that's why there's so little head-room. For deep water you lower the plate; so, in one way or another, you can go practically anywhere.'

I was not nautical enough to draw any very definite conclusions from this, but what I did draw were not promising. The latter sentences were spoken from the forecastle, whither Davies had crept through a low sliding door, like that of a rabbit-hutch, and was already busy with a kettle over a stove which I made out to be a battered and disreputable twin brother of the No. 3 Rippingill.

'It'll be boiling soon,' he remarked, 'and we'll have some grog.'

My eyes were used to the light now, and I took in the rest of my surroundings, which may be very simply described. Two long cushion-covered seats flanked the cabin, bounded at the after-end by cupboards, one of which was cut low to form a sort of miniature sideboard, with glasses hung in a rack above it. The deck overhead was very low at each side, but rose shoulder high for a space in the middle, where a 'coach-house roof' with a skylight gave additional cabin space. Just outside the door was a fold-up washing-stand. On either wall were long net-racks holding a medley of flags, charts, caps, cigar-boxes, hanks of yarn, and such-like. Across the foreward bulkhead was a bookshelf crammed to overflowing with volumes of all sizes, many upside down and some coverless. Below this were a pipe-rack, an aneroid, and a clock with a hearty tick. All the woodwork was painted white, and to a less jaundiced eye than mine the interior might have had an enticing look of snugness. Some Kodak prints were nailed roughly on the after bulkhead, and just over the doorway was the photograph of a young girl.

'That's my sister,' said Davies, who had emerged and saw me looking at it. 'Now, let's get the stuff down.' He ran up the ladder, and soon my portmanteau blackened the hatchway, and a great straining and squeezing began. 'I was afraid it was too big,' came down; 'I'm sorry, but you'll have to unpack on deck —we may be able to squash it down when it's empty.'

Then the wearisome trail of packages began to form a fresh stack in the cramped space at my feet, and my back ached with stooping and moiling in unfamiliar places. Davies came down, and with unconcealed pride introduced me to the sleeping-cabin (he called the other one 'the saloon'). Another candle was lit and showed two short and narrow berths with blankets, but no sign of sheets; beneath these were drawers, one set of which Davies made me the master of, evidently thinking them a princely allowance of space for my wardrobe.

'You can chuck your things down the skylight on to your berth as you unpack them,' he remarked. 'By the way, I doubt if there's room for all you've got. I suppose you couldn't manage —'

'No, I couldn't,' I said shortly.

The absurdity of argument struck me: two men, doubled up like monkeys, cannot argue.

'If you'll go out I shall be able to get out too,' I added. He seemed miserable at this ghost of an altercation, but I pushed past, mounted the ladder, and in the expiring moonlight unstrapped that accursed portmanteau and, brimming over with irritation, groped among its contents, sorting some into the skylight with the same feeling that nothing mattered much now, and it was best to be done with it; re-packing the rest with guilty stealth ere Davies should discover their character, and strapping up the whole again. Then I sat down upon my white elephant and shivered, for the chill of autumn was in the air. It suddenly struck me that if it had been raining things might have been worse still. The notion made me look round. The little cove was still as glass; stars above and stars below; a few white cottages glimmering at one point on the shore; in the west the lights of Flensburg; to the east the fiord broadening into unknown gloom. From Davies toiling below there were muffled sounds of wrenching, pushing, and hammering, punctuated occasionally by a heavy splash as something shot up from the hatchway and fell into the water.

How it came about I do not know. Whether it was something

pathetic in the look I had last seen on his face — a look which I associated for no reason whatever with his bandaged hand; whether it was one of those instants of clear vision in which our separate selves are seen divided, the baser from the better, and I saw my silly egotism in contrast with a simple generous nature; whether it was an impalpable air of mystery which pervaded the whole enterprise and refused to be dissipated by its most mortifying and vulgarising incidents — a mystery dimly connected with my companion's obvious consciousness of having misled me into joining him; whether it was only the stars and the cool air rousing atrophied instincts of youth and spirits: probably, indeed, it was all these influences, cemented into strength by a ruthless sense of humour which whispered that I was in danger of making a mere commonplace fool of myself in spite of all my laboured calculations; but whatever it was, in a flash my mood changed. The crown of martyrdom disappeared, the wounded vanity healed; that precious fund of fictitious resignation drained away but left no void. There was left a fashionable and dishevelled young man sitting in the dew and in the dark on a ridiculous portmanteau which dwarfed the yacht that was to carry it, a youth acutely sensible of ignorance in a strange and strenuous atmosphere; still feeling sore and victimised; but withal sanely ashamed and sanely resolved to enjoy himself. I anticipate; for though the change was radical its full growth was slow. But in any case it was here and now that it took its birth.

'Grog's ready!' came from below. Bunching myself for the descent, I found to my astonishment that all trace of litter had miraculously vanished, and a cosy neatness reigned. Glasses and lemons were on the table, and the fragrant smell of punch had deadened previous odours. I showed little emotion at these amenities, but enough to give intense relief to Davies, who delightedly showed me his devices for storage, praising the 'roominess' of his floating den. 'There's your stove, you see,' he ended; 'I've chucked the old one overboard.' It was a weakness of his, I should say here, to rejoice in throwing things overboard on the flimsiest pretexts. I afterwards suspected that the new stove had not been 'really necessary' any more than the rigging-screws, but was an excuse for gratifying this curious taste.

We smoked and chatted for a little, and then came the problem of going to bed. After much bumping of knuckles and head and many giddy writhings I mastered it and lay between the rough blankets. Davies, moving swiftly and deftly, was soon in his.

'It's quite comfortable, isn't it?' he said, as he blew out the light from where he lay, with an accuracy which must have been the fruit of long practice.

I felt prickly all over, and there was a damp patch on the pillow, which was soon explained by a heavy drop of moisture falling on my forehead.

'I suppose the deck's not leaking?' I said, as mildly as I could.

'I'm awfully sorry,' said Davies, earnestly, tumbling out of his bunk. 'It must be the heavy dew. I did a lot of caulking yesterday, but I suppose I missed that place. I'll run up and square it with an oilskin.'

'What's wrong with your hand?' I asked sleepily on his return, for gratitude reminded me of that bandage.

'Nothing much; I strained it the other day,' was the reply; and then the seemingly inconsequent remark: 'I'm glad you brought that prismatic compass. It's not really necessary, of course; but' (muffled by blankets) 'it may come in useful.'

From 'The Riddle of the Sands' 1903

Part II

SO MUCH TO LEARN

'*Dabchick*, bound for Ipswich!' I yelled with pride.
'You'll soon be back,' was all he shouted as we swept past.

Maurice Griffiths: *Magic of the Swatchways*   81

R T McMullen

THE LEO

NOTHING could seem more ill-omened than the first incident related in the log for 1850, at the very commencement of my novitiate.

The day the *Leo*, 3 tons, left the builder's yard, she was so carelessly moored by the man who had charge of her, that she grounded during the night on the edge of a camp-shed at Charlton, between the Marine Society's ship and the shore. Being a deep boat, only half-decked, and heavily ballasted, the tide flowed into and filled her. Words will not describe the intense feeling of disappointment and mortification I experienced when I went down the next morning to try my new boat, and saw only a few feet of the mast above water.

With assistance kindly rendered from the Society's ship, she was got up at the following low water, and taken to Greenwich to be cleared of the mud and filth with which she was well plastered inside.

Since that time I have launched two new vessels and took the precaution to have them christened in due form; my neglect of that ceremony in the case of the *Leo* being, no doubt, the pretext for Father Thames taking it into his own hands.

The first sail was as far as Gravesend and back, with a waterman in charge, and this was the only apprenticeship I served. A confiding kinsman, whose judgement was almost equal to my own, accompanied me, and, his opinion coinciding with mine, that there was nothing to do which we could not easily do ourselves, I resolved to dispense with pilotage services from that day as a waste of money.

My first attempt, with only the boy on board and a chart for guide, though a very mild and unambitious little cruise from Charlton to Erith and back, was not concluded without a narrow escape. Passing between the collier brigs off Charlton at ten p.m. to anchor for the night, I made allowance for the two I wished to pass ahead of, and then discovered a third vessel at anchor by itself, upon which we were helplessly driven by the tide. Our mast-head fouling his bowsprit, the *Leo* was beginning to fill, when the crew of the brig got the mast clear and she righted.

The second cruise was regularly planned and more pretentious. It was voted a jolly thing to drop down to Gravesend on the afternoon of the one day, and start early next morning for a sail round the Nore, my confiding kinsman to do duty as mate upon this grand occasion.

Great was our rejoicing when the anchor was let go at Gravesend, after having providentially passed safely inside the ships to the anchorage below the Custom House. After tea, which was made in a bachelor's kettle on deck, all hands turned in—the boy, the bachelor's kettle, and sundries occupied the forecastle, in which there was just room for all when properly packed. We, the quarter-deckers, of course occupied the cabin. Though the boat was only three tons, each had a properly constructed berth six feet by two feet, with bed and leeboard complete. Nothing could be more comfortable, if you could only remember that the deck beams were within six inches of your head. What with glorious anticipations for the morrow, bright ideas that would not keep, but must be communicated immediately, and what with laughing and giggling, being too hot and too cold, and the novelty of the situation generally, there was not a wink of sleep got all night.

At last the day broke on which we were to make our mark in the sailing world. O dear! I shall never forget that day, though a veil is thrown over it in the log-book where it is mentioned in these suspicious terms: 'Sailed out the first season in the Thames, &c., &c., &c. Once venturing to the Nore; but in this adventure got into such trouble that there was no chance of repeating the attempt until the recollection of it had quite blown over, which was not earlier than the following year.' Nevertheless, as an act of penance for unpardonable rashness, I will confess a few scrapes.

After washing and dressing in the sharp air of an early June morning, with a nice breeze from the westward, we got the anchor up at five a.m. This was no sooner done, and the jib set, than we fell athwart a yacht, about ten tons, which brought out two wrathful and unlucky wights in their night shirts, who, with chattering teeth and much bare flesh exposed to the fresh wind, worked well and successfully to get us clear. Having given us a parting benediction, they dived precipitately below, and no doubt drank health and success to us in a well-earned glass of brandy. I must further confess that, being in a state of bewilderment on account of the getting athwart hawse not being in the day's programme, we did nothing whatever towards clearing the vessels, nor even thought of thanking the gentlemen for their exertions until they had probably fallen into a sound sleep again.

It is usual, I think, after a confession to find, if possible, some excuse for the fault you have confessed. Now my excuse for getting athwart hawse was this: after much cogitation I made up my mind to cast the boat's head to the northward, but happening to spy a swell on board a yacht close by, with a gold band on his cap and a great many gilt buttons on his coat, I was greenhorn enough to think he knew something, so modestly asked his advice, and followed it to our grief and confusion.

Since then I have grown older, and have learnt one or two little secrets which I will disclose for the information of brother greenhorns. When you hear a man talking so loudly that you are in doubt how many yachts he owns, be sure his nearest approach to ownership is knowing a friend, who is or was an owner. Therefore be careful not to ask the name of his yacht. And when you see a yachting gilt-bespangled dandy, trust rather to your 'Seaman's Manual and Vocabulary of Sea-terms,' and do not disgust the gentleman with awkward questions before company unless you wish to make an enemy.

Running down the *Hope* under all sail on a beautiful sunny morning was such a delightful novelty, and so exhilarating, that confidence was restored sooner than might have been the case if we had not been able to charge our first misfortune upon the lubber with the gold band and gilt buttons. After a good breakfast we were in high spirits, and every fresh gust of wind was answered with an inward chuckle of satisfaction.

All went merrily as a marriage bell until we were about a mile below the Nore, when our enjoyment was at its height, and it was thought time to turn back. Finding, on coming to the wind, that it was necessary to take a reef down, we ceased all at once to see beauty anywhere, had misgivings, and secretly began to 'wish we were at home'.

A nasty short sea having got up, I had sense enough to keep the weather-shore, but quite forgot there was a Nore sand until frightened out of our wits by the vessel bumping on it. Our hair had scarcely time to stand on end before she came off again, having crossed the sand from the inside into the rough water of the fairway. Now began another trouble. The sea in the tideway was so violent, and the wind so strong, that sail was shortened to close reefs, which, though indispensable to our safety under the circumstances, would have been unnecessary, had I known how to sail the boat. In this hampered state we just managed to fetch above the Chapman Head at high water, when an accident happened which, but for presence of mind on my part, and a sudden conviction that there was no time to lose, would have been attended with horrible consequences to myself. The mainsheet was attached to the sail in two parts, viz., a single block and a pair of sister-hooks. To prevent the block from striking our heads I put it in the upper cringle and the hooks in the lower. The hooks not being moused, as they should have been, one of them, unobserved by me, shook adrift while the boat was in stays. The sail in passing over to leeward happening to hit my face, the hook caught me in the right eye, and would have dragged me over the lee gunwale if I had not seized the sail with both hands and extricated myself as soon as possible. It could not have dragged me overboard if I had chosen to resist with the weight of my body, but anyone who has had a cinder or other foreign substance under the upper eyelid will understand that, the hook having got all the eyelid in the deepest part, its leading was irresistible. My companions were horror-stricken when I told them what I thought was the matter and called for help. However, before they could get to me, it was all over. Never before or since have I felt such a sense of joy and thankfulness as when, having applied a handkerchief to the wound. I caught a glimmer of daylight. As the mate had only seen a tiller and never handled one, we were compelled to hail a schooner for assistance. There happened fortunately to be two Greenwich watermen on board, who left in their boat, which had been towing astern, and boarded us after a little hesitation. There is no doubt that the *Leo* looked dangerous in the sea, and was dangerous, being at that time only half decked and deep with ballast. She had a shifting wash-board to keep water out, but it was a very imperfect arrangement. The men, finding her better than they expected, shook out a reef and ran for Yantlet, where we left her heeling over on the ground, and walked up to the village of Allhallows to dry our clothes, which were wet through, and to get, if possible, a hot dinner. Though very anxious to see a surgeon and get relief for my wound, which was extremely troublesome, I had to bear the pain and the doubt as to what injury was done until the next day. Having supplied our necessities at a decent little inn, we all walked down again and went on board to wait for the tide; the men lashing their boat to the *Leo*'s gunwale to assist her in rising, about which we had doubts.

Shortly after midnight, with two reefs down, we started again, towing their boat with our little punt stowed inside it, and arrived at Gravesend about 4.30 a.m., where the mate and I landed very wet with spray, cold and miserable, to take the first train to Woolwich.

On landing we certainly did not find *terra firma*, for everything seemed to be in motion. For several hours on the previous day we had been greatly annoyed by a stone bottle full of beer rolling about on the cabin floor. After the boat began to jump about, I wouldn't leave the helm, and the mate didn't care to be groping about securing things below, because I must have battened him down the while to keep the water out, and his health, though good in the open air, might have taken a sudden turn down there. For nothing is more calculated to ruin one's sea legs than crawling on hands and knees in a heavy sea, in a space so confined that it was like crawling under a table. Besides, they say it is the last straw that breaks the camel's back, and he had a suspicion that *that* would be the last straw for him. Therefore we let the bottle roll and bang about all day.

While dozing in the train up to Woolwich and in our beds the following night, we were both pitching and rolling about, the sensation of motion being accompanied by the wretched sound of the rolling bottle. We have since had many a laugh over this.

The mate having qualified for sea so far as he considered necessary for passing an examination at one of the Inns of Court, resigned his appointment and has never been seen on board a yacht since.

Upon submitting my wound to surgical examination, the eye was pronounced not to be injured, though its escape was a miracle. It was closed, however, for a fortnight, and nearly a month elapsed before it could take its turn of duty and be properly considered a 'weather eye'.

After being so badly handled at the first venture, I could not get under way or go in amongst the ships to bring up without having a taste of brimstone in the mouth from excessive anxiety. I envied the bargemen their coolness and evident self-possession, and looked forward to the time when I should feel the same confidence. My plan was to persevere in sailing by day or night in all weathers, and never to let want of confidence stand in the way. In this manner, getting into scrapes and getting out of them, I learnt more of practical sailing in a few months than I should have learnt in several years if I had hired a man to take the lead in everything.

E. E. Nott-Bower

INITIATION

ON a certain day in 1945, I was wandering despondently about Richmond looking for a place to put a caravan. I see now that it was rather a ridiculous thing to be doing. The fact was that I possessed a caravan, and it seemed a pity not to live in it, rather than in the bed-sitting room in London which gave me a permanent nightmare. Passing over Richmond bridge, my eye lighted on a collection of craft moored to the bank upstream. On the whole they were deplorable craft, but one among them seemed, even to my untutored eye, to possess an air of belonging to the open seas rather than to the Thames at Richmond.

I made my way round to get a closer look. A small man with a beard was in occupation, and he asked me aboard. He was obviously a proper seafaring type, and as he showed me round, conversing in language pleasantly decorated with fruity technical terms with which, at that time, I was only vaguely familiar, I fell into a sort of salty trance, from which I have never properly recovered.

Commenting acidly on the indignity of having to endure autumn leaves on the deck of a sea-going vessel, he led me down to the cabin where, over mugs of beer, he continued his discourse. I gathered almost at once that *Smew I* was for sale, at a figure not much in excess of the price of a caravan. My eye wandered round the sunny cabin with its large sky-light, its comfortable bunks, its bookcase, brass clock and barometer and, I blush to admit it, I then and there decided to buy her. I did not tell Edward so, for he, not having realised the full depths of my ignorance of nautical matters, was enjoying his sales talk as much as I was.

Had I not been in a trance, I might have been awed to learn of *Smew's* great age (fifty-three—a year more than my own), and of the equal antiquity of her rig; I might have made some show of prodding her timbers with a knife, or of testing her auxiliary motor. Instead, I just sat there drinking beer, and hearing how *Smew* was well known before the war as an able little vessel capable of going anywhere; often to be seen thrash-

88

ing down-Channel in dirty weather, or hove-to, riding out a gale, and shipping never a drop of water; a bit slow to windward perhaps, but I didn't want one for racing, did I?; was registered at Lloyds (a telling point, since I knew Lloyds to be a kind of maritime Tattersalls); was suspected of having been involved in smuggling activities in her earlier days ... and so it went on.

It was some time before the fact emerged that Edward had never sailed in *Smew* himself, and that in fact he had acquired her only a few months previously, and had brought her from Southampton in a lorry. But I persisted in maintaining my belief that he was an honest soul, and that his views on sailing-boats, even those he wished to sell, were worthy of deep respect. I was quite right as it turned out.

For decency's sake, I went away and pretended to think the matter over for a few days, but actually I had already decided. I would buy *Smew* and live in her; I would acquire and read every book I could lay my hands on concerning seamanship and navigation; I would spend my week-ends, and any other spare moments, in beautifying *Smew* and making her ready for the sea; and on the day that I retired I would sail her out of the Thames into the Channel.

All these things I succeeded in doing. Some were pleasant, such as reading Slocum, Voss and Claud Worth, or varnishing the cabin-top on a sunny day; some unpleasant, such as filling the bilges with ballast on a dirty January night. Under skilled supervision I moved *Smew* under power from Richmond to London Docks, and later I took my courage in both hands and ventured forth alone on the waters of the Thames. I was not apprehensive of shipwreck or disaster, but I felt rather like a new boy at school and expected some person in a peaked cap, probably connected with Trinity House or some such fearsome institution, to roar at me 'What the hell do you think you're doing?' I just wouldn't know. There were probably hundreds of crimes which my books had forgotten to mention. But I need not have worried. It was two years before anyone addressed an angry word to me afloat, and that was when I tried to enter the naval harbour at Gibraltar without permission.

I continued my acquaintance with Edward, and have done so ever since to my great benefit. The more I saw of him, the more I realised how much he knew that I wanted to know, and the more he realised what a public danger I might become if something was not done about it. My previous experience of sailing had been confined to three or four brief episodes in dinghies and large rowing-boats equipped with lugsails, none of which tended to advance my prestige as a mariner. I could not conceal this from Edward for very long.

He used to come and spend occasional week-ends with me, and steep me in a strong solution of brine. We would proceed with the rigging of *Smew*, every detail of hull and gear being

89

explained. When a splice was required, I was shown how to splice; when a leak in deck or cabin-top was bothering me, I was shown how to stop leaks; when a small hole was found in a sail, I was shown the use of palm and needle. When it was too dark to do any more, we would repair to the 'Steamship' or the 'Prospect of Whitby' for beer and nautical conversation, to be followed by a meal at a Chinese restaurant, where Edward would produce a pair of ivory chopsticks and display, at any rate in my untutored view, astonishing skill in their use.

It was an exhausting life, as I had a busy job in London which occupied me until late in the evenings, so that the 'homework' which Edward set me between his visits had to be done at nights; but the satisfaction of seeing *Smew* steadily progress towards completion, and of feeling my knowledge of her increase in proportion, was very ample repayment. Navigation held few terrors for me, as I had studied topographical survey as part of my military duties as a Sapper, and this often involved thinking in inches or less as a standard of accuracy. It was a comfort to reflect that at sea one could usually be satisfied with a possible error of a few miles.

My personal equipment as a mariner on the eve of setting out on my first passage amounted to having messed about in dinghies and rowing-boats at odd times during my life; for over six months I had lived aboard *Smew*, mostly in cold, wet weather, and under expert guidance had got her rigged and fit to venture out to sea; I had read many books on sailing and seamanship, some by experts to show how things should be done, and some by novices to show how they should not; and I had a fair theoretical knowledge of navigation and chart work. But I was acutely aware that all this, although providing an essential background, was little enough qualification for having personal charge of a vessel at sea.

Smew was designed for a Colonel Smee by Mr Trew, so the name, being also that of a lesser-known sea bird, was inevitable. Apart from the installation of an auxiliary engine in 1937, she is the same now as when she was built — a gaff-rigged cutter, clinker built, with heavy spars and gear capable of standing up to all kinds of rough treatment. She has a tall topmast, which can be housed in bad weather, and carries a topsail and jib-topsail. Her reefing gear is of the old-fashioned type. She is 30 feet long overall (26 feet on the waterline) with a 10-foot beam, and draws only about 3 feet 8 inches. This shallow draught enables one to take her through inland waterways, but ⌣y no means precludes deep-sea cruising. She has a straight iron keel of about a ton, and carries a ton of lead ballast inside. She comes under the generic term of 10-tonner, though she is actually rated at eleven.

When I bought her from Edward he had just constructed a tabernacle, in which the mast is pivoted, enabling it to be lowered with the minimum amount of trouble. There is a roomy cockpit with a high coaming, which gives one a feeling of great security in rough weather, a cabin, and a large fo'c'sle. There is no companion from cockpit to cabin, and the easiest way to get down is backwards—one knee on the cockpit deck, and the other leg down to cabin level two feet below. A pace back now, and one can stand erect underneath the skylight. This is of great importance, for it is here that we dress and wash in turns, using a basin on the table; wash up, and navigate.

There is a small low gap in the bulkhead between cabin and fo'c'sle. This gap is at the root of all the rude health we fully enjoy in *Smew*. Getting through it entails a ducking motion which exercises practically every muscle in the body. If one has come in to cook, one now sits on the locker on the port side. The canvas cot above the locker is hinged, so that it can be swung up against the ship's side. It is normally kept in this position with some spare bedding, empty kit-bags, etc., stuffed in behind it. The similar cot opposite is kept down, and is loaded with stores of all kinds, from tea to sea-anchors.

Seated on the locker, one is in a comfortable and commanding position to select pots, pans and kettles from the opposite locker, and foodstuffs from the shelves on one's right hand. The twin gas-rings are on the floor immediately in front. Pots and pans seem to cling with extraordinary tenacity to these gas-rings, and even if they come off, they usually only skate about the floor the right way up. This cooking position is very comfortable, and I think I would prefer it to a stand-up galley. The fo'c'sle also contains the spare sails and bosun's stores.

Two people can sail *Smew* quite easily, and for day sailing, when one puts into harbour every night, two is the most convenient number. A body living in the fo'c'sle, unless it is an extremely small, agile, non-complaining body, is inclined to be a hindrance to the manifold activities which take place there. On a long passage, however, involving nights at sea, it is perhaps worth while to have three. Since there is always one on deck, the cabin bunks can be used in rotation.

I had made no very definite plans for the first year, beyond sailing *Smew* along the south coast to some place within reach of my home in Devon. After that the itinerary would depend on how she behaved at sea, on how much confidence I could achieve in my handling of her, and on who I could get to sail with me. I am surprised, on looking back, that I had taken so little account of the latter question, which is one on which so many sailing plans are shattered. It solved itself, as you shall hear.

When I sailed from London Docks in April, 1946, I was accompanied by Edward, but I could count on him only as far as Dover. The trip was to be done in two week-ends, during the first of which we hoped to reach Queenborough, near Sheerness. I say I sailed from London Docks, but this is not quite correct. I had looked upon that hour as marking not only my release from the bondage of office work in London, but also the end of my labours, at any rate of the more unseemly ones, on *Smew*'s preparation. I pictured myself at the helm, gliding peacefully down the Thames with that air of efficient indolence exhibited in such perfection by the crews of sailing barges. In the event I was below, trying to trace a mysterious ignition fault in the engine. *Smew* was being ignominiously towed by a friendly craft, and Edward was at the helm. The wind was dead in our faces, and I was hot, dirty and disappointed.

After an hour the friendly craft had to leave us, and the tow-rope was cast off. I abandoned the engine and, setting sail, we beat down river to Gravesend. That I enjoyed, as anyone must enjoy his first sail in a boat of any consequence. It was not exactly indolent, for we must have gone about every five minutes on an average, but I quickly came to understand the illusion of leisure which the sailing of a fair-sized boat conveys to the onlooker. Everything happens much more slowly than one expects, and there is never any hurry about doing anything—at least, if there is a hurry, it is nearly always due to lack of elementary foresight. In fact, one can judge the efficiency of the crew of a sailing-boat largely by the apparent lethargy which they display. Edward, for instance, you would often imagine to be in a deep coma until a leisurely but precise movement demonstrates his continued consciousness.

We anchored at Grays that night, and sailed to Queensborough next day. I then had a week to do and collect all the things I had forgotten, and I found it none too much. Edward joined me again late on the following Friday night, and on the way back from the station we discussed the prospects. The B.B.C. forecast had been 'moderate to fresh north to north-east wind', and I confess I had a shade of doubt as to whether this was an entirely appropriate setting for a small untried vessel on a sea passage round the Foreland after many years of idleness. Edward, however, had no doubts at all, and as soon as we were aboard we began preparations for a start about four a.m., which would give us a fair tide for the greater part of the day.

We inspected all gear, and took two reefs in the mainsail, to avoid the possibility of having to reef in the dark while sailing. The wind, even in harbour, appeared to me to be more fresh than moderate, but Edward refused to allow it more than Force 3. Its direction was NNE, and we therefore hoped to make the Longnose buoy, off North Foreland, from our departure point without tacking.

At half-past three we ate a large meal, but what with nervous excitement and the fact that large meals have never had much appeal for me at that hour of the morning, I cannot truthfully say I enjoyed it.

At four o'clock I started the motor, the anchor was weighed, and we were off. It was still dark, and I found the number and variety of lights confusing. Edward, however, knew the neighbourhood well, and we picked our way out to Sheerness without difficulty. Off Garrison Point there was a very sizeable sea, but I was much reassured at the way *Smew* rode over the waves rather than going through them. Soon our course enabled us to make sail, and the engine was stopped. It was now just getting light; *Smew* was behaving beautifully under sail, and sea-sickness had shown no signs of rearing its ugly head. We were making our course fairly comfortably close-hauled, and once round the Foreland we should have a fair wind for Dover. I felt like indulging in a snatch of song, but thought better of it, having a suspicion that Providence might disapprove of a display of elation at such an early stage and get it back on me.

My log records that at 6.20 we passed the Mid Spaniard buoy, and that at 6.35 the dinghy broke adrift. We wore the boat round and brought the dinghy alongside, but the sea was considerable, and we found it impossible to grab and hold the dinghy while a fresh rope was rove through the towing-ring. Eventually we achieved it by means of throwing a heavy fender, attached to a line, over the dinghy thwart. By this I held the dinghy while Edward hung over the stern and managed to get a rope through the ring. At last we were on our course again, but things were not quite the same. The sea looked more unfriendly, the wind seemed to have increased, the sky was grey, Edward was looking thoughtful, and I had no further desire to sing.

Some two hours later, on reaching the SE Margate buoy we found we could no longer make our course to the Long-nose as the wind had slightly headed us. I asked Edward if we could now assess the wind at Force 4, and to this he reluctantly agreed. I then inquired how I should describe, for entry in the log, the state of the sea. 'Rough' was the only word I could think of, but Edward preferred 'confused', and this was duly entered.

Two tacks, and we were off the Longnose. The old boat seemed sluggish so I took a look inside the cabin and found an alarming quantity of water. I shouted to Edward and we hove her to and got on to the pump. A few strokes and it jammed. We removed the plunger to find a mass of shavings, matches and such like in the valve. We cleaned and re-assembled it but it jammed again about every ten strokes.

It was raining now; water was washing about the cabin floor, and all the charts had shot out of their rack and were floating about on the oily surface of the bilge-water. The motion of the ship was intensely uncomfortable, and I was definitely feeling very far from well. As I staggered about the cabin, making efforts to reduce the shambles, Edward informed me that the plunger of the bilge pump had fallen off into the bilges under the engine. During the next hour I tried to comfort myself with the reflection that in all the sailing books I had read the writers invariably maintained that moments of this sort were compensated for by subsequent periods of ecstatic happiness, and that the balance of enjoyment was unquestionably on the right side.

'This,' I mused palely, 'is a formidable overdraft to record on the first page of the account.'

We collected a bucket and a saucepan, and took up some floor-boards. Edward filled the saucepan from the bilges and poured it into the bucket. When the bucket was full I bore it on deck and emptied it into the sea. Every ten buckets we changed jobs. I was disgracefully ill, and I believe I have never enjoyed an hour less, but strangely enough, though *Smew*'s motion has often been equally unseemly, I have never since been sea-sick.

After an hour and a half of this we got sailing again, this time south with the wind on our quarter, and the motion consequently easier. The sea nevertheless was to me definitely alarming, and when the dinghy tow-rope again broke I was not at all surprised that Edward, who was at the helm, watched it disappear without a comment. It was a new dinghy for which I had an intense affection, but it would have been impossible to recover it in that sea.

We ran past the Goodwins between two and four o'clock. The scene was one of unbroken greyness. Low grey clouds were scudding up from aft across the sky, the big grey seas were breaking in the banks, and a forlorn grey light-vessel was bobbing about in the distance like a lost cork. I shuddered and felt I never desired to see the Goodwins again, not even if the alternative were to stay quietly at home weeding the garden for the rest of my days. But I was feeling decidedly grey myself; I had had no sleep the night before, and I was extremely cold, wet and sea-sick.

It was soon after six o'clock when, with infinite relief, we dropped anchor in the outer harbour at Dover. After we had cleared up, Edward suggested we should cook a meal. With the best will in the world I could only regard this as a display of shameless braggadocio, and climbed firmly into my bunk, to remain there till late the following morning.

From 'Ten Ton Travel' 1950

Maurice Griffiths

A CHILLY INTRODUCTION

I T was on a Saturday night in January some twelve years ago, and having just acquired sole ownership in a little two-ton cabin-sloop called *Dabchick*, which was lying at Woodbridge in Suffolk, I had enlisted the enthusiastic help of an old school friend, Derek, who I gathered had done a little sailing in and out of this river before, to fetch the boat round to the moorings that awaited her at Ipswich.

To look at, *Dabchick* left a good deal to be desired if one's ideas ran on yachts glistening in the sun on the Solent. She was a converted ship's boat of uncertain age, with a transom stern, 17 feet overall, 6 feet beam, and drew 3 feet, with a small, lead keel bolted on the bottom of a short, false keel. Someone with a certain amount of optimism and an obvious contempt for post-war yachting parties had converted her for use as a small hireling on the Broads, and she had, in consequence, a rather neat lifting cabin-top with Willesden canvas flaps at the sides, a mast in a tabernacle, a large mainsail that was only intended for Broads sailing, plenty of lockers round the well, and a minute cabin which was my chief pride because it had two plush-cushioned berths and was fitted almost entirely in well-chosen varnished pitch-pine, while the floor was covered with real blue lino!

That the little wretch was hard-headed, slow in stays, almost dangerously tender, narrow-bowed, and, being ballasted too much by the head, was very wet and suicidal in a seaway; and that her rig of standing lug mainsail and large jib was about as mad a combination for sea sailing as could be devised, only occurred to me—by degrees—later. So also did the fact that her hull had seen better days and at least two of the planks were pulling away from their fastenings.

The man who had sold me the boat had told me he would have her ready to sail away and lying at anchor at a spot called 'Kison', about a mile below the town, where we should also find the dinghy on the beach. Here she would be able to lie afloat at low water and we could go aboard her as soon as we arrived by the evening train.

As we picked our way cautiously along the slippery sea-wall that the local people of Edward FitzGerald's native town refer to as The Promenade, stopping occasionally to retrieve one or other of our packages as they fell in rotation, we began to anticipate all the excitement of a 'sea passage' (as we called it) on the morrow. It was still snowing in drifts, and as we stopped for a short rest under the lee of Everson's boat-building shed, the wind roared savagely through the poplars overhead, their tall heads waving violently against the gloom of the sky, while the fury of the gusts made us stagger like drunken figures.

Somehow, as the lights of the little country town were left behind and we trudged on into the nothingness that was the river, the humour of the situation, which had been buoying up my spirits since we had begun our shopping, left me, and I began to wish I hadn't been so enthusiastic about getting the boat round this week-end. That's the trouble with Derek, I was thinking; you mention a possible trip in a rash moment and he overwhelms you with his enthusiasm. The idea of going aboard a cold, cramped and obviously damp little boat on a night like this with the intention of rising early and sailing round to the Orwell became more and more repugnant as we stumbled along.

'By Jove, if we've got a breeze like this tomorrow,' Derek called boisterously over his shoulder, 'we ought to make a quick passage of it, oughtn't we?'

'Oh yes, rather, just the breeze we want,' I shouted back in the kind of voice Captain Kidd might have used to encourage his crews, hoping my friend hadn't heard my teeth chatter.

At last we had reached the strip of shore at Kingston Quay and begun to search for the dinghy. My heart gave a leap as I caught sight of a dim white shape a few yards off shore and could actually hear the water washing against the bows of my new boat. Excitement and the thrill of ownership banished all misgivings I had entertained on the sea-wall.

'I say, it's a bit thick!' Derek's voice sounded plaintive in the darkness. 'That old fool's left the dinghy too far down, and the water's covered her anchor.'

Someone had to retrieve the thing, and we tossed for it — with my usual luck. I should like to draw a veil over the next few minutes of cold misery when I slipped off my nether garments and waded in with icy water over my knees, found the dinghy's anchor by treading on one of its flukes, and then spent five minutes in the biting wind (blessing the merciful darkness, all the same) running up and down the beach to dry myself before dressing again. And when we eventually got aboard the little *Dabchick* and found the damp-smelling cabin filled with berth cushions, blankets, a sail and a heap of gear which had all been bundled on to the floor by the late owner, I would have given anything for a hot bath and a warm bed in a good hotel.

Yet an hour later we were reclining on the two berths facing one another through an atmosphere you could have cut with a knife, while the remains of a hot meal lay huddled on the locker lid which did duty as a table between us. The cabin lamp was putting up a brave fight and casting a soft, warm glow over the interior of the kennel-like cabin, while a Primus was roaring cheerfully on the floor, heating up a saucepan full of good coffee.

As I lay back on my berth and gazed with glassy eyes through rings of tobacco smoke at the cabin-top beams, I would not have changed places with any other mortal in the world. It would have called for too much effort, for one thing. The little boat, sheering about in the squalls and snubbing occasionally on her anchor chain, was quivering with life and warmth and companionship, the wind was moaning through her rigging (the expression attracted me at the moment) and the little waves were breaking along her clinker-built sides with sudden rushes of sound. The possession of one's first boat and all its attendant interests and novelties is an experience which is to be remembered for the rest of one's life.

And later that night, as we lay in our berths under warm blankets, sleep withheld her spell for a time while we listened to all the unaccustomed noises, trying to diagnose each one. The sudden rasp of the anchor chain on the bobstay, the *tap, tap,* of a halliard on the mast, the occasional squeak of a block in its eye-bolt, the *scrunch* of the water against the lands of the planks, and over all the continuous roar of the wind in the trees that sheltered this snug anchorage.

Once, as we dozed off, the cry of a curlew, faint and shrill, came from far down the river. It sounded plaintive out there in the cold, windy night, while in here it was so warm. . . .

I awoke with that peculiar stiff and uncomfortable feeling that one gets from sleeping in an unheated boat in winter. The temperature in the cabin had undergone a change during the night. In fact, it was now so nearly arctic that staying in one's bunk with the hope of getting warm again was out of the question. We had left the cabin-top raised to give us air, and the draught that was pouring in through the gap above the door penetrated the blankets like a knife.

I shut up the air inlet and lit the Primus, but it was not until the coffee was put by to keep warm and the bacon was sizzling in the pan that my companion fully opened the eye that had been fluttering for some time and made a poor pretence at waking up with a start of surprise.

'Good Heavens, I haven't overslept, have I?'

I said, Oh no, he surely knew that I was by nature an early riser? Apparently he did not.

'But—it's hardly light yet.'

I glanced out at the grey sky that was only just beginning to pale in the east.

'No, it's only seven o'clock; you needn't get up yet. I thought you'd like breakfast in bed.'

He sank back with a sigh of relief.

'By Jove, Maurice,' he said magnanimously. 'Your brain must be as good as new.'

If we had hoped for considerably less wind (although neither of us had dared express the wish) we were disappointed, for it was blowing as hard as ever when we started to get under way about nine o'clock, and the squalls were coming out of a grey, snow-laden sky. The wind had backed more to the west, but it was every bit as piercing.

'Now for a fine s-sail!' Derek cried as he started to tie in reef-points, but the remark, begun well, ended on a slightly *tremolo* note that rather spoilt the effect. I dared not risk my voice and remained silent.

We tied in the second reef, for we found that the big lugsail, intended for the Broads, had only two reefs. There still seemed a great deal of it when it was set, slamming about in the gusts. There was, we found, only one jib, and that was big enough to fill the whole fore triangle when set on a 5-ft. bowsprit.

'Never mind, she'll carry it!'

Derek's enthusiasm was infectious, and when he broke out the anchor, *Dabchick* started off down the narrow channel like a rocket. The little boat almost took charge, and it was all I could do with both hands wrenching at the short tiller to keep off the bank.

At the first bend we had to gybe. Derek began to haul in the mainsheet.

'Keep her going until I get this swigged right in,' he said breathlessly, and as he did so the boom flew over with a crash and laid *Dabchick* on her side until the water poured over the well coamings, then she righted herself.

We were so surprised to find the boat upright and the mast still standing that we shook hands over our good fortune. And while my attention was thus taken up, *Dabchick* took a wild sheer and nearly mounted the bank. However, the interval gave us time to breathe, and the flood-tide, aided with the boathook, floated us off in a quarter of an hour, and we continued our somewhat erratic progress down the river.

Off Waldringfield the channel widened, and even on this cold, blustering day the Deben looked pretty in the pale light of an obscured sun. The bare trees were waving their branches at us as the squalls tore through them, stripping them of twigs, while their nakedness was enhanced by the white patches of snow that lay here and there in the fields.

As we rounded into Ramsholt Reach we brought the wind forward of our starboard beam, and with her sails sheeted in *Dabchick* lay over in the squalls until the water lapped into the well. At times she was overpowered, and we had to ease the jib sheet to let her luff up a little into the wind. This jib of hers was too big for the reefed mainsail and was holding her head down, causing her to carry lee helm. It had no reef-points, and neither of us knew enough then to take in a temporary reef with 'stopping' at the head.

It was about high water now, and by the time we were passing the collection of forlorn-looking motor-boats and fishing craft moored above Felixstowe Ferry, the ebb had begun to race out through the narrows between the shingle banks.

The sight that met our inexperienced eyes as we turned the last corner and opened up the bar made our hearts miss a beat. The entrance appeared to be an unbroken mass of white foam with leaping crests, whose tops tumbled over and were carried along like steam by the wind. For one moment it was on the tip of my tongue to suggest running back, but there was a six-knot ebb carrying us ruthlessly towards that barrier of shoals and broken water, and, sailing her hardest, *Dabchick* would not have been able to forge against it.

There was no turning back now.

As he had professed a slight knowledge of the lie of the channel over this bar, Derek took the helm while I held on to the weather coaming and watched the banks of shingle on either side racing past. A coastguardsman came running down to the point from the Martello tower, and as we drew abreast he asked our name and where we were bound.

'*Dabchick*, bound for Ipswich!' I yelled with pride.

'You'll soon be back,' was all he shouted as we swept past.

A minute later we buried our bowsprit into the first of the breakers, a sea leapt up, filled our jib and the sail burst with a noise like a gunshot. At the same instant our keel hit the shingle with a jarring crash that pitched us both to the lee side of the well.

Dabchick lifted her foredeck clear of the welter of water, rose on a comber, staggered on and crashed once more on the hard shingle. A third time she lifted and fell, while a sea broke on to her weather deck and poured into the well, and then she lay on her beam ends while the furious tide swirled around her, pressing her harder on to the dreaded bank and bringing the pram dinghy alongside to leeward.

'My God!' cried Derek, as he scrambled up to the windward side. 'I've piled you on.'

The remnants of the jib were flogging away to leeward in long streamers, the violence of their antics shaking the masthead. All around us was a seething welter of foam and water, while the roaring of the seas on the bar and the continual thuds as they broke against our weather side filled our ears with a terrifying tumult of sound.

My attention was arrested by my companion, who was hurriedly slipping off various garments without a thought to his innate modesty or the perishing cold. The horrible thought occurred to me that the strain had been too much for him — Derek, I had always thought, possessed a delicately balanced mind, and now in this emergency —

'I've put you on, old man,' he explained, looking rather like a ballet girl as he fluttered, so to speak, in the wind, 'and I'm jolly well going to get you off. So here g-goes!'

And before I could protest he had slipped overboard up to his waist. The boat moved as soon as he jumped from her, and when he put his shoulder under her quarter she gave one more scrunch and sailed off, dragging him with her.

'I'm all right!' he cried, as I tried to haul him aboard, 'keep her going till we're over the bar.'

The next few minutes were a nightmare, for the little boat was quite unable to cope with the steep, curling seas and simply dived into the heart of them, burying her foredeck to the mast and wallowing under the weight of water. Every moment I expected to feel her hit the ground again, but mercifully she was swept clear into deeper water, where the seas were more regular, and I was able to round her up into the wind and help my friend aboard.

'Near thing. All my fault; I hugged the shore too close,' was all he said as he disappeared into the cabin to dry himself. My thanks seemed absurdly inadequate in the circumstances.

When he came out into the well again, fully dressed, and took the helm, I clambered forward to take in what remained of our jib. It looked too much like a signal of distress to be left up.

Sitting astride the mast tabernacle, I hauled in the flogging strips of canvas while the lean-headed little boat dived into half a dozen successive seas, drenching me and sending a lot of water below, squirting through a dozen places in the forehatch and cabin-top.

For four hours we tried to beat against the strong ebb that was pouring north against us, while the squalls laid us almost flat and the salt spray and sleet blinded us. The boat, with no headsail and a mainsail that was obviously too large, reefed as it was, proved almost unmanageable, carrying prodigious weather helm and getting into irons every time we went about. Had I known then how to counteract this, I should willingly have hove-to and moved half the ballast further aft. As it was we thrashed on, grimly fighting every inch of the way and anxiously watching our pathetically slow progress each time we stood in on the port tack towards Felixstowe.

That was the coldest and most miserable passage I have ever made. We were able to stand only short spells at the helm, and I well remember the agony of aching hands as one sat in the bucking cabin, trying to get back one's circulation in the brief spell below, while the increasing bilge water surged up on to the lee berth.

By the time we had brought Landguard Point at the entrance of Harwich Harbour in sight through a break in a sleet squall, the ebb-tide had eased, and another board allowed us to fetch through the shallow swatchway that used to lie in those days between the end of the jetty and the deadly Platter Sands.

Here an unexpected cross sea suddenly rose above us to windward, tumbled over and fell with a thunderous crash on our deck, seething over the cabin-top and surging into the well. For one sickening moment, as the water boiled around our feet and burst open the cabin doors, it seemed that the little boat had filled and was going down under us; but she slowly shook herself free of the water, lurched on and rounded the point into the harbour, very much down by the head with the weight of water inside her.

While we raced up the smooth water of the harbour I bailed with a bucket until the bilge water was below the floorboards once more; then I lit the Primus and handed out a mug of steaming Bovril to the mate who had so unselfishly risked his life for the sake of my boat.

An hour later, when we lay snugly on my moorings at Ipswich, with the gear stowed and a hot meal under way, we sat in the cramped little cabin, drying ourselves, and declared that, now it was over, it had been a 'great' passage and the boat herself a 'wonderful sea-boat' to have stood it. And the joy of ownership that I felt then, the mounting enthusiasm that swept over me like a flood, glossed over all its trials and hardships, its dangers and miseries, and I wanted to do it again, to go and explore other rivers and estuaries in her—for she was mine. My boat!

The joy of that moment lingers still.

Claud Worth

IANTHE

IN 1885 I bought a clench-built ship's long-boat for thirty shillings. As the result of many weeks' work at Christmas and Easter, of two friends and myself, with occasional help from a local carpenter, this boat grew into my first 'yacht'. We named her *Ianthe*. She was 22 feet long and 6½ feet beam. We raised her topsides one plank higher, and put in six heavy sawn oak floor timbers and about a dozen bent timbers. We decked her all over, with the exception of a well 6 feet long and 2½ feet wide. The ballast was 8 cwt. of old furnace bars bedded into her bottom with Portland cement. A false keel made her draught about 2½ feet. We rigged her as a cutter, with long bowsprit and long running topmast. The mainsail was made by a coast-guard out of a larger second-hand sail which I bought at King's Lynn. A large square-headed gaff-topsail, staysail and three jibs of stout calico were sewn by a housemaid in my father's house and roped and finished by our friend the coastguard. He also taught me how to use a needle and palm, to turn in an eye-splice in wire, and many other things. The cabin, as we called it, under the deck was like the space under a dining table. There was barely room to sit upright on the floor.

One of our first passages, from King's Lynn to Boston, nearly ended in disaster. We arrived in Boston River on a spring tide about an hour before high water and brought up with our twenty-pound anchor and a small hemp rope, and went ashore. On the first of the ebb she tripped her anchor and sheered into the bank. We got back just too late to push her off. We made fast a rope to a post ashore and set it up to the mast-head with the main halyards, the bank being so steep that she would otherwise have rolled over. We spent a miserable night watching her until she floated at about six next morning. In a sense, the accident proved fortunate, for we decided that one anchor was not sufficient. We bought the only anchor we could get, an enormous rusty thing weighing seventy or eighty lbs. and fifty fathoms of stout coir rope. The gear half filled the well, but I remember how opulent and well-found we felt when we were able to refer to our other anchor as 'the kedge'.

The passage from Sutton Bridge to Lowestoft I shall always remember. We left Sutton Bridge early one morning on the top of a spring tide, so were able to sail over all the banks. A pleasant SSW wind carried us to the Bays Channel off Hunstanton and over the flats past Blakeney to Cromer. Soon after this the wind drew ahead, and the rest of the passage was a beat to windward. We lost ground on the ebb but made good progress on the flood, though it was very wet with wind against tide.

Next day, late in the afternoon, we sailed into Lowestoft and moored between the pier and a dolphin, wet through and tired, but happy. We had reached a strange and distant port, and everything was new. Much water had found its way below by way of the open well and through imperfectly caulked seams, but our bedding and spare clothes, stowed in oilskin bags, were dry. While my two friends were decorating the rigging with wet clothes and I was baling the North Sea back into its proper place, a man and two women from a steam yacht stood on the pier and stared down at us. As they were turning away, the man said: 'Good Lord, do they call that pleasure!' I shall never forget our astonishment and disgust at the silly remark. It had not occurred to us that there *could* be a more delightful holiday. We had made a good passage, and were immensely pleased with our vessel because she was our own. The glamour of the sea always makes one's first boat a thing of strength and beauty.

Next year, 1887, we planned an ambitious cruise from the Wash to the Thames and then down Channel as far as we could get in the time available. Fortunately the first Jubilee year had a very fine and settled summer. It had gradually dawned upon each of us that the boat was rather tender, though it would have seemed almost disloyal to discuss it even among ourselves. But when we reached the London River and saw other boats of our size with whole mainsail while we had two reefs, even we had to admit that she was very much over-canvased. So we decided to shorten the mast and cut the first reef off the mainsail. The jibs and staysail, being already too short, would not need alteration. By the advice of the skipper of a barge we went into Greenhithe Creek for this purpose. We had cut about two feet off the lower end of the mast and I had begun turning in the new splices in the rigging when the owner of a yawl yacht, which was fitting out in the creek, came and spoke to us. When we told him that we proposed sailing down Channel we felt grateful that he did not, like everyone else, try to dissuade us. Though the names conveyed nothing to us at the time, the yawl was *Orion* and the owner R. T. McMullen. His parting remark was characteristic, 'If it looks like blowing hard on shore, get in somewhere in good time or else give the land a very wide berth.'

One afternoon we had just managed to save our tide round Dungeness when it began to breeze up from the southward.

By the time we were off Fairlight the wind was too strong for the close-reefed mainsail; so we lowered the mainsail and ran for Rye under staysail only. We had no plan of the place and could make out no entrance. When we were within about a mile of the breakers we set the close-reefed mainsail again and tried to claw off. *Ianthe* barely held her own and was in imminent danger of capsizing. I nursed her as well as I could while Green and Dalrymple passed the end of the coir rope outside the rigging and made it fast to the big anchor. Then we got the canvas down and pitched the anchor over from the well. The bowsprit was already housed right in, and the topmast down on deck. The boat rode wonderfully well and did not drag. The motion was very violent and much water washed along the deck, so that we had to bail continually until the breeze died down at about four o'clock next morning. We called it a gale, but probably it would be about as much as *Tern III* would want for a whole mainsail. When we got under way, with a light fair wind, we were so frightened of the land that we passed Beachy Head almost out of sight. We were learning.

From 'Yacht Cruising' 1910

Hilaire Belloc

COMPASS COURSE

WITH the afternoon the wind freshened, and, as it freshened, went right round by north to a little east of north, whence it blew steadily enough, and gave us about four knots at the fall of darkness.

My companion had never held a tiller, but he was very expert at all sports, and I thought to myself, 'I will see whether so simple a thing as steering a boat cannot be easily accomplished by a man at the first trial. Then shall I be able to get what I badly need, which is a little sleep.' So I lighted the binnacle lamp, I explained to him the function of the lubber's mark, and gave him the point on the card which he was to keep on the lubber's mark. I said to him: 'If it comes on to blow a little harder and the card swings, and the boat tends to yaw a little, don't mind that, but keep the lubber's mark on the average at the point I have given and that will be enough.' He said that he understood all these things, and for the first time in his life set himself to steer a ship. But I, for my part, went down to sleep, confident that if it should come on to blow at all hard it would awaken me there and then, so no great harm could come. I slept for many hours, when suddenly I was awakened by my companion giving a loud cry of astonishment. I tumbled up on deck quickly, and I found him pointing at a light which shone brilliantly upon the horizon, dead on our bow. He said to me: 'Look, look, there is a light dead ahead!' I said to him: 'Of course!' and that it was the light of Strumble Head, outside Fishguard; and I asked him what he would have expected. I had given him his course, and, naturally, he had lifted the light in good time. But he, for his part, could not get over it; he thought it a sort of miracle. He kept on repeating his amazement that so clumsy a thing as a tiller and a rudder, and so coarse an instrument as an old battered binnacle compass, should thread the eye of a needle like that; it was out of all his experience.

A W Roberts

A SHORT CUT TO LONDON

MANY years ago when I was mate of a small barge trading up the rivers and creeks of the Thames Estuary, I sat in a pub in West Mersea in company with a hoary-headed old stalwart who was then seventy-five and had been trading in those parts in sailing barges since he was twelve. His face was much the same colour as a barge's mainsail and his hands bore a striking resemblance to a pair of main sheet blocks.

Over a pint of ale, duly followed by other pints of ale, he was giving me a bit of advice. I was in need of both the ale and the advice because my skipper had gone to hospital with a damaged hand and the owners had shown sufficient trust in me to suggest that I took the barge to London as she was wanted there to load middlings. Blown up with fresh pride, I assured them that I was capable of doing so but now that I had come to grips with the task and felt the weight of a skipper's responsibility I did not feel so brave about it.

'If you can keep ahead of them other barges coming out o' Colne tomorrow you'll load first and be back and unloaded afore the last of 'em's got a bag in the hold.'

'That's all very well,' I said, 'but some of those chaps were sailing in barges before I was born and if they don't know how to beat me up to London then they'll never beat anybody.'

'Ah,' said the ancient with a wag of his head and a suspicion of a wink, 'o' course you needn't say I told you nothin'. You needn't say you seen me at all. An' if you gets up there first they'll think you must have had a lucky slant or done right more be luck than judgement as the sayin' is. But you do what I tell you and you'll be in the Millwall Dock and ready to load while they're still turning up Halfway Reach—that is, if you take every advantage and don't chuck away what you've gained or let Bowline Jack and the likes of him slip by you in the night.'

I told him that I intended to get through the Raysand
Channel as soon as there was water in the morning and then
blow down to the Ridge and over the sand to come out into the
West Swin above the 'Sheers' (which is the name bargemen
always use for the Maplin Spit because there used to be a little
lighthouse there on sheerlegs).

The old chap lit his pipe and blew a stream of strong smelling
smoke across the table.

'And then Bowline Jack'll be over the Buxey and up with
you and beat you to Sea Reach on the next flood.'

After a bit more banter and another couple of pints we finally
got down to brass tacks.

'Well, come on,' I said, 'What would you do?'

Silently he drank up his ale. Then he sucked the last draws
from his pipe and slowly knocked the ashes out on his heel.
He always used to do that when he had something important to
say. He used to reckon he could only do one job at a time and
that there were too many people in such a hurry that they tried
to smoke, drink and talk all at the same time and did none of
them properly.

'It's low water at five in the morning, wind west and tides a-
making. You muster from the Nass beacon where you now lay
on the low water. Give her the sail (mainsail, topsail and foresail) and half a leeboard and haul her short across the spit into
the Raysand. Don't slack your sheet and you'll have water time
you're there. Let her go straight over from the sou'west Buxey
and hold her nicely below Foulness. Then keep your luff, watch
your leeboard and use your lead if you ain't sure. And don't
come off the sand until you can see the Admiralty beacons.'

The landlord called time and we went out into the night.
My venerable companion and adviser walked with me down to
a cottage near the hard where he was staying with his daughter's family while his barge was unloading timber at Maldon.
As we said good night at the gate he tapped me on the shoulder
and pointed meaningly up at the heavy cloud rolling down over
the moonlit Blackwater from the westward.

'You'll have a nice sail tomorrow. Do what I told you and
you'll beat 'em all by miles—miles and miles.'

I did what the old fellow said. With the help of my temporary
mate I got the barge under way just as the tide was creeping up
past the Nass. It was dark then but daylight before we reached
the shallow water of Batchelors Spit. The half leeboard just
smelt the bottom and had to come up a foot. There was just
enough water in the Raysand to allow the barge to heel. Off
Foulness I began to get worried and had to heave the leeboard right up and once her chine did stir up a bit of sand.
But I stuck to my faith in the old man's words and soon we
found a foot or two more water. Sometimes with only a matter
of inches under her it was a great temptation to keep her full
and reach out into the deep water of the West Swin Channel.

But I could see several barges stretching up along the Maplin Edge and I knew that some of them were faster than my barge and handled by wily old fellows who knew more about sailoring than I did. So I kept her on the wind, cut inside the hump on the end of Blacktail Spit and finally came into four fathoms by the lower of the Admiralty Beacons.

By that time the other barges were encountering a dead nose ender as they turned to and fro between the Maplin and the West Barrow. They were some five or six miles astern with about two and a half hours of flood left. As I got into the stronger river tide it was easing where they were and we drew further and further ahead. I fetched the Lower Hope at high water and other barges were out of sight with their anchors down along the edge of the sand between Shoebury and Southend. On the night tide we mustered again and just scrambled in the dock via the South West India entrance. The tide would not have lasted to have sailed right round the Isle of Dogs to use the Millwall Dock entrance which opens into Limehouse Reach. But there is a cutting through from the other side so we were able to berth alongside our steamship ready to take in cargo from her in the morning. Twelve hours later Bowline Jack's barge came sailing up the dock.

'When the hell did you get here?'

'Berthed this morning.'

'Was that you skatin' across the sand Sunday morning?'

'Yes. I could see you down by the Sheers.'

'Takin' a bloody chance weren't you. I don't know where you learnt them tricks but there ain't much water there and you might easily come to grief. Your ol' skipper'd have a fit if he knew you had brought her over there. Another time you let her run down below the Ridge and fetch the Sheers. That's the safest. Too chancy that way you come.'

My old friend's words still rung in my ears and I said nothing. 'You needn't say I told you nothin'. You needn't say you seen me at all.' So I said nothin' and when I left the dock and sailed away for Rochford, Bowline Jack was just beginning to load.

Weston Martyr

SAILOR IN SEARCH OF SMOOTH WATER

WHEN Harris invited me to cruise on the Broads, I said:
'No. I wouldn't be seen dead there. I spit on the Broads.'
Harris, who is not a sailorman, said: 'Oh! Why? I cruised with
a chap up there last summer and it was charming. The place
is full of birds, too, and I thought you said you liked bird
watching.'

I said: 'I do, but not the kind of bird which I hear infests the
place these days. I'm a sailor, I am; not a dance band boy.'

Harris said: 'Well, well. Pity you won't come. I've chartered
something they call a thirty-five-foot Bermuda sloop. She's
lovely. Four spring-beds and a pressure gas cooker. I'm taking a
jar of Navy rum. And Sam's coming. He's got a case of pre-war
gin and a Suffolk cured ham.'

I said: 'It tempts me. But I dare not come. If my sailing
friends heard I'd been yachting on the Broads, my reputation
would be gone forever. They'd guy the life out of me. And I'd
certainly be excommunicated by the Ocean Racing Club gang.
Did you say that ham was Suffolk cured?'

Harris said: 'Yes. And Sam says there's twenty-odd pounds
of it.'

'Then I think it's my duty to come,' I said. 'I need building
up badly. I *will* come. But, whatever you do, Harris, don't you
dare tell anybody.'

We ran Harris's hireling craft to earth at her home port of
Wroxham. The port consisted of a reedy river, fifty feet wide
with a maximum depth of four feet, and it was bung full of
houseboats, motor boats, swans, lounge lizards presumably
male, and a giggling crowd of near-nudes most obviously
female. Harris's boat was moored to a petrol pump and her
name was *Perfect Lady*. She looked to me like a perfect bitch
because she had (*a*) a fifty-foot mast in a tabernacle and no
preventer backstays, (*b*) a maximum draft of two feet with

six feet six inches minimum headroom, (c) she was painted pink with chromium fittings, (d) her cockpit was full of silk cushions. Her owner surprised me very much by looking like Cautious Conrad's bad brother. He said: 'Your name Harris?'

I said: 'No. That's Colonel Harris. And don't you try to sting him for damages if that mast carries away. It'll be your fault for not fitting backstays.'

He said: 'Huh! It's easy to see *you're* no sailor, even if you do try to sound like one. It's the pitching wot carries masts away, Mister. And in these waters there ain't no seas—what *you'd* call waves. So there ain't no pitching. So that mast's stood up ever since I put it there, even if every week a new crowd of blurry landlubbers does do their damndest to jibe it out of her. Backstays!' He snorted. 'D'you think I want to spend *all* my time fitting new booms? Now, you come aboard and I'll try to show you something. I say I'll try—but gawd help us!'

He did try. He showed us how to steer with a tiller, to lower the mast, to make sail, to trim sheets, to pump out the W.C., and to lower the cabin top. This latter operation was something I was glad to learn as it reduced the skyscraper on deck to reasonable proportions.

His parting words were these: 'Your water tank's full. So is your cooking gas cylinder, and there's a spare in the fore peak, if you know where that is. You've got ten cork fenders, and I wish it was a hundred. Don't hit anything, but if you must, hit something soft. And watch out some other mug don't hit you. Don't go trying to reef. You'll only muck it up and tear my mainsail. If it blows too hard for you, run her into the nearest bed of reeds, lower everything and quant her—shove her along with them two poles. Don't lose 'em overboard, mind! If you do you won't never get nowhere. If you're starting, you'd better start quanting now. Wind's dead ahead, so I shouldn't try sailing her, Mister, if I was *you*. You've got to be a real sailor to sail a boat in these waters.'

I said: 'Oh, go to hell. Harris, lash those poles on deck. Sam. Up mainsail. Set the jib. Let go the shore lines. Shove her head off and we'll show the bastards.'

The breeze filled the *Perfect Lady*'s tall sails and I waited for her to forge ahead. Instead, she slid broadside on across the river and crashed into a gold plated houseboat heavily laden with blondes. We carried away her radio mast and a string of Chinese lanterns and I felt glad I had forgotten to get our flock of cork fenders inboard.

C. Conrad's nasty brother roared: 'Down jib and quant her, you silly old sucker. Rig a preventer backstay round your neck and choke yourself before you sink her. Why didn't you bring your nurse?'

I said: 'Unlash those damned quants, Harris. Get some headway on her with them and we'll try it again on the other tack. We'll sail her out of here yet, or bust.'

We bust. We did get her sailing. We even made a little to windward on our second tack, and I was getting her to shoot a bit into the wind when she brought up all standing to the sound of crashings from aloft. My previous sea experience had not taught me that one cannot pass a fifty-foot mast beneath the overhanging branch of a forty-five-foot tree. I hadn't seen the darn thing, anyhow.

I hung my diminished head, while Sam and Harris quanted us to hell out of there. I was glad when we rounded a bend in the river, because there was a sound in my ears as of a herd of plastered jackasses hee-hawing. It was those despised Broads boys and girls, laughing.

For the next three hours we beat to windward and made about three miles. Then we had to bring up to let the jib sheets cool off. They were red hot. If you do not believe this, try working a thirty-five-foot skimming dish with no keel along a fifty-foot wide river around whose every bend the wind keeps dead ahead. During those three hours we tacked ship every nine seconds, or well over 1,000 times. And if the Bermuda or Fastnet courses can provide any tougher job than that, I am glad to have missed it. I also understand now, fully, why Broads yachtsmen managed to get along without preventer backstays.

We brought up for lunch in the lee of a salient landmark called the Ferry Inn. In fact, we got stranded on the bar there. When we floated ourselves off I apologised to Harris for having sneered at the Broads. I admitted there were features about Broads sailing that had the blue water racket beaten by miles.

We proceeded. Presently a big, black squall loomed up to windward and I thought of oilskins and getting wet and sweaty putting two reefs in the main. Then I remembered the advice of C. Conrad's horrible brother. I rammed the boat full tilt into a thick bed of reeds, let the sheets fly—and there she lay like a perfect lady asleep in her bed. We went below, lit our pipes and rested until the wind and rain blew over. And I said: 'Shipmates. Once upon a time, if you'll believe it, I sailed all across the Atlantic and back again. I understand, *now*, what a fool I was.'

We shoved our *Lady* out of her snug bed and, it now being dead calm, quanted her down the river. This sounds easy, but it is, in fact, the most heart- and back-breaking method of marine propulsion I have ever perpetrated. You plunge your quant into four feet of water and a full fathom of mud. You put your shoulder to the quant and walk aft—where you find yourself involved in a struggle to retrieve the dern thing. You pull desperately, and succeed in pulling the boat further astern than you managed to push her ahead. After a little of this, three distinct Schools of Thought on Quanting were evolved aboard the *Perfect Lady*. Harris who is a Royal Engineer and scientific, reasoned that if you wanted to progress eastwards per quant, you must head your boat west and strive to progress westwards.

Sam argued that the thing to do was to plant the quant ahead of the boat, when the pulling-out process should result in progressive, instead of retrograde, motion. I advanced a beautifully reasoned and strongly-worded disquisition entitled: 'Why Quant and get Nowhere and Hot and Sweaty when you can sit on your Fanny and Wait for Wind?' I then organised 'The Anti-Quant Club' and Sam and Harris became its Founder Members. We had just decided, unanimously, that only a damn fool would try to move a boat with a damn quant when we observed a little sloop slipping along towards us down the windless river. She was manned by an elegant young gent and his girl, and they passed us at a good three knots, wielding a couple of quants with easy grace and utmost dexterity.

Sam watched them go and then he said: 'Hell.' Harris said: 'Yes. Pure Hell.' I said: 'That's cured one intolerant old sailor of sneering at Broads yachtsmen. I guess I've still got a lot to learn.'

I had. The Broads taught me another lesson that same evening. We were making short, quick tacks down the river against a rising wind. Presently a motor yacht caught us up from astern. We were zigzagging so quickly across the narrow river that she had no chance to pass us. She had to slow down.

Harris said, 'I think he wants to get past.'

I said, 'To hell with him. It's our right of way. Let him wait.'

He waited, patiently. I continued to tack the *Perfect Lady* across his bows, until it occurred to me that I was hardly behaving like a perfect gentleman. I put the sloop against the bank and motioned the motoring nuisance on. As he went past he waved a friendly hand and said:

'Thank you. I'm so sorry. Look here! It's coming on dark, this reach is three miles long and it's full of mosquitoes. Won't you let me tow you to the next Broad? A good berth and no mosquitoes. There's a decent pub there, too.'

As we went ahead at the end of that motor boat's towline. I said to Harris and Sam, 'The man's a sailor and a gentleman, dammit! And I've been going about for years, saying all motor boatists were no-sailors and cads.'

I am glad to take this opportunity of apologising to the motor boating fraternity for maligning them for so long. I met a lot of motor boats on the Broads. There were rather too many of them for this old sailor's fancy and I still do not like their noise and smell. But their crews certainly did teach me that motors as well as sails can hatch out good men.

It was an old gentleman who had never sailed a boat anywhere but on the Broads, who gave me my final lesson. He was sailing alone aboard a twin of our *Perfect Lady*. We brought up near him for lunch one day and, when he observed our jar of rum, he came aboard us for a gam. Emboldened by the rum, I challenged him to a race to Potter Heigham. This involved a beat, almost dead to windward, along a reach of river as straight and as narrow and with banks as step-to as a canal. I made a beautiful start, getting well ahead by dint of giving the word to start myself, while the old gentleman was still busy hoisting his mainsail.

Away I went, dashing to and fro across the river, doing seven tacks per minute, with Sam to port and Harris to starboard, working the jib sheets like lightning. I remember I laughed at that poor old lone gentleman. Then I remember my laughing stopped. For that old man played an old Broads trick on me that I had heard about but, up to then, hadn't believed in. He reached across the river until his boat was moving fast, trimmed the boom in flat, steered parallel to and almost touching the lee bank and *kept there*, with most of his mainsail lifting excepting for the upper leach. But this kept him moving ahead and, so long as he kept moving, he did not make any leeway, because the water compressed between the wedge of his lee bow and the steep bank pushed his bow up to windward. And he kept his helm *up*, just enough to keep his bow pressed against the water cushion forward and just enough to keep his stern clear of the bank aft. This is how he did it. Either that, or it was magic. Take your pick.

It was, of course, a delicate operation. I tried it and failed completely. Every now and again the old man lost headway when he had to reach across the river and back to get going again. The fact remains that he took about ten tacks against my 500 odd. And he beat me by fifteen minutes.

We berthed alongside him, and Sam and Harris went aboard to tell him what a wonder he was. I stayed where I was, but the ports of both cabins were open, and this is what I heard:

Sam: 'By Gosh! You did give us a beating. Well done!'

Harris: 'Yes, by Jove! And do you know *who* you've beaten? The man who was sailing our boat is an internationally known ocean racing man and *you beat him*. Let me tell you you've beaten no less a person than . . . *Weston Martyr*!!!'

Old Gent: 'Never heard of him.'

Robert Hunter

A SHIP IS LAUNCHED

THE first thing to do when you want a yacht built is to find a ship-yard. We have one here, not so very far away. It nestles on the shores of the wide Atlantic, in a village that goes by the name of Innishbunnion. I approached the yard owner. Yes, he thought he could do it.

The order was placed in September. This would allow at least eight months before I needed the ship: masses of time, so I thought; but I did not know much about ship-yards—then. Now I do not want to bore anyone with pernickety details, so suffice it to say that the length of the yacht was to be thirty-three feet; it would have oak keel, stem, stern and frames; mahogany planking and pitch-pine decks. There was to be an auxiliary engine and a hollow mast. The designer lived somewhere in Scotland. No one could design round Innishbunnion.

Henry, the owner of the yard, was as enthusiastic as I was. 'I'm after ordering the oak from Kilkenny, Major,' he told me as I arrived at the yard one fine September day; ' 'tis grand timber, with less knots than eyes in m'head.'

Henry was a splendid person, always smiling and humming; not perhaps a first-class organiser but a good honest craftsman. When he hit a nail he hit it on the head, not on one side. He had not, however a good idea of Time. Things tick over slowly at Innishbunnion. Tomorrow is as good as today; the day after tomorrow, better. Remembering this, I asked him when the timber would arrive.

' 'Twill be here any day. I'm after telling them in Kilkenny 'tis urgent.'

On my next visit, a fortnight later, the oak had not yet come. I walked to the Innishbunnion post office and sent a telegram to Kilkenny. 'If timber not sent by Thursday cancel order procuring elsewhere.' The timber came four days later.

There were signs of activity at the ship-yard the next time I went. They had actually got the keel down and heaps of rounded pieces of oak were lying around the place. The men seemed busy too; there were only four of them. There was Paddy Donovan, aged about seventy, the world's greatest pessimist. It might be a glorious day but Paddy would say it would rain tomorrow. He had been coxswain of the local life-boat and had invariably told his crew, when they set off on a rescue job, that there was not a hope of saving a soul.

Then there was Mike Downey, young, strong and rather a daredevil, as quick at his work as Paddy Donovan was slow. His favourite weapon was an adze which he handled as if it was a cricket-bat. I always kept well away from Mike with the adze in his hands; its head was loose in its socket.

Next came Steve; I never discovered his surname, neither did I discover his actual job. Sometimes he would be shaping a piece of wood, two minutes later he would have left the piece of wood and be drilling holes in a lump of iron. After five minutes of this he would leave the job and go and paint somewhere. Number four shipwright was Peter Sullivan, a middle-aged man without, so far as I could see, a tooth in his head. He was for ever rubbing his stomach and complaining of indigestion. When I asked him why he did not get himself a set of false teeth he said they were on order. Like everything else in that yard, teeth were on order but slow in coming.

Henry the builder was like Steve; here, there and every-where. One day he would be on my job, another on a broken-down fishing-smack and yet another day he would be helping a man with his engine. But he always left his job when he saw me arrive.

'Now then, Henry,' I would say, 'what about those chain-plates, and the mahogany for the planking, and the brass screws you said you needed — have they arrived?'

Of course they had not. Nothing ever seemed to arrive at Innishbunnion ship-yard.

'But they *must* come,' I declared. 'Time's getting on, you know. Have you sent them a telegram?'

'Well, no — but there's the train tomorrow. 'Tis certain I am they'll come tomorrow.'

And off I would go to the post office and send more telegrams. The girl at the counter had come to know me quite well, taking as much interest in the progress of the yacht as I did myself. She invariably said she would send the telegrams off immediately and would then proceed to talk about Peter Sullivan's teeth, saying she was waiting every day to see them arrive. Then she would get on to the yacht again, so I had to be firm and refuse to discuss teeth or anything else until she sent the telegrams; which only meant 'phoning them to her next in command, ten miles away.

Everyone in the village knew me; not surprising, when you remember there were only some two hundred souls. Small boys stopped me in the street and asked how she was getting on: 'she' being the yacht. Then there was the schoolmaster, himself a keen yachtsman, who delighted in telling me the timber we were using was not up to standard; that we should

use brass keel-bolts, not iron, and that when the time came to
get the yacht out of the shed she would be too high to come out.

It was about the latter end of January that I began to have
misgivings. Henry and his merry men had been on the job four
months or more and how far had they got? A cursory glance
reassured; for one could at least see that a yacht was being
built and not a giant perambulator or a coal-truck. Keel,
forefoot, stem, stern and deadwood were all in position and so
were the floors and frames. But if you looked behind all this you
saw nothing. The planks were not yet on, neither was the decking, nor was there the slightest sign of any joinery work below
where the decks should have been. There was still no cabin, no
cockpit, no forecastle, no bulkheads, no partitions —nothing but
empty space.

I drew Henry to one side. 'Henry,' I said, 'are you sure you'll
be ready in time?'

He smiled reassuringly. 'Don't be worrying, Major. 'Twill
all work out according to plan. You could perhaps send another
telegram for those special bolts.'

These bolts were on order from Dublin and had to do with
the lavatory fittings. Why Henry should be worrying about
such things, when the lavatory itself had not arrived, rather
puzzled me, but I did not say anything. Instead I asked about
the keel. He took me out of the shed to an open space at the
back. There lay a mysterious black object which reminded me
of a large stuffed dugong I had once seen at Aden.

' 'Tis the show of the world. I made it myself,' he proudly
declared. 'We send this to Dublin for them to copy.'

It was certainly a neat piece of work, and with pencil marks
along the top to show where the keel bolts would go. But was it a
proper fit? Well, I just did not know. Having expressed my
appreciation of the job I asked when he would be sending it off.

'There's no train today, Major, but 'twill be the fiercest hard
luck if it doesn't go tomorrow.'

Ten days later, that was my next visit, the stuffed dugong
was just where it had been. Henry had his answer. ' 'Twas
fierce—every truck flowing over with whiting. Wonderful
hauls of whiting they're after getting. They'll be taking the
model tomorrow—if there aren't too many whiting.'

I went straight to the station-master-cum-porter-cum-signal-
man. I was firm and emphatic. The station-master promised to
do his best but would not go further than that. They took it next
train, but only because the fish merchant agreed to sell the
appropriate number of whiting locally. That's what I call being
obliging.

To show Henry I was really getting worried I stayed two days
in the village, being looked after splendidly by one of the
publicans. I talked to each shipwright in turn. 'How are we
getting on? I want her in May, you know. Will she be ready?'
'Ready by May—hardly.' Peter Sullivan was as gloomy as

Paddy Donovan; one could scarcely expect a dyspeptic to be otherwise, 'I wouldn't like to be saying which'll be ready first; your yacht or my teeth. You'll be as tired of waiting as I am.'

To let off steam I sent wires flying in all directions. I wired the Dublin foundry to be sure to cast the keel the moment the model arrived. I wired the firm in Glasgow to hurry up with the fittings we had ordered. I wired the Clydeside mast-maker for an estimated date of despatch and I wired the English sail-makers to make sure work was up to schedule.

My stay at Innishbunnion bore some sort of fruit. The men were working hard, perhaps a little too hard; for some of their dovetailing jobs made a few pieces of wood look as if suffering from hammer-toe. But I left the village feeling slightly more cheerful. Although there were as yet no deck-planks laid, one could at least see the beams they were to lie upon. I also saw signs of a settee in the making. I felt so cheerful that I postponed my return by ten days.

But when I did get back I was horrified. Nothing seemed to have happened at all and not a soul was working on the yacht. Steve was carrying iron pipes across the yard, Mike Downey appeared to be hacking a grimy old trawler to pieces, Paddy was painting the sides of a punt, and Peter was perched half-way up a mast scraping at something. Henry, the yard owner, was down on the quay helping a man with his engine. I realised I was not the only pebble on the beach so far as Innishbunnion ship-yard was concerned, so could not do very much. What I did was to retire to my friend the publican and suffocate my anxieties with a litre or so of stout.

March came in like a lion and went out like a lamb. Lion-like or lamb-like there was no effect on my yacht. She remained in her chrysalis, indifferent to everything. I took Henry to a pub, thinking I might get more out of him if away from that yard. I talked to him like a father. Two more months and where would that yacht be? Still in her bed, of course; engineless, cabinless, mastless, ballastless, cockpitless. I said it was not good enough and stood him one more whiskey. We staggered to the yard together. The men were taken off their other jobs and put on to the yacht. Henry, tears in his eyes, swore to me that he and his men would work all day, all night, every day and every night, to have the yacht ready in time.

April came and April went. The yacht now had her ballast-keel in position, half her decking done and the lavatory from Scotland was nearly installed. I examined the keel; had it really fitted? Well, not exactly, but then they never did. Liquid lead had been poured in to make good the deficiencies. I asked why they had not finished the decking. They had run out of pitch-pine. And where was the rudder? They had run out of elm. Then what about the cabin-top, a mere matter of larch? They had run out of larch. Well, why didn't they get on with the samson-posts and tiller? They had run out of oak.

May came and May went: perfect sailing weather: no yacht. The Clydeside mast was there, a beautiful glittering spar; lying out in the sun, for there was nowhere else to leave it. There was no sign of sails. I wired the makers twice in four days and on the fifth day got a reply, 'Sails despatched soonest'. Now what did they mean by 'soonest'? We painted her in May; three coats of white above the waterline and three of red below.

June came and June went. Still perfect sailing weather; still no yacht: at least, no yacht that ever looked like taking the water. I bit my lips with rage. What seemed to be one of the 'finest ever' summers was rushing madly past me and I was impotent to stop it going so fast. The engine was lying where it always lay, and when I remonstrated with Henry he told me the engineer from Castle Oliver was after getting phlebitis and could not come. Very well, then, I would sail her away under sails only; but I had not got any sails, they were to come 'soonest'. I spent the greater part of my time sending telegrams. Replies came spasmodically. The sails were held up at Liverpool. No, they were held up at Southampton. No, they had gone by goods to Fishguard. I wired the authorities at Liverpool, Southampton and Fishguard. None of them knew anything about my sails.

I turned again to Henry. 'I'll trace those sails or die,' I cried; 'but meanwhile why don't you get on measuring up the rigging-wire and splicing it?'

' 'Tis fierce. I sent for Pat Connolly. He's away at a funeral.'

'How long ago did you send for him?'

Henry, who could be most deliberate when he wanted, counted the days on his fingers. ' 'Twould be four days back.'

'Four days! He can't still be at that funeral, unless he was the corpse.'

'I know, I know,' muttered Henry, genuinely put out. 'He'll be here tomorrow.' But an Innishbunnion tomorrow is everyone else's any-time. I insisted they put Paddy Donovan on to the job, since, after all, he had been a rigger twenty years ago.

July came and July—no, it did not quite go. On the tenth of the month I got a message from Innishbunnion to say the ship was ready for launching. Unable to believe the good news I dashed over at once. Henry met me at the yard entrance beaming with pleasure. 'She's ready, Major. Just say the word —and away she goes.'

'No time like the present, Henry,' I replied in my delight. 'We won't be too fussy about the launching ceremony. Rig up a bit of tape and I'll produce a bottle of booze. Your little girl can do the naming. I'll tell her what to say.'

'But she can't be launched today, Major.'

'Why not? Tide's right. What's to prevent it?'

He turned my eyes seawards. Poised delicately on the cradle I was supposed to be using, and exactly on that part of the slipway where my yacht was supposed to be coming, stood a lifeboat.

'Here for painting. Lifeboats are priority jobs. 'Tis the fright of the world.'

There was nothing I could do. One cannot order lifeboats off slipways just like that. I asked Henry how long the painting would take and he told me two days. 'But why aren't the men working on her now?' I asked, for there was not a man in sight.

' 'Tis the paint we're waiting. 'Twill be here tomorrow,' said Henry.

Four days later I happened to be on a headland looking out to sea, when a lifeboat passed quite near. It was the one I had seen at the yard; I was positive about this. Cutting short the picnic I tore across to Innishbunnion and cried to the first man I saw, who happened to be old Paddy Donovan, 'She's gone. The lifeboat's gone. I've seen her.'

Paddy looked at me in his usual sad way and spoke in his usual sombre tones, 'She's after leaving all right. Now there's a fisherman in. She's on the cradle — in for repairs.'

He was of course quite right. There *was* a ship on the cradle. Henry, who had spotted my arrival, faded quickly away. Everyone belonging to the yard faded away. Only the trawler-men, standing on their damaged decks in the ship that was on the cradle, wondered what had happened. I chased Henry round the village and got him at the post office, not at the counter but having a drink. I was as calm as I could be.

'Am I never to get my ship launched? Do you think this weather will last for ever? She was promised for May and it's now July. Are we in Innishbunnion or are we in Southampton? Is this perpetual stream of shipping ever going to stop?'

I said a great deal more but forget what is was. The post office girl had hidden behind her counter; Henry was shifting his empty glass from one hand to the other with every remark I made. When I allowed him to speak it was to say that the fishing-boat would be off the slipway very soon. He had hardly liked to refuse them. Was it not their means of livelihood?

I made him swear that the moment the fishing-boat was off the cradle, my yacht would be put on. Then no matter what came in I would have priority. There was not much more I could do, so I cleared out. But three days later I was back again. The yacht was still in her shed. True, she had moved a few inches towards the slipway but nothing more; because she could not. That know-all schoolmaster *had* been right. She was to tall to get out of her shed.

Mike Downey was up a ladder hacking away at an enormous oak beam. Steve stood below propping up an iron girder. Henry was down on the quay helping a man with his engine. Before the yacht could proceed, the oak beam would have to come out and the iron girder be put in its place. I glanced at the tide. There was not a hope of launching that day.

I was back again next day. The beam had been removed and the girder put in its place. The yacht could now come out —

and why hadn't she? And why was there not a soul in the yard?
I went to the nearest pub. Didn't I know it was an Obligational? To the uninitiated, an Obligational is a religious
holiday. No farmer and no shipwright works in Southern Ireland on an Obligational; even if they do work on bank holidays.
I found most of the village squeezed into the local lifeboat
listening to a hurley match on the lifeboat's radio. Henry was
there too. He told me the launching was definitely arranged for
tomorrow.

And for once an Innishbunnion tomorrow came. When I
reached the yard the yacht was out of her shed and a few yards
down the slipway. She looked beautiful. Mike, Steve, Paddy
and Peter were all busily painting on the anti-fouling. I have
never seen them work faster. Henry was at the back of the yard
fiddling about with the engine that controlled the launching
hawser. In half an hour the anti-fouling was on. The ship
was ready to be launched.

A little girl was standing near the yacht, dressed in her
Sunday best. This was Molly, Henry's daughter, ready to do
the naming ceremony. I went to the pub and bought a bottle of
whiskey. Then I changed my mind and bought gin instead,
and then decided to have both, for I guessed they would be
needed. It was not every day that a yacht was launched at
Innisbunnion.

I gave Mike Downey the gin bottle and asked him to tie it
on to the tape they had rigged up on the stem. Then I went to
Henry and asked him if everything was ready. Henry handed
over his job at the engine to Paddy Donovan who knew all
about it. Paddy started the engine. Henry and I returned to
the yacht in her cradle. I went across to Molly and took her by
the hand. I assured her there was nothing to be scared about.
All she had to do was to repeat the words as I said them.
My final instructions were that she was not to let go of the
bottle till I told her. I then pressed it firmly into her small
hand. Paddy Donovan had his hand on the engine clutch-
lever; the rest of the men were round the cradle armed with
crowbars.

'Now then, Molly,' I said soothingly, 'let's get started. Just
say these words after me.' I then began in loud, resounding
tones, Molly repeating them in her own piping way. 'I CHRISTEN
THIS SHIP — I christen this ship — ARETHUSA — *Arethusa* — MAY
GOD BLESS HER — may God bless her — AND ALL THAT SAIL
IN HER — and all that sail in her.' Perfect! Even down to the
delightful Irish brogue.

'Let go!' I cried. 'Let go of the bottle.' But Molly did not
seem either able or willing to do this. 'Let go!' I cried again with
a trifle more sharpness in my tone. And then she did, but it was
a shocking attempt, for it missed the yacht by metres. She had
another shot and missed again, so I seized the bottle from her
hands and flung it at the ship myself. I got it fair and square;

there was a frightful splash of gin and Henry, who had come forward to encourage little Molly, got most of it in his face.

'The clutch, Paddy; the clutch,' they all yelled; for nothing seemed to be happening, except that Paddy was red in the face from his energies. Henry went up to see what had happened and returned looking rather glum. 'The clutch's after jamming. We'll have to lever her down by hand.'

The process was slow and laborious, but inch by inch she moved. And then there was a sudden débâcle. The lethal rate of progress became in the twinkling of an eye the speed of a super-sonic fighter. Paddy had got the clutch to work, but now the brake-lever had jammed. Never could man-made ship have struck natural element with such resounding force. The harbour was one sheet of foam; we were all of us drenched. *Arethusa* was the length and breadth of that port before we could say Jack Robinson.

She had to come to rest somewhere. Her stern met the flanks of a heavy old fishing-boat moored the other side of the quay. This stopped her; perhaps just as well, or she would have gone through the quay. 'Twas the fiercest thing they had seen. That the poor little *Arethusa* had been given a bump that would have knocked out an elephant, and that the inrush of water had gone right through her exhaust pipe and into the engine, and that the engine would have to be completely stripped and dried before she would function, were of minor consideration. The ship had been launched.

CRUISING IN YACHTS

'Must be Zeebrugge,' I said. 'We'll steer for it.'
We did. Where was the Mole?

John Seymour: *By Sail and Oar Again* 123

George Millar

SERICA CROSSES THE CHANNEL

UP the river the yachts lay that night with their flanks in nests of soft mud, deep mud said to be dangerous. The mud swallows everything; objects such as knives it devours, but lighter-density objects are sucked down slowly, slowly. Old men come to the yacht yard with metal cages on the end of poles. They sift at the creamy edges of the mud and lift out carpet slippers and egg-whisks, which they regard with capricious interest before returning them to that smooth, all-consuming maw. How many yachtsmen have dismembered their mistresses and slid torsos, femurs, clavicles, and delicate, folded ears into the Lymington mud?

Beside the creek the agreeable town of Lymington slumbered with dignity, its sash windows reflecting the shining velvet of the night. An airless night, the sky clear of any shred of cloud, and unusually hot for June. The people of Lymington pushed down their all-wool blankets, and lay in the half-life of sleep, covered only by sheets.

At four a.m., when Isabel and I went on deck, the tide had whispered its moon-drawn saunter over the mud-banks, lifting the yachts, including ours, from their nests. The creek had become a river, wide, sullen, leaden, with the tide chuckling and the nervous yachts shivering against each other's fenders. Tall masts pricked a low sky that seemed to be a greater version of the river; some of the masts were painted white, but the majority, our own included, were varnished to display the golden wood that is known as silver spruce.

Aware of those who lay sleeping near us, we whispered, and stepped delicately on rubber soles as we set about the unfamiliar business of getting under way. It was a Saturday morning. Empty cars were herded in the yacht yard between the creosoted sheds. Week-enders were going sailing. An ocean race was to begin later that morning.

No wind . . . our engine proved to be unusually silent. Soon we were moving downstream between two lines of moored boats, past the Isle of Wight ferry, past the Royal Lymington Yacht Club, whose balconies were empty, whose slips, clustered round with snub-nosed, short-bodied, broad-bosomed dinghies, were deserted. On the balconies the telescopes on tripods stretched out their glinting eyes to the Solent and the mist-enshrouded island.

While, in the murmurous interior of the yacht, I was setting breakfast dishes on a tray I felt from a liberated swing of movement that we had cleared the river mouth. Isabel called from the cockpit: would I give her the bearing to pass the Needles? That landmark should have been visible, but we were brushing through a heat haze. Above us the sun was a sphere whiter than the surrounding whiteness, around us white tendrils were heaped on the smooth water. No wind. . . . Now and then the mists trembled to the bray of a big ship probing up to Southampton with pilot, echo-sounder, radar.

On the radar screen we were visible as the smallest of small dots moving toward France. A forty-ton yawl came out from the coast of the Isle of Wight and crossed our bows, motoring. Her sails hung damply. Her professional skipper, perched behind the wheel, was rolling a cigarette. He gave us a nod, knowing, confident, neither friendly nor hostile. We saw no land after the sedgy mouth of the Lymington River (and were to see none for two days and a night). The red eggs of buoys, Trinity House spawn marking the channel between Hurst Point and the Needles, appeared out of the haze and vanished.

As the waking sun began to lick the haze off the water a flicker of wind came from the west. We hoisted the mainsail and the big Genoa. It was an unusual English Channel, flat, oily, hot. Even in the cockpit, under the sickle-shaped scoop of the mainsail, it was hot. Gently she sailed south, and while she sailed we felt her tiller and watched the ripples her form swept into the smooth water, and listened to her sailing noises. We lunched in the cockpit: omelette fines herbes, watercress salad, strawberries, Stilton, iced lager. . . . The light airs that were sending *Serica* along at four and five knots would scarcely have filled the mainsail of a slower type of boat.

At the end of May we had determined to sail *Serica* to foreign waters. She had then been for twenty months in a shed on dry land. We hurried south from Sutherland (at the northern end of Britain) to Lymington (at the southern), lived aboard while the fitting-out was done—and now we were at sea, bound for the Mediterranean.

We had made no detailed plans before setting out, but had contemplated sailing down-Channel for Brest, or for the north-western corner of France. Now, with the Westerly fading and hot stillness all around, we chose to go to Guernsey, and began to study the Sailing Directions, charts, and Tide Tables, with a view to entering St Peter Port. I was perplexed by the tidal data because, apart from a rushed crossing from the Hamble River to Le Havre in *Truant* (before thankfully squeezing the ketch into the canals of France), my navigating had been done in the all but tideless waters of the Mediterranean and the Ægean, or on the stones and grit of the Libyan desert. There is nothing complicated about navigating in tidal waters (I was soon to learn) once the navigator knows where to look for information in Admiralty or other publications. I was more seriously worried by my compasses, which differed by a margin that could only be termed enormous, namely eleven degrees. An experienced yachtsman (who writes *practical* books about yachting) had advised me to buy a hand-bearing compass of a type used by the Royal Air Force. I had mounted this instrument on a teak bracket inside the doghouse. By taking it out and sighting it along the yacht's centre line I could check the bearing on the big steering compass, mounted centrally at the forward end of the cockpit.

'The error will be in the big compass,' I said.

'The big one looks the more reliable to me," Isabel said.

Although I had little respect for such reasons as she advanced for her preference, I decided to steer on a mean between the two compass readings, and at eight p.m. we heard a fog signal booming ahead that we identified as the diaphone on the Casquets. We were therefore on our course for St Peter Port.

The wind had died. Isabel suggested that since the weather was so remarkably peaceful we might go to bed. The last few days had been exhausting. . . . I took down the Genoa, double-reefed the mainsail (more to see if I knew how to do it than to accomplish any useful purpose), and lashed the tiller. The evening was so sultry that we felt the need of air, and we lowered the dinghy overboard in order to clear the saloon skylight. I hung the riding light on the forestay, and we were soon in bed and asleep.

A few hours later I woke. *Serica* was sailing herself in narrow circles, and at the same time was being carried by the powerful tide. Occasionally I would hear the cold beat of a ship's engines. I had convinced myself that the tides would take us north and west, and believed that there was no chance of our hitting land that night. But at three a.m., hearing more wind as well as tide, I could stay in bed no longer. Isabel, less nervous, slept on.

I eased the main sheet, hoisted the Genoa, and found myself sailing on a southerly course. When I had the feel of the yacht in the darkness—and very lively she was—I lashed the short tiller and shook out both reefs in the mainsail. The pram dinghy danced after me, pushing before its raised prow a boisterous moustachio of foam. When Isabel came on deck we hove to.

We lifted the dinghy, lashing it to its chocks on the coach roof, and continued with mainsail and No. 3 jib.

That day the south-east wind was gusty, and raised a short, grey sea. We sailed through morning, afternoon, and evening, at six or seven knots, close-hauled, and spent much of the time wondering where the devil we were. The horizon was banked with clouds that formed mirages, land and citadels and hamlets and the openings of mighty rivers.

Although the yacht had almost ceased to make water when on an even keel, she was now sluicing her white topsides, which had dried out and become porous during her long sleep ashore; she leaked so copiously that I had to pump every hour. (The bilge pump, excellent so far as its capacity for spewing forth water is concerned, is an exhausting contraption; the operator, kneeling on the floor under the doghouse, turns a brass handle in a horizontal clockwise movement.)

Wind and sea stiffened during the dark afternoon. The yacht increased her pace. Her decks were wet enough, since her sharp bows sliced through the tops of the seas and the wind flung the spray aft, but in the cockpit, protected by the curve of the dog-house and by the coamings, we were dry. Wondering about our landfall on a dangerous and unfamiliar coast in worsening weather, I was yet exhilarated by the lightness of the tiller in my fingers, the steadiness and drive of a balanced sailing machine, the long, tormented thread of our wake. Isabel dosed herself with a new medicine to prevent seasickness, and said that the effect was a kind of paralysis. She took her turns at the tiller, and between turns slumbered at my side.

In the evening I woke her and announced with distaste (since navies at sea are often a nuisance to yachts) that I had sighted ahead the combined fleets of the Russophobe powers. Those fleets, the B.B.C. had early informed us, were doing exercises off the coasts of France. Looking through the binoculars (which were encrusted with salt) I picked out the aircraft carrier H.M.S. *Implacable*, which was, I knew, flying the flag of Admiral Sir Rhoderick McGrigor.

We soon realised that the fleet, though we could see foam at the bows and sterns of all the units, was stationary, and when we had sailed a mile or two nearer we saw that it was no fleet but a collection of grey rocks upon the bases of which the sea rushed with a fury that, like aerial bombardment, was as terrifying as it was senseless. A Breton fishing-smack was working nets close to the rocks. She was about three times the size of *Serica*, but as she carried no sail she behaved stupidly, standing on end and rolling her scuppers under, while we, by comparison, were steady and nimble. We sailed close to her, and hailed.

'*Où sommes nous?*'

The dripping men on board answered in a chorus that came to us like the barking of sea lions. At length we made out:

'Les Roches Douvres.'

We gybed *Serica* (for the first time) without difficulty save for a contretemps with the jib sheets, whose pull I had underestimated, and sailed with wind and sea on our port quarter, heading south-west. Now there was a flurry of charts and Sailing Directions. Where was the nearest anchorage? (With us in such circumstances the nearest is always the best.) A place called Lézardrieux situated some distance up the tidal Rivière de Pontrieux, of whose dangers the compilers of the Sailing Directions write in a tone even more tartly warning than usual. Lézardrieux it would have to be.

The light had slipped away; I was not sure of my compasses and had had no opportunity to test the patent log. What little was to be seen of the land to port more than confirmed the nightmarish outlines on the charts. Was this indeed the coast of Brittany, land of pink shrimps and cider, and butter white as Irish linen, this growling line of rocky defences so thick, so venomous?

I am of an inequable temperament, prone to sudden and foolish exaltation or despair. That evening I was low, miserable, puny, and afraid. Although Isabel always has a stouter heart, the anti-seasickness medicine seemed to be relaxing its druggy grip at the very moment when elements and circumstance were increasing their pressure. It was she who pulled us together . . . she made out a buoy which she identified on the chart, and that buoy was the key to the river.

Fate is a queer bird. The night before I had ordered my charts Mr Adlard Coles had climbed down our ladder to have a look at us and *Serica*. He happened to mention the anchorage at Lézardrieux. So I had ordered, with some seventy charts covering the coasts between Lymington and Italy, a full-scale one of the Pontrieux River. On the chart the river looked small, but in the darkness (and we were entering at approximately high water) it proved to be vast. A sea writhed and in places boiled on the bar, but we buffeted through it. I had been so obsessed with navigation and so keen to get somewhere as quickly as possible that it had not occurred to me to reduce sail. Sailing at that speed with breakers audible and sometimes visible on either hand was too much for me, and I got down the mainsail. I had vaselined the track and the slides, and was agreeably surprised at the ease of handling a Bermudian sail. The engine started at the first touch of the button. We passed beacons, buoys, a cluster of wind-flattened islands, and then entered the land between hills. Leading lights guided us up the main channel. A bend, more leading lights, and the swell had changed to a ripple. The patent log showed ninety-five miles for the day's run. We dropped anchor in eight fathoms at the top of the last reach before the village.

How welcome, how precious the steadiness, the calm, the land-lockedness of the anchorage! Wind hissed through the trees on the slopes above us. Down-river roared the sea. And there we were alone, comfortable, suddenly hungry. No matter how rough the passage, you have but to find good anchorage and there, in the boat, are warmth, light, food, books, alcohol, tobacco, comfortable beds, violins, daggers. It is to enhance such contrasts with the sea and the wind that the truly wise yachtsman sails in the company of a beautiful or an intelligent woman—it may be his wife.

From 'A White Boat from England' 1951

Hilaire Belloc

THE NORTH SEA

Such as it was, there it was, and trusting in the wind and God's providence we lay criss-cross in Lowestoft South Basin. The Great Bear shuffled round the pole and streaks of wispy clouds lay out in heaven.

The next morning there was a jolly great breeze from the east, and my companion said, 'Let us put out to sea.' But before I go farther, let me explain to you and to the whole world what vast courage and meaning underlay these simple words. In what were we to put to sea?

This little boat was but twenty-five feet over-all. She had lived since 1864 in inland waters, mousing about rivers, and lying comfortably in mudbanks. She had a sprit seventeen foot outboard, and I appeal to the Trinity Brothers to explain what that means; a sprit dangerous and horrible where there are waves; a sprit that will catch every sea and wet the foot of your jib in the best of weathers; a sprit that weighs down already overweighted bows and buries them with every plunge. *Quid dicam?* A sprit of Erebus. And why had the boat such a sprit? Because her mast was so far aft, her forefoot so deep and narrow, her helm so insufficient, that but for this gigantic sprit she would never come round, and even as it was she hung in stays and had to have her weather jib-sheet hauled in for about five minutes before she would come round. So much for the sprit.

This is not all, nor nearly all. She had about six inches of free-board. She did not rise at the bows: not she! Her mast was dependent upon a fore-stay (spliced) and was not stepped, but worked in a tabernacle. She was a hundred and two years old. Her counter was all but awash. Her helm — I will describe her helm. It waggled back and forth without effect unless you jerked it suddenly over. Then it 'bit', as it were, into the rudder-post, and she just felt it — but only just — the ronyon!

She did not reef as you and I do by sane reefing points, but in a gimcrack fashion with a long lace, so that it took half an hour to take in sail. She had not a jib and foresail, but just one big headsail as high as the peak, and if one wanted to shorten sail after the enormous labour of reefing the mainsail (which no man could do alone) one had to change jibs forward and put up a storm sail—under which (by the way) she was harder to put round than ever.

Did she leak? No, I think not. It is a pious opinion. I think she was tight under the composition, but above that and between wind and water she positively showed daylight. She was a basket. Glory be to God that such a boat should swim at all!

But she drew little water? The devil she did! There was a legend in the yard where she was built that she drew five feet four, but on a close examination of her (on the third time she was wrecked), I calculated with my companion that she drew little if anything under six feet. All this I say knowing well that I shall soon put her up for sale; but that is neither here nor there. I shall not divulge her name.

So we put to sea, intending to run to Harwich. There was a strong flood down the coast, and the wind was to the north of north-east. But the wind was with the tide—to that you owe the lives of the two men and the lection of this delightful story; for had the tide been against the wind and the water steep and mutinous, you would never have seen either of us again: indeed we should have trembled out of sight for ever.

The wind was with the tide, and in a following lump of a sea, without combers and with a rising glass, we valorously set out, and, missing the South Pier by four inches, we occupied the deep.

For one short half-hour things went more or less well. I noted a white horse or two to windward, but my companion said it was only the sea breaking over the outer sands. She plunged a lot, but I flattered myself she was carrying Caesar, and thought it no great harm. We had started without food, meaning to cook a breakfast when we were well outside: but men's plans are on the knees of the gods. The god called Aeolus, that blows from the north-east of the world (you may see him on old maps—it is a pity they don't put him on the modern), said to his friends: 'I see a little boat. It is long since I sank one'; and all together they gave chase, like Imperialists, to destroy what was infinitely weak.

I looked to windward and saw the sea tumbling, and a great number of white waves. My heart was still so high that I gave them the names of the waves in the eighteenth *Iliad*: the long-haired wave, the graceful wave, the wave that breaks on an island a long way off, the sandy wave, the wave before us, the wave that brings good tidings. But they were in no mood for poetry. They began to be great, angry, roaring waves, like the chiefs of charging clans, and though I tried to keep up my courage with an excellent song by Mr Newbolt, 'Slung between the round shot in Nombre Dios Bay', I soon found it useless, and pinned my soul to the tiller. Every sea following caught my helm and battered it. I hung on like a stout gentleman, and prayed to the seven gods of the land. My companion said things were no worse than when we started. God forgive him the courageous lie. The wind and the sea rose.

It was about opposite Southwold that the danger became intolerable, and that I thought it could only end one way. Which way? The way out, my honest Jingoes, which you are more afraid of than of anything else in the world. We ran before it; we were already over-canvased, and she burried her nose every time, so that I feared I should next be cold in the water, seeing England from the top of a wave. Every time she rose the jib let out a hundredweight of sea-water; the sprit buckled and cracked, and I looked at the splice in the forestay to see if it yet held. I looked a thousand times, and a thousand times the honest splice that I had poked together in a pleasant shelter under Bungay Woods (in the old times of peace, before ever the sons of the Achaians came to the land) stood the strain. The sea roared over the fore-peak, and gurgled out of the scuppers, and still we held on. Till (Aeolus blowing much more loudly, and, what you may think a lie, singing through the rigging, though we were before the wind) opposite Aldeburgh I thought she could not bear it any more.

I turned to my companion and said: 'Let us drive her for the shore and have done with it; she cannot live in this. We will jump when she touches.' But he, having a chest of oak, and being bound three times with brass, said, 'Drive her through it. *It is not often we have such a fair wind.*' With these words he went below; I hung on for Orfordness. The people on the strand at Aldeburgh saw us. An old man desired to put out in a boat to our aid. He danced with fear. The scene still stands in their hollow minds.

As Orfordness came near, the seas that had hitherto followed like giants in battle now took to a mad scrimmage. They leapt pyramidically, they heaved up horribly under her; she hardly obeyed her helm, and even in that gale her canvas flapped in the troughs. Then in despair I prayed to the boat itself (since nothing else could hear me), 'Oh, Boat,' for so I was taught the vocative, 'bear me safe round this corner, and I will scatter wine over your decks.' She heard me and rounded the point, and so terrified was I that (believe me if you will) I had not even the soul to remember how ridiculous and laughable it was that sailors should call this Cape of Storms 'the Onion'.

Once round it, for some reason I will not explain, but that I believe connected with my prayer, the sea grew tolerable. It still came on to the land (we could sail with the wind starboard), and the wind blew harder yet; but we ran before it more easily, because the water was less steep. We were racing down the long drear shingle bank of Orford, past what they call 'the life-boat house' on the chart (there is no life-boat there, nor ever was), past the look-out of the coastguard, till we saw white water breaking on the bar of the Alde.

Then I said to my companion, 'There are, I know, two mouths to this harbour, a northern and a southern; which shall we take?' But he said, 'Take the nearest.'

I then, reciting my firm beliefs and remembering my religion, ran for the white water. Before I knew well that she was round, the sea was yellow like a pond, the waves no longer heaved, but raced and broke as they do upon a beach. One greener, kindly and roaring, a messenger of the gale grown friendly after its play with us, took us up on its crest and ran us into the deep and calm beyond the bar, but as we crossed, the gravel ground beneath our keel. So the boat made harbour. Then, without hesitation, she cast herself upon the mud, and I, sitting at the tiller, my companion ashore, and pushing at her inordinate sprit, but both revelling in safety, we gave thanks and praise. That night we scattered her decks with wine as I had promised, and lay easy in deep water within.

From 'On Sailing the Sea' 1939

Claud Worth

SEAWORTHINESS

SEAWORTHINESS is a relative term. One man in speaking of a good sea-boat means a capable week-end boat for semi-sheltered waters: another perhaps is thinking of a vessel in which he can make an ocean voyage in safety. Again, the term may be applied either to a safe vessel or to one which is easy in her motion.

When accounts appear in the newspapers of some Western Ocean liner having her decks swept and heavy steel stanchions twisted up like wire, it may be asked, 'What would have happened to a ten-ton yacht if she had been out in that gale?' There is no reason why the yacht should not go through it safely. In a gale, say off Dover or in the Irish Sea, the liner might bridge over two or three seas and be very steady when a yacht would be making heavy weather of it. In a great Atlantic sea whose length is greater than her own, the liner will still make good weather if the seas are not too frequent. But a long vessel pitches and scends slowly: like a long clock pendulum she has a long period of longitudinal oscillation which cannot be shortened except to a very slight extent. Suppose, for example, that three is her maximum number of oscillations in a certain time; if she is driven against a head sea so that she meets four seas in that time she will be unable to keep step and will drive her bows into it. A little vessel yields to every movement of the sea—herein lies her safety. I remember, as a passenger in a large liner, witnessing a striking example. We left Liverpool during a westerly gale. Off the Saltees we shipped a great sea which smashed one of the boats. Off the Old Head of Kinsale the engines were running at reduced speed, but she was shipping heavy water over the bows. A small pilot cutter sailed close under our stern. She was taking things quite easily and with nothing more than spray coming on board.

In the discussions about seaworthiness of cruising yachts, which from time to time are carried on in the yachting papers, one man perhaps advocates a long keel, another prefers a cut-away forefoot, a third likes a light displacement and all the ballast outside, while a fourth pins his faith to inside ballast and plenty of it, and so on. Each in turn proves his contention by referring to yachts which have made long voyages or gained a great reputation. No agreement is ever reached, or ever can be reached, because the points under discussion are not the most essential. By far the most important factor in determining the seaworthiness of a yacht is the crew, next comes the gear, and last of all the form of the hull.

A small yacht, by making a long voyage in open water, may perhaps gain many advocates for her particular type when her success may really have been due to her having a competent skipper. Similarly, many a good little boat has acquired a bad reputation merely because she has never been owned by a man who understood her.

The Skipper must not only know his vessel and how to handle her, but he must be able to navigate her and must know the sea. He must be watchful and careful. He needs 'nerve', coolness, and endurance, this endurance being a mental rather than a physical quality. Above all he must not be liable to panic in a sudden emergency. I have known men who, faced with an awkward situation and knowing exactly what should be done, lose their heads and do something quite different—perhaps run for a difficult harbour on a lee shore, thereby taking a risk twenty times greater than that which they are trying to avoid. They, fortunately, are exceptions. Of the average man R. L. Stevenson has truly said: 'It is a commonplace that we cannot answer for ourselves until we have been tried. But it is not so common a reflection, and surely more consoling, that we usually find ourselves a great deal braver and better than we thought. I believe this is every one's experience.'

Roger North

ROGER NORTH'S CRUISE

ANOTHER of my mathematical entertainments was sailing. I was extremely fond of being master of anything that would sail, and consulting Mr John Windham about it, he encouraged me with a present of a yacht, built by himself, which I kept four years in the Thames, and received great delight in her.

This yacht was small, but had a cabin and a bedroom athwartships, aft the mast, and a large locker at the helm; the cook-room, with a cabin for a servant, was forward on, with a small chimney at the very prow. Her ordinary sail was a boom-mainsail, stay-foresail, and jib. All wrought aft, so we could sail without a hand a-head, which was very troublesome, because of the spray that was not (sailing to windward) to be endured. My crew was a man and a boy, with myself and one servant, and, once, making a voyage to Harwich, a pilot. She was no good sea-boat, because she was open aft, and might ship a sea to sink her, especially before the wind in a storm, when the surge breaks over faster than her way flies; but in the river she would sail tolerably, and work extraordinarily well. She was ballasted with cast lead. It was a constant entertainment to sail against smacks and hoys, of which the river was always full. At stretch they were too hard for me; but by, I had the better; for I commonly did in two what they could scarce get in three boards. And one reason of the advantage they had at stretch was their topsail, which I could not carry.

The seasons of entertainment were the two long vacations, Lent and autumn, especially towards Michaelmas, for the summer is too hot and calm; unless by accident, those times are cool and windy, without which the sea is a dull trade. But these were for long voyages, as down below bridge to Gravesend, Sheerness, &c., which lasted for the most part five or six days. But for turning up the river, and about the town above the bridge, I could, given time, have the yacht at any stairs for an afternoon's entertainment, as I saw occasion and found the tide serve. Once on the last seal day, we top practicers in Chancery, as usual, made merry together, and in a frolic would go to sea, as I used to call it. I sent for the yacht, which had lain all Trinity term in the heat uncaulked, so that her upper work was open, though her bottom was as tight as a dish. We went aboard, and when the vessel began to heel the water came in at her seams and flowed into the cabin, where the company was, who were too warm to perceive such an inconvenience, till at last they were almost up to the knees, and they powdered out. We called for boats and went ashore, and the yacht was run ashore to prevent sinking downright. This made much merriment when we came together again, discovering what a present we had like to have made to our friends at the Bar by sinking and drowning the premier practicers, and so making way for the rest.

I used to make frequent visits at Bellhouse to my relations there, because it lay near Purfleet, from whence I could walk thither.

When I prepared for one of these voyages I used to victual my vessel with cold meats in tin cases, bottles of beer, ale, and for the seamen brandy. And I mention this because I was sensible from it that all the joy of eating which gluttons so much court, consists in appetite, for that we had in perfection, and though our meat was coarse (beef for the most part) yet no epicure enjoyed that way so much as we did. Once being bound for Suffolk, I layed in a pilot at Greenwich, who understood the North course out of the river well being used to carry lampreys into Holland I thought it a strange trade. It seems they fish for cod with them. They are a small lamprey, having nine holes on each side in lieu of gills. These they put in flat wooden vessels of water, and carry over alive. If dead, they are unfit for use. And the keeping them alive on board employs many hands, for they must be perpetually stirred in the water by putting in cords, and then drawing them along the bottom, else they die. With a good gale I got in one tide as low as the Ooze Edge and there anchored, and lay for the next tide. This is a great way below the Nore, opposite to Thanet. There is a small sand that lies within the river, above the Nore, called the Middle Ground; and a small thread runs from that to the Ooze Edge, where is a buoy, to warn sailors of it, whereby it notes that the current is there a little divided, but upon the sands themselves a great deal, so that it does not set with that force as elsewhere. And I observe that all those shelves have a manifest cause from the coast, for where a place is sheltered from the current, as at the point between Thames and Medway, there a shelf as at the Nore, grows. The windmill point above bridge is a visible instance of the same. For there the current sets straight from Lambeth one way, and from the bridge the other way, on the shore opposite to the point; so for want of a stream to scour, a shelf grows there, and is dry at low water. In the evening the wind slackened, and the surge yet wrought, which was a most uneasy condition, to lie stamping and tossing without a breath of wind to pay our sail which wrought and flapped about most uneasily.

Here I observed that there was wind aloft, though I was too humble to enjoy it. For empty colliers came down with topsails out, full-bunted, and bows rustling, which did not a little provoke me, but patience is a seaman's capital and necessary virtue.

Next morning it was hazy, and an inward bound vessel hailed us to know where they were. We answered, at the Ooze Edge. They immediately dropped anchor, for fear of the sand, till the day should clear enough to discover the buoy. When the tide was made we weighed, and the wind freshened, and we stood down the king's channel, and the gale holding, we stemmed the neap tide coming in, and it being high water at the Spits, we ran over all past the Gunfleet, so that the neap ebb by evening carried us into Harwich, where we anchored, and went on shore to refresh.

At the point of the low country between the Thames and Malden waters there is a very ugly shelf, and a great mast is set down at the point which they call the Shoe (that is the name of the shelf) beacon. The Naze, or Nose point, before we make into Harwich, appeared to us at noon, for it is high land, and we saw it at great distance. There was little remarkable in this day's voyage, only that I, with my friend Mr Chute, sat before the mast in the hatchway, with prospectives and books, the magazine of provisions, and a boy to make a fire and help broil, make tea, chocolate, &c. And thus, passing alternately from one entertainment to another, we sat out eight whole hours and scarce knew what time was past. For the day proved cool, the gale brisk, air clear, and no inconvenience to molest us, nor wants to trouble our thoughts, neither business to importune, nor formalities to tease us; so that we came nearer to a perfection of life there than I was ever sensible of otherwise.

At Harwich we were asked if we had left our souls at London, because we took so little care of our bodies. For our vessel was not storm proof, and if that had come we must run for it, not without danger, but that is pleasure to the eagerness of youth. After our visit in the country we returned on board at Ipswich, having tidied up the yacht. We rode sixteen miles in the night to take the head of the tide, and used a boat down to the first broad, where the yacht was fallen down. It was cold in the boat, and strange to see what invincible sleep seized us; all dropping like so many dead things. We had a fierce gale, about S.W., wherefore we were forced to turn it out of the harbour; but then made but one run to the Spits, and came to anchor, intending to put through in the night by the soundings, without sight of the buoy, as we did, it being tide of low ebb. And, keeping in two and three fathoms, we succeeded well, and anchored again in deep water, expecting the tide. The reason of our putting through in the night, as the pilot told me, was to have a consort, or a resort in case of distress; for there lay in the King's Channel, above the Spits, four great East Indiamen, and if a storm had rose we could not have rode it out in the Wallet where we lay, nor safely put through to come at the great ships much less shifted in the night by making to any port. As soon as the tide of flood was made, we sailed, turning up the King's Channel, ahead of these Indiamen, that weighed not till the morning, and, being ahead, we dropped again, not to lose our friends, if need should be, and lay till broad day. I could not but concern myself in all this important naval conduct, though most of my crew, except the sailors, slept. And at midnight, in the air, the eating cold meat and bread, and drinking small beer, was a regale beyond imagination. I can say, I scarce ever knew the pleasure of eating till then, and have not observed the like on any occasion since.

Work being over, I took a nap, but before I lay down the pilot asked, 'Master, if the ships send us a bale of goods, shan't we take them in?' I answered, 'No,' considering that if I was caught smuggling, as they call it, I should be laughed at for being condemned to forfeit my vessel at the custom-house, where my own brother was a ruling commissioner, as he had certainly done. It was not ill advised to resolve against such a temptation, for next morning a custom-house smack came aboard us, and searched every cranny, supposed we had been dabbling. It was not unpleasant to observe the desperate hatred the seamen had to these water waiters. One vowed he could scarce forbear to run his knife in their guts, for he was at his breakfast; and they would snarl and grin, like angry dogs, upon all such searches, which frequently happened to us in the river, but durst not bite, or scarce bark at them, by which I see the trade which such men drive upon the river.

In the morning when we weighed we had only the tide to carry us up, for it was a dead calm, and no glass was ever so perfectly smooth as the surface of the sea; the reflection of the heavens was as bright and distinct from the water as above, scarce a sensible horizon; and there was everywhere about us much small craft bearing up in the tide. This posture was dull, and if it had been hot weather would have been very painful. We found we had good way by assaying the lead, but otherwise we could scarce know we moved. After a considerable space found the buoys begin to enlarge, which the pilot called raising the buoy, which was an indication we had advanced. About nine of the clock the seaman called out a wind was coming. I looked out as sharp as I could to see this wind, wondering what it should be like; at length, with my glass I could perceive in the horizon at E. as it were a thread, almost imperceptible, whereby only the horizon was a little more sensible than in other places. It was always strange to me that the seamen would descry by their bare eyes things at a distance as well as I could by my glass, though a good one. And I often proved this by asking what a vessel was, how she stood, and what tack she had aboard, and the like; all which they would plainly describe when I could scarce with my bare eyes perceive anything. But looking and distinguishing or judging by the eye is an art made by practice as other arts grow; by being used to sea views they sooner spy little extraordinaries than they to whom all is unusual. Criticism of all kinds is a habit of nicety, for when much time is spent in being acquainted with the ordinary instances any little thing extraordinary appears. The coming of this wind due east was great joy, because so favourable, and it was a great diversion to observe among the craft, which had it and which not; now this, and then another, for it came with much uncertainty, as one might imagine supposing it had been visible as smoke is, and we laid our sails as fair for it as we could, and at last it came and fluttered us a good space, for, as I said, upon the edge it was very rolling and uncertain, till at last we were full paid, and stood in with wind and tide and stemmed good part of the ebb. At last, the wind failing, we came to an anchor within the middle ground, upon the coast of Kent, above St James' Point. And there shall end the relation of this voyage, which I have made more largely than pertinently, supposing it might, at least, shew the strong inclination I had to action and the pleasure it gave me; for, otherwise, I could not have had such an impression from it as not to forget one circumstance. And I must needs recommend it to all persons that are fond of pleasure to gratify all inclinations this way, which makes health the chief good we know, rather than those which weaken nature and destroy health, and, by that, with vain shadows deprive us of the substantial part of life—ease, and freedom from pain.

This I have related as one of my mathematical entertainments, for the working of a vessel, its rigging, and position of the sails, do exercise as much of mechanics, as all the other arts of the world.

J D Sleightholme

SHE'S YOURS CHUM

SLEEP has been a disjointed business and full of voices and roaring, with snatches of vivid dream and nightmare—a kind of idiot's Ball. You come out of it suddenly like a bird fluttering out of a thicket, but full consciousness still hangs back. You are aware of your belt buckle and the tickle of your sweater-neck damp with your breath.

There is a gleam of light on the deckhead and feet thud down a ladder, somebody is whistling through his teeth. An awful suspicion comes into your mind; slyly, you shut your eyes, thinking it out but full well you know what's coming. Then there is a hand—quite disembodied—holding out a mug. You eye it with black hate from your warm nest of blankets and you notice that the hand has acquired an oilskin sleeve— a wet one. 'She's all yours, chum,' says the hand. On one elbow you grope for the mug. 'O.K., O.K.,' you mutter.

Tea must be drunk sitting on the edge of the bunk, or you may go to sleep again. You do this and the boots thud back up the companionway. You begin to work it out. The ship is lively and your backside rolls back and forth on the keen edge of the bunk-board. It's raining up there and plenty of wind. On the bulkhead your oilskin is doing a shuffle and you give it a sour look. The tea is tasteless because of the mean taste in your mouth. 'Like a parrot's cage,' you reflect, 'or a horse's crupper,' you improve, but you drink it because it is all part of a formula, and the same will hold when you relieve 'him' in four hours' time.

'Why does he have to be so bloody gay?'

Putting your boots on is an annoying process and you curse steadily, then there is a sock stuffed deep into one toe and off comes the boot again. Meanwhile she lurches and you crack your elbow. There's a towel to wind round the neck and a shirt and sweater to be stuffed back into your pants. Sleeping all-standing always produces this crumpled belly business, 'you'd think they'd invent something!' Now the oily, and you totter about struggling into the sleeves, flapping like an old crow in a chimney. There's a button missing. 'Some fool must have done it. "Him" of course.'

You mount the companionway, mastering your irritation and looking as cheerful as you can, which is about as much as a wet paper hat.

'Ha,' you say, struggling in the narrow door, 'whoops, dearie!' Secretly you give it a vicious side-kick.

The wind greets you with a stinging slap in the face and you use a word normally saved for blocked toilets. 'He' is at the wheel yelling something, and you clutch your way aft to him.

'—and that's the Ile de Bas light behind the port shrouds and Sept Ile is back there but . . . expect to . . . rather tends . . . ruddy feet frozen.' The wind has digested most of his words, but you nod and grunt. 'Hang on,' you say, 'I'd just like a peep at the chart.'

'The what?' he asks. 'Chart, chart!' you repeat. He roars with laughter, so that you detest him. 'Oh, it sounded like "tart".'

Five minutes reprieve while you try to focus on the chart. You're trying to force yourself into the centre of things — you, the ship, the shore and the direction. Later, as you sit at the wheel, you will 'feel' your position. You're the missing bit of jig-saw, wriggle into your hole and all those lights will become friends and you'll feel the forward thrust of the ship along the coast.

You battle out into the night again. His backside disappearing below is a hateful sight. 'Cocoa or tea when I call you?' you yell after it. It doesn't hear you.

There you are, then, pull your oilskin around your knees, and the back of your sou'wester outside your collar, wriggle your neck and settle down to it. His final words remain in your mind. 'North eighty West.' They stick in your brain like the shadow of newsprint on a polished table.

The port light rolls down and the foam goes red — and up and down again. The roaring of wake — and sea — and rigging are the familiar sounds of your dream and it's going to go on for a long time. There's rain, of course, and that wasn't any part of sleep.

'Why in hell am I here?' you ask. 'It's cost me money and time and ambition to be here. Why in hell?'

You have a wrist-watch and it's a sly little engine. An hour passes before you look at it. Held out to the light of the binnacle it grins at you pityingly like a bus-conductor. 'Twenty-five minutes, mate,' it says. You know damn well how it raced and rattled away your time below. The thought occurs that time is only a relative thing and you think some more about the theory and you feel clever.

'I'm enjoying this,' you tell yourself, 'this is the life for me,' and you begin to whistle and then sing. You do the 'Old Bold Mate of Henry Morgan' because you can manage the bass bits. You conclude with a dispirited 'Lily of Laguna' which gets lost in the flogging of the jib ten minutes later.

You sail on in silence.

Have you noticed how the lighted bowl of the compass card looks at you? Inside that clean little house it looks lazy and comfortable. It's like looking into a warm, brightly lit room from a winter's night, and inside, the occupant moves slowly and confidently, at ease and relaxed. If one could get in . . . and the bland whiteness is like a moon. The ship fades and there is only the binnacle's face enveloping you, the roar of water is muffled and the darkness is only a blanket over your head.

The wheel spins, rapping your knuckles with a blur of spokes. You jerk awake and curse, looking guiltily around.

She won't quite sail herself under the small jib and so to leave the wheel you must slip the becket over it, and this you do at regular intervals—more frequently perhaps than you need. You take a series of fixes and they stride along the chart heading west. As the tide goes fair the strides are longer and it becomes a sort of game. Ile de Bas comes abeam and the lights of the Morlaix entrance look like people with flash lamps searching behind a hedge. Sleepiness has gone now and you are alert to it all. Half the watch is over.

On the wheel you feel important and vital and very tough. You think of men you dislike and sneer to yourself in the dark at the thought of them doing this. 'Merry, hawk-eyed you spinning a wheel before the dawn.' You laugh aloud and promptly feel idiotic.

Another hour and you have cramp and your feet are cold — 'he' said something about that. Your eyelids are two half-lowered portcullises and time is dragging again. 'If I put the kettle on in another twenty minutes and if it takes a quarter of an hour to boil, an' five minutes to make the tea, that'll leave ten minutes left for "him" to get up.' You look at your watch and settle down to think about women for a while.

Ten minutes to four, and the darkness is less complete. 'Does one ever see a real dawn like an insurance advertisement, with banners of light, heraldic colours and the rest? Why in hell does dawn come creeping in like a lodger in the pantry?' The night is diluted with dirty water until you suddenly find that you can see the jib fairlead and the side-lights cease to stain the water.

The teapot handle is fisted with string, and care must be taken but you whistle as you pour, then for'ard you go, mug in one hand, torch in the other, shouldering along as the ship lurches.

'All right, she's yours, chum,' you tell him. He struggles up and glowers. 'O.K., O.K.' he mutters.

Sir Alker Tripp

THE CRUISING SPIRIT

To my shame and sorrow I own it; I do not possess the full and true cruising spirit. That lot cannot be the lot of everyone, and I am one of the poor specimens; I am simply not in it with some men I know, as regards that placid and adaptable frame of mind which is the true fruit of the cruising spirit.

It is not that I have found myself wanting in times of stress or trouble. Even among the poorest of us such a failing is seldom encountered; and I, like all the rest, have generally muddled through somehow. But my inferiority comes out even there; for I do it with the utmost expenditure possible of nerve-strain and foreboding. Until things are *really* bad I spend my imagination in thinking out, and providing escape from, all sorts of awkward predicaments which may never happen. I believe a good many other people do the same, though they do not always own up. And I believe that they also, like me, only become reasonably placid and contented when the awkward predicament has really arisen. Then the fight against odds brings its own inspiration, making a man even of the abject.

I am not thinking, however, of that aspect of matters just now—but of the ordinary everyday cruising outlook. I was shamed into realisation of these things the other day when, lying in a mud-berth in my yacht (not yet fitted out), I heard a song as glad as that of a skylark. It was some fellow singing; he may not have had high musical proficiency—on that point I am not competent to speak—but for sheer joyousness and freedom I have seldom heard his music matched. It had the merry note that only a man who is happy to the core can put into a song.

And guess where my songster was! Thigh-booted, he was knee-deep in the mud. On Easter Monday he was shovelling the mud away from the keel of his yacht which, had she only floated from her winter berth (as, by all the rules of the game, she ought to have done) would have taken him for his projected Easter cruise to the Channel Islands. The spring tides on the South Coast since January had all been short; even the March tides, usually bumper ones, had failed to float his vessel. He had lost his Easter cruise, and was spending his holiday digging out his yacht instead. Grumble? Not he. Every time you met him his happiness was infectious and did you good. At low-water he was digging, and at high-water he was on deck with marlinspike and knife, hard at work at rigging jobs which he had intended to carry through in mid-channel on his cruise.

The poet says

Had Fate
Made me as hapless, I had been as great.

Speaking for myself, I am sure that I shouldn't have been. I should have groused. I should have been telling people about it all and expecting their sympathy. But *he* had the cruising spirit to its uttermost, and the chances of the game were all one to him.

He came on board me for a yarn once or twice, at intervals between his labours. I mentioned Newtown River, I remember; and he smiled reminiscently.

'What was it?' I asked.

'A double casualty,' he laughed. 'I was in a twenty-four-tonner, and there isn't much room, as you know. But I had brought up in a snug berth, making myself a nuisance to nobody—unless perhaps the oyster people. And I was rather pleased. Then another pilot-cutter of about my own tonnage came in, and—went bang aground.'

He paused. Good Samaritan as he was, I might have known that he went to the rescue. So he did.

'I thought I could fetch him off with my auxiliary,' he went on, 'but I couldn't.' He paused. 'The fact is I went aground myself on the other side, and we both dried out. Drawing seven foot six we both lay over at a mighty angle, so that, while some of the berths on board were quite comfortable, the ones opposite—weren't!'

'So your week-end was spoiled?' I hazarded.

'Not a bit,' he answered. 'We found all sorts of things to do. We made a great bonfire ashore, for one thing, I remember. I daresay I never enjoyed a week-end better in my life.'

There you have it; the genuine article. That is the spirit.

Yet once again, a week or two after, I heard that cheery note of song. The neaped yacht was afloat by now, and she came proudly in from sea. Her sails were soon off her. A kedge was down as well as the big anchor, and some pulley-hauly was in progress to the merry tune of a shanty. The same note of utter happiness was in his voice. Then my hero came ashore, and I noticed that the bridge of his nose was gashed and his nose itself newly blooded.

'What on earth—?' I asked.

'Oh, the block of the tops'l halliard fell on it,' he explained.

'When did it happen?' I asked.

'Just this minute, as I was getting the tops'l off her,' he laughed.

And he went striding off, the happiest man you ever met.

Eric Hiscock

SAVAGE FORCE ELEVEN

AFTER our easy, almost carefree, passages in the steady trade wind belts of the North Atlantic and East Pacific, Susan and I have found the Western Pacific to be a difficult and sometimes a dangerous place for little ships. The weather there is unreliable, the trade wind often failing and occasionally giving place without any warning from the barometer to strong gales with heavy rain, and a great many vigias are marked on the charts. A vigia is a reported shoal, the position, even the existence of which, is doubtful; although some of these have been disproved in recent years, enough remain to be a source of anxiety and perplexity to the mariner, especially on a dark and windy night.

When we left Pago-Pago in American Samoa we were bound for Vavau, the northernmost inhabited island of the Tonga group which, under the rule of capable Queen Salote, is the last remaining kingdom of the South Seas. The wind was strong and forward of the beam so we had a wet and uncomfortable passage, and as we proceeded on our way the weather worsened; there were solar and lunar haloes and an increasing quantity of low, oily, black cloud while the wind steadily freshened. On the morning of our third day at sea, and after mistaking several low cloudbanks for the island, we made a landfall.

It was a gloomy morning with drizzle from a leaden sky, and as we approached Vavau the wind increased to Force eight; half the mainsail was rolled down and we had the second staysail set, but the latter soon had to come in as the wind strengthened and even then the yacht was over-canvased. It was impracticable to roll down any more of the mainsail and I did not wish to set the trysail because we would shortly have to beat nine miles through a twisting channel to reach the only anchorage, and *Wanderer III* does not go to windward very well under that sail. As we closed with the land the drizzle developed into a downpour which obscured everything, but as we knew the bearing of the headland which we must round in order to enter the channel, we held on until its 600-foot cliffs loomed up no more than a couple of hundred yards ahead. At that moment the gale hardened suddenly to a savage Force eleven, sixty miles per hour or more, the strongest wind we had experienced, and *Wanderer* was overpowered. With surprising ease we got the mainsail down, the Gibbons' slides running easily in the lightly oiled track, muzzled it and got some tiers on.

It was then noon. We were both soaked and our teeth were chattering for the thermometer had fallen lower than it had been since we were in England; so we left the yacht to look after herself while we changed into dry clothes and had a meal of soup and fried corned beef with onions, quickly prepared and appetising.

Apart from its normal diurnal rise and fall the barograph was steady, so we expected an improvement in the weather soon, when we intended to make sail and beat up for the harbour. But no improvement came. The hours went by and the gale continued to shrill its high-pitched scream in the rigging. With it just abaft her beam *Wanderer* had a list of fifteen degrees and was moving in a northerly direction at about four knots with the helm free. As she drew away from the island's lee the sea increased and by the late afternoon some heavy crests were beginning to break aboard over the stern. We therefore decided to stream the sea-anchor in order to slow her down.

This is of the pyramidal type, its mouth (2½ feet square) being kept open by stout oak crossbars which are held together by a brass bolt at the point where they cross. It is strongly made, the canvas being a heavy flax, and it is roped throughout with 1¾-inch rope the four parts of which, each having passed through a hole at the end of the crossbars, are brought together at a large thimble to form the bridle. A lead weight secured to one of the crossbars keeps the anchor submerged and prevents it from spinning. Previous experience had convinced me that the modern yacht with her deep heel and shallow forefoot will not ride head to wind with the sea-anchor streamed from the bow unless she can set a riding sail aft; so we put the anchor out from the stern on a thirty-fathom warp of two-inch hemp secured to a samson post on the port quarter. With the helm lashed amidships *Wanderer* made a course straight down wind, but we did not wish to drift in that direction because to leeward of us lay the small, low island of Toku with a breaking rock a mile from it, and beyond an active volcano, Fauna Iai. Neither is inhabited. With blinding rain driven horizontally by a gale of such strength that we could show no canvas to it, these were uncomfortable neighbours to have under one's lee especially with night coming on; so we lashed the tiller to starboard, thus bringing the wind out on the port quarter, and hoped that the yacht would work across the wind sufficiently to carry her clear of the dangers. She lay safely, only occasionally taking aboard a dash of spray, and there was no strain on the rudder; in my opinion, that is the most important advantage of riding by the stern.

Nights in the tropics are always long, and as it was then midwinter in the southern hemisphere we knew there would be at least twelve hours of darkness. With the low, heavy, rain-filled sky night came early, and to us, lying uneasily in our bunks, it seemed interminable. The sea was increasing all the time and being on the quarter, it threw the yacht heavily to leeward again and again with a crash which, we thought, must surely start a seam or butt, and on the swift upward lurch after each leeward roll the rigging howled a shriller note and something aloft vibrated furiously, shaking the mast and the whole ship. Several times during the night I looked in the bilge to see if she was making any water, but there was no more than usual there and I blessed William King's good men at Burnham-on-Crouch who had built the little vessel so honestly and well.

First one then the other of us would struggle wearily over the bunkboard, stagger to the hatch, slide it back a few inches and have a look round, for the proximity of the unlit islands under our lee caused a constant nagging anxiety; but there was never anything to be seen in the blackness except our own masthead light. Dawn came on leaden feet and it was with a feeling of great relief that we watched the first faint grey light of day creeping through the ports. A sickly yellow streak low in the eastern sky signified sunrise, and by this time the wind had moderated to about force nine.

Breakfast was a sordid struggle with sliding crockery and squeamish stomachs, but we managed to keep it in its place. Afterwards there was a temporary clearing on the horizon and we saw Fanau lai, grey and sinister with jets of smoke spurting from its crater. It was several miles distant and no longer to leeward, so throughout that worrying night *Wanderer* had succeeded in working across the wind and taking herself well clear of the dangers.

We could then have put the helm amidships and drifted straight down wind in greater comfort, but such a course would have taken us farther from such slight shelter as the Tonga groups of reefs and islands still afforded and, of course, farther from Vavau which we still hoped to reach when conditions improved. So we left the helm as it was, crawled into our bunks before noon and, except for periodically renewing the chafing gear on the sea-anchor warp where it passed through the fairlead, remained in them until next morning.

On the third day the wind moderated to force eight, but the rain continued; the sea was larger than before and the motion even more violent. The galley stove persisted in leaping out of its gimbals until we lashed it in with seizing wire, and again and again heavy crests broke aboard to find the weak spots in our sun-shrunk decks. All the spare towels were in use protecting our books from the drips, and a trickle of dirty green water seeped past the perished wedges and ran down the white enamel paint on the mast.

That evening at dusk I opened the hatch to have one last look at the dismal scene around before night settled in. I was standing in the companionway with my head and shoulders outside, when a crest heavier than anything we had previously experienced came aboard. It tore away the canvas dodgers, filled the cockpit and flooded the deck fore-and-aft, knocking me down the companionway and coming below after me. It ran right through the ship into the forepeak, climbing into my bunk on the way and into the bookshelf above it; it inundated the chart stowage where lay 300 Admiralty charts, and even succeeded in breaking one of the lamp chimneys which was five feet above the cabin sole. I at once took a bucket and bailed the cockpit, for the cockpit drains are too small to deal quickly with a large volume of water and I was fearful lest, held down by the weight of water aft, the yacht might fail to rise to the next big sea. If I have a criticism to make of the design of *Wanderer* it is that, bearing in mind the weight of gear we have to carry in the stern lockers, she lacks sufficient reserve buoyancy aft; she would be better either with increased freeboard there or else with a short sawn-off counter; a refinement which I would have liked to incorporate but could not afford.

Much of that night was spent mopping water from books and charts, and we noticed with that strained attention a long drawn-out gale begets that there were occasional lulls when the shrill voice of the wind in the rigging dropped a note or two. The gale was blowing itself out.

Next day the wind was down to force seven and the sun shone fitfully so that I was able to get sights and fix our position. They showed that during the four days we had lain to the sea-anchor we had drifted a total of 120 miles, our average speed being 1¼ knots, and that we had made almost a square drift just as though we had been hove-to under sail; the wind had been south-east and our course west-sou'-west. We were then 120 miles from Vavau and 150 miles from the nearest islands of the Fiji group. Lack of sleep, anxiety and the wild motion had so tired us that we felt in no fit condition to attempt the hard beat back to Vavau against the sea then running, so we decided to make a fair wind of it for Fiji.

Gilbert Wheat

NOWHERE AND BEYOND

TEN degrees north and 135° west, a sailboat creaks and groans through the swells of an endless tropic sea. The hot sky forms a hard metallic shell, its horizon edges rimmed by distant thunderheads. The huge orb of the sun burns nearly in the zenith.

North-east trade winds blow steadily against two triangular staysails hung out on either side of the boat's mainmast. An untended tiller flops back and forth. To the eye of an observer, perhaps from an airplane diverting its course to dip low in curiosity, the scene is one of desolation and suggested tragedy. No one is on deck. The boat seems to drift aimlessly downwind—coming out of nowhere, going into nowhere. It moves slowly, its wake vanishing in a few yards. But a closer look reveals signs of life aboard and a plan of travel. A sea turtle lies upside down on the foredeck waving a flipper at the sun. Two wool shirts and a blanket flap from a lifeline, drying in the wind. A glistening filament of fishline trails aft.

It is midday. Down below a man sleeps in the boat's only bunk. His lean body stretches moist and naked on a blanket. Matted hair and an untrimmed beard cover most of his face. It is midday, but if he sleeps during the dark hours there is a chance of being run down by another boat. Though he sails now on an empty ocean, he has come by habit to rest in the day and stand his cockpit watch by night. A hermit of the sea, content to be a thousand miles from the nearest human being, he sails away from the complexities of society, and sails alone because he cannot sail with company. He is his own confidant, his own guardian, his own enemy.

The close air in the cabin mixes with the smells of kerosene, tar, putty and musty canvas. Hard bunk boards rise and fall beneath him, and his head, in sleep, rolls from side to side.

Waves slosh along the thin sides of the wooden hull, sending their muted drumbeat echoes through the cabin. A one-burner stove squeaks in its gimbals, a can of beans in the food locker rolls back and forth (click, click, *clack*, click, click, *clack*). Overhead and forward, the turtle spanks the deck with leathery thumps; and from high aloft come the wrenching, vibrating sounds of the rigging. But the man sleeps on, for these sounds are normal. Should the hull move through the water in a new motion, should the rigging change its tune only slightly, some inner signal will wake him.

The sun drops toward the west, sending a shaft of yellow light into the cabin. The beam crosses a rifle strapped to the overhead, its breech and barrel plugged with grease. As the boat rolls, the sunbeam moves up and down in the sparse cabin, touching on a rack of charts and navigational books, a tarnished lamp on the bulkhead, a pile of folded canvas and coiled line. The beam moves over the man's face. He stirs and rouses himself from sleep.

An hour before sunset his burnt face appears at the top of the companionway. He wears nothing but a ragged pair of dungarees cut off at the thigh. The boat still sails itself, wind and sea have come up only slightly. He goes forward and urinates over the lee rail, his bare toes gripping the gunwale, his elbows locked around the mainmast shrouds. He thinks of his greatest fear — falling overboard. For the thousandth time he imagines himself in the wake, swimming desperately after his moving boat. But, as always in his imagination, the boat sails efficiently away from him until the mast top disappears from sight.

He checks the pieces of rough canvas tied around the sheets to prevent chafing. He moves one piece of gear to a point where the two lines barely touch, knowing how easily one line, with an almost imperceptible rubbing motion, can saw the other line in half. He scans every yard of his canvas sails for pinholes, which a sudden gust of wind can expand into angry, shrieking rips. Not a shroud, not a turnbuckle escapes his attention. The parting of a shroud in strong winds, followed by the sickening crash of the mast, could deprive him of his only means of propulsion. In a matter of seconds he could be as helpless as a piece of driftwood.

Squatting in the cockpit he studies his steering compass. The boat's heading vacillates between two zero zero and two one zero magnetic. Things seem normal, or nearly so. He takes the tiller by hand once more and wedges himself into a corner of the cockpit.

He lives by the wind and the cloud shapes and the state of the sea. The size and curl of the waves, the increased tension on the rigging in the last hours tell him the weather will soon change. Toward the south, low clouds are growing in size and blossoming into new formations. The faint fluttering of the staysails warns of a change in wind direction. He cannot wait until wind and sea become too much for him. His boat is very small. He did not build it for speed or comfort but to withstand anything he thinks the elements can marshal against it. If he has outfitted the boat correctly, the only error will be his.

While there is time and light, he takes down the two stay-sails and sets a mainsail and a small storm jib. His changed rig will not work well down wind, but it will allow him to tack or head into the storm. The sky in the south turns dark and wet, and mechanically he reviews each step of his preparations. He has forgotten one thing, the open porthole forward. He closes it, then returns to the tiller.

From his seat in the cockpit he keeps an eye on the kerosene stove in the galley under the ladder. In five minutes the pot will rattle with boiling water. He peels two potatoes, knocking off the green sprouts with his rigging knife. If the storm is just a squall, the gimbaled stove will balance his boiling pot without spilling water. After the potatoes come out, there will be enough hot water for a big mug of black coffee. At midnight he will eat half a box of raisins and a chocolate bar.

His nautical almanac promises no bright moon for another five nights, so he will sail through a darkness lit only by stars. If the squall comes and goes quickly, leaving in its wake a dry clear sky, he will risk a catnap before sunrise.

From a compartment in the lazaret he takes a Very pistol and removes its waterproof wrapping. He breaks it down and looks for corrosion. There is no corrosion, and he puts it back beside a sealed box of flare shells. The pistol was an unusual acquisition for him—expensive, an occupier of space, but long ago he changed his mind about having one aboard:

Sailing south from Portland along the coast of Oregon, a gale had caught him. He flew his storm trysail, a tough scrap of canvas, but the mast carried away, snapping off cleanly at deck level. It toppled into the sea in a tangle of wire and canvas, and he had to work himself forward at the end of his safety line and part the shrouds with boltcutters because the broken butt end of the mast was ramming the hull. For fifty exhausting hours he fought the storm, struggling to keep his boat afloat.

Fifteen days later, drifting south, he ran out of food and water. His navigation told him he had passed the latitude of San Francisco and was in a shipping lane, and one night a passenger liner ploughed towards him through the fog. She moved slowly, sounding her foghorn at intervals. She came toward him, but suddenly he realised he was unprepared for rescue. He shouted, he pulled of his heavy sweater and waved it. The liner thundered by, so close he could make out figures along the promenade rail. They waved at him, and he saw one man clasp his hands and shake them above his head in the victory salute. But no one made a move towards rescue. The liner held course and speed, her rows of yellow lights going by like windows of a triple-decker train. Her white bows came out of the fog at him, followed by a great city of warm cabins, and her broad white stern disappeared back into the fog the same way.

Where were her lookouts? Why wasn't he on their radar? A few days later a purse seiner towed his boat into San Diego, and the fisherman told him he was a fool not to carry a flare gun. One bright flare in the sky and any landlubber would know he was in trouble.

In his log he writes his estimate of wind velocity and direction. He makes notes on the weather and estimates his course and speed since morning. Then he writes the number of days at sea. They now total forty. He keeps track of the day of the month since he must know this to punch his almanac tables. Nothing out here will remind him it is Sunday or Wednesday or the Fourth of July or June 30th. Hours, days, weeks weave themselves together in one long unbroken rope of time.

He also puts down his approximate position. It is only a guess, but before sunrise he will shoot stars and later plot a fix. By navigating this way, at dawn instead of dusk, he will have morning sun to light his folding chart table in the cabin. Three mornings ago, under clear conditions, he plotted a good fix from Deneb, Capella and Aldebaran. In that pre-dawn moment, when the high-magnitude stars still glowed and the dark line of the horizon first became visible, he went forward on deck with his sextant lashed to his wrist. Bracing himself against the mast, he carefully moved his mirrors to bring the points of starlight to the horizon. He noted the altitude of each star and, with a pocket watch, the time of observation. Then, he went to the cabin, opened his books and worked slowly and painfully at his plotting board. Half an hour later three pencil lines crossed, forming a small triangle, and with a certain pride at making no errors he drew a heavy black dot in the centre of the triangle. Within a mile or two he was definitely located — in the middle of nowhere.

He is forty days at sea, and the pencil line on his track chart comes closer and closer to the island of Eiao in the Marquesas. If he can sail his boat thirty-five miles a day, allowing a slow passage through the doldrums, he will sight the island in another month. No one lives on Eiao, but he will rest there and dive for reef fish and lobsters. He will kill a wild goat with his rifle. Meanwhile, in the doldrums, he can trap rain water in his cockpit awning. When food runs low he will sharpen his hunting knife and butcher the turtle. He studies the turtle's horny carapace. The oily meat can be dried, the innards trailed for bait. There will be steaks near the flippers and several days of high-protein soup from the bones and tough muscles. His turtle will rock back and forth until its day of execution, three flippers waving like the parts of some giant toy, the fourth flipper tethered to the mast. He remembers how easy it was to capture the turtle. When he first spotted it, sleeping in the sun with its round shell completely dry above water, he merely sailed the boat alongside it, ran forward to the bowsprit, and gaffed it through one of the back flippers. The turtle weighed a hundred pounds or more, and the boat heeled almost to the gunwale as he worked it aboard between the lifelines.

But now the wind hauls around, blowing at him from the southeast. He trims the sheets and sails close-hauled toward the squall, through freshening wind and gradually steepening seas. He pulls in his fishline and coils the stiff wet filament into a cockpit locker. His white jig, a handful of sea-bird feathers wired to a strong hook, is still intact. He wonders if it will be worth while to trail turtle innards as bait. This far away from continental shelves and islands, only chance will send him a mackerel, an off-course barracuda or dolphin. But later on in the calms of the doldrums the innards might draw small brown sharks, small enough to be gaffed and dragged aboard.

There are no birds in the sky, nor have there been for twenty days. Long ago, when he left the California coast, a thin-winged albatross had flown silent escort for him. It flew above his mast top at night and made long circling flights during the days, always coming back to him. Sometimes it landed in the swells ahead of the boat, ruffling its feathers as the slow wash of the boat rocked it. Then one day it turned back in the mid-Pacific, as though even this small boat were going too far for it.

Here the man sees nothing in the sky or sea. The ocean is brilliant blue, as it has been for days, but it is a dead ocean. No colloids of bay or river silt and no micro-organisms deflect the sun's rays. He floats through a vacant world. The sky is still light. He opens a paperback novel and reads aloud to hear the sound of his own voice.

The squall line spreads, and he estimates the rising wind at twenty knots. But the boat drives forward, and he is not worried. The sun disappears in a flaming wash of reds and oranges; the squall clouds tumble toward him—damper and blacker, expanding by the minute. A sudden lift in the wind picks the scud from wave tops and sends a film of spray into the cockpit. The rigging hums, the boat heels sharply to starboard and the turtle slides heavily to the lee rail, its tethered flipper pulled tight. Two hundred yards ahead a wall of slanting rain begins to flatten the sea, and the man goes forward to the mast. With quick turns around the cleat he releases the main halyard, gathers in the flapping mainsail and lashes it to the boom with three canvas stops. His beard tips bristle with salt spray, and the sea water bubbles over his feet, rushes down the lee rail and overboard through the scuppers. With the jib pulling hard and the tiller lashed amidships, he studies the onrushing squall. It is mostly rain, not wind. He decides the boat can take care of itself. He swings himself into the cabin and slides the top hatch shut. A deluge of rain falls on the boat, drumming like hailstones on the resonant cabin top. He listens to the jib flutter as the boat comes into the wind and loses way. Down in the cabin, already dank from lack of ventilation, the man hunts with a flashlight for cabin leaks. He finds one trickle of water running into his bunk and another forward in the chain locker. He makes note of the exact places to work in more putty. Then, with a bar of soap, he climbs on deck to catch the last of the squall shower. The fresh water courses down his body, washing off a week's accumulation of perspiration and sticky salt crystals. Back in the cabin, still wet, he puts on a shirt for the night watch.

The squall passes. The air is murky, and scattered eddies of wind flap the sail, but the weather is clear to the south. Above him stars begin to glow. He studies the sky a while for new signs, then changes his rig back to the twin staysails. Once again the boat moves slowly southward in front of a strengthening north-east breeze. The rudder snaps and clicks without strain against its underwater hinges. The two sails belly against the night sky, and the pale red light above the compass card shows the heading at two one zero.

The man fills his pipe and studies the blue smoke as it streaks forward and dissipates above the cabin top. The wind blows dry and cool, and the boat sails briskly at three knots. The black-onyx night waves rise and fall and stretch out forever in front of him, and he senses, rather than observes, a new steadiness coming into the north-east wind. It is almost time to eat his potatoes and make black coffee, and after that he will have the long night ahead of him. He is at peace with time and nature.

During the coming hours his mind will touch on half-forgotten things of the past—a city, a love, a friend, a lost career. But he is not in harmony with such things. They exist for others, and in another world. Nature is his natural environment, and if he is less an observer and admirer of her beauties, it is because he is a real part of her. The wind, the sea, the sky are elements to be understood and used. The constellations of the zodiac, the romantic names of Virgo, Sagittarius, Pisces are only navigational signposts. The dawn and sunset clouds, for all their shapes and colours, are only indications of weather. The stars tell him where he is, the wind and sea tell him what sails to set.

Most of his books tell him how to do things. They tell him about first aid, special knots and the correct way to stitch a sail. His bible is a copy of the *Sailing Directions*. It tells him what to expect at his next anchorage—fresh water, food supplies, how many natives live in the main village. Sections of the book describe weather in his ocean and when he can expect to make hurricane-free runs from one land mass to another.

Other cruising yachts, bulging with equipment and gregarious crews, meet the lonely single-hander in all the anchorages of the world. He visits people and places and tells his stories, but he rations his time with society, anxious for the simplicity of the sea. The single-hander's boat is small, and so is his pocketbook. Ashore, he works alone. He repairs and provisions his boat to suit himself. He combs the ragged waterfront for spare line, canvas and metal fittings. What he eats, what he wears are secondary to what goes into his boat. He careens his boat on deserted beaches, propping it up in the sand with borrowed lumber. Working fast against the incoming tide, he scrapes the bottom clear of barnacles and checks his rudder. He works for no man, is responsible to no one but himself. His work is thorough.

He may sail into port bearded, thin, sick, given up for lost a hundred days before. But when his boat is ready he sails again. A few dock watchers cast him off. They wonder if anyone will ever see him again. They wonder what kind of misfortune will claim him—a leak, a sickness, a reef, a storm. He tempts fate: he seems to ask for a chance to die alone and unreported, blotted out in some wet, howling fashion.

He pushes off from the dock and waves a shy farewell. Even before his boat clears the protective shores of the harbour it heels over in capricious winds. He trims the sheets, comes about to new tacks and at the same time unrolls a harbour chart. He is on his own once again. His boat may be in sight for hours, a white scrap of hull and sail growing smaller and smaller. Eventually there will be no sign of him anywhere on the horizon.

John Seymour

BY SAIL AND OAR AGAIN

Willynilly spent the winter in a yard in Brightlingsea, and in July I started making journeys in my van from Orford to paint her, and get her ready for the voyage. I intended to sail to the Kiel Canal by easy stages—but not too easy. Then cruise for a few weeks in the Baltic. Several people had offered to come with me but one by one had dropped out—the pressure of life being too much for them. In the end—when I was quite reconciled to sailing alone, a young friend of mine named Mogador made up his mind to come with me and—although he was quite inexperienced sailingwise—he is as good a shipmate as I ever had.

As the time got nearer for departure there seemed to be more and more things to do—until the fatal day when we said: 'We'll just go regardless!'

I journeyed from Orford to Brightlingsea with Sally, my wife, Mogador, a boy named Dickie, and the van heavily overloaded with large objects. Without Sally we would never have sailed. She skilfully stowed away (helped by Mogador and Dickie, watched by me) four heavy iron and wood skids (for dragging *Willynilly* up the beach), a large block tackle to help with the same job, iron pickets and a sledge-hammer to drive into the beach for a purchase, sacks of sand ballast, a Primus stove in a biscuit tin, a water container, a paraffin one, a meths one, a boat compass, some dozen charts (all 1915 vintage) given to me by the Harbour Master of Pin Mill, spare rope galore, a tent, an awning to go over the after part of the boat to sleep under, sleeping bags, kit bags of spare clothes, and food. Three loaves of Sally's own bread, our own butter from our own cow, our own home-canned mutton from our own (late) sheep. We were not to starve.

We sailed away on a gentle westerly breeze—only to notice that we didn't have a watch and we sailed back to cadge Sally's off her. Then we said goodbye again—to Jack Tué as well for he moved heaven and earth to get us away—and I don't blame him for all the uproar was terrible—then off we went again. Gently round the point, on the ebb tide, off that charming place Jaywick, and—bang—the breeze fell away and came up again fresh and happy from due eastward!

We were flummoxed.

I was not going to try to tack across the North Sea, I was not going back to Brightlingsea. There were two things I could do. Beach at Jaywick, or sail south. I did the latter—groped through the Ray Channel and ran into Burnham. If the east wind held I'd sail for Calais and then coast-crawl.

Burnham is a place full of memories for me. When I am there I live in the past. I had an honorary uncle (Andrew MacMeekan) who was, in his lifetime, a great yachtsman there, with two 6-metres (The *Gypatus* and the *Gybo*), and when a small boy I used to spend all my holidays with him and sail down to Cockle Bank (the farthest he ever went in those days) and picnic. I remember Burnham when it was still half a fishing village and a very good place it was too.

We slept on board, under the awning, on somebody else's moorings, and spent the morning trying to buy a chart of the Thames Estuary. Now you would think that if there is nowhere else in the world where every single shop from the butcher to the haberdasher would stock a chart of the Thames Estuary it would be Burnham—but we were forced to sail at eleven—without a chart. There just wasn't one. Nobody had ever heard of one. I know it's easy to say:

'What do you want with a chart? You only draw two foot, etc., etc.'

I still don't like wandering about among all those blasted sands and buoys without knowing where I am—within a little anyway. We couldn't get a weather forecast—it's a feature of the Burnham telephone system that you can never get any attention from the exchange—and it's not automatic. It was a question of either spending the rest of the day dialing 'O' hopelessly, or going without. We went without. We had a westerly breeze and a foul tide, which we stemmed happily enough. Once outside the Crouch and down Swin we lay a course for the Galloper.

Lovely day—breeze strengthening. We got to the Galloper at lighting-up time and by then she was really galloping. We sailed close—shouted for a weather forecast. The sole watchman held up six fingers and shouted 'Force six—nor'-west!' If he had said Force twenty it wouldn't have altered our plans much—we had to go on. We were running down hill.

The darker it got (it was a long July day) the rougher it got. We could still carry full sail (we had a new mainsail) and *Willynilly* plunged along like a bird. We sailed through a fleet of Belgian trawlers—fairly bouncing about in the waves. We had to reef and in the middle of the night we had to reef again.

Willynilly was sailing too quickly for safety. We had a hurricane lantern hung on the side of the boat inside to see the compass. The North Hinder loomed—two flashes every ten seconds, then we had to pull down a third reef. It was really blowing up now—the waves enormous (to us!) with breaking tops. The coble rode like a bird. It was morally unwise to look astern. If you did you felt you were sure to be engulfed. The waves looked enormous and our free-board is only a few inches. But every time the stern lifted just at the right moment—we surfed forward in an exhilarating manner then slid backwards into the trough. Womp!

Sometimes a slop came over but never more than a slop. Mogador had steered while it was light. I didn't dare let him in the dark—a broach-to would have been embarrassing. It was an awful long time before we actually saw the naked light of the North Hinder. It was very hypnotic trying to steer in that sea, to two faint loom flashes every ten seconds. The sky was overcast and there were no stars. To look at the compass was to spoil your eyes for the horizon. An occasional ship went by and it was damned rough.

They say cobles are dangerous running before the wind and a big sea. I never heard such a lot of nonsense. *Willynilly* was beautiful to steer, and I've never run before a bigger sea in a small boat and hope never to again. Her big rudder gave perfect control even in the nearly dead water of a wave. There was never any danger of broaching-to—unless the steersman had gone to sleep. There was a danger of that—it was so very dark, and so hypnotic—looking for those two flashes.

A couple of times the wind eased and I shook out a reef—once two—but by the time we got to the North Hinder, at first light, we had all three in again and needed them. In fact I was wondering whether to drop the sail and just show a jury sail. I chucked a large warp over the stern as a steadier. The North Hinder was trying to stand on her head.

I had intended to go to the North Hinder and there make up my mind whether to steer for the Hook, or Flushing. I plumped for Flushing. Me, I just wanted inside somewhere quick. We didn't sight the buoy, but we saw some ships. Then we passed out of the shipping channel over the sands that run along the coast thereabouts. The sea goes from fourteen or fifteen fathoms to five or six on these ridges, and I thought that maybe it was that which made the sea get so very nasty every now and then. I ate some of Sally's bread and a half tin of bully beef—like fools we had forgotten to get a thermos and couldn't light the stove in that wind. One keeps saying to oneself,

'I won't look at the watch, not for another hour. Then the hands must have moved a decent way and I shall know we shall be getting decently near the coast.'

The North Hinder's a long way out. It's one of the lonelier

places. Then, when we were really browned off with the whole thing, we saw a trawler. We spoke her.

'What's the bearing for Flushing?'

'*Suid-suid-ost!*'

We had been steering south-east. Like fools we altered course. Then, very long afterwards, in the hazy light we saw a town. High buildings—like skyscrapers—very compact.

'Must be Zeebrugge,' I said. 'We'll steer for it.'

We did. Where was the mole? Couldn't be Zeebrugge. No mole. Must be Ostend. It's very hard to look at a chart when you're steering and holding the sheet and the boat is trying to stand on her head. Particularly when there's some spray coming over and the chart is getting soggy. Mogador steered sometimes but even then conditions weren't perfect for chart reading. Then we saw a lighthouse on the end of a pier and decided to run for it. There was a long curving piled jetty—we nearly went the wrong side of it—straight for a beach on which a colossal surf was breaking. At the last minute we saw that the entrance to the harbour, if harbour there was, was west of the pier. So in we shot—helped by curling waves which were obviously feeling the bottom. Most exciting. Into a long calm harbour entrance, widening out into a fair-sized basin. Just eleven o'clock—24 hours from Burnham.

I had always thought Ostend was a much bigger place than that. There was a floating staging with a lot of yachts. A boatman helped us tie up to it.

'England rules the waves,' he said looking at *Willynilly*.

We went into a café, had a bowl of soup and some wine. After a lot of trudging about we found a cheap hotel that would take us (any smartness that we may have had in our attire had worn off) and we went to bed.

When we woke up the sun was shining brightly outside but there was still a stiff breeze.

'Lovely morning!' said Mogador. 'Shall we have bacon and eggs here or go to a café and have *croissants* and coffee?'

'My dear Mogador,' I said. 'We sailed into Ostend at eleven o'clock in the morning. We wandered about for, say, two hours. We can't have slept for thirty-six hours. It is today —not tomorrow.'

The sun seemed to us though to be in the east. We had a surrealist argument as to whether it was today or tomorrow. We were still dog-tired. Finally we went downstairs to ask. It seemed the only way. But try asking in school-boy French whether it is today or tomorrow? Try asking in English even. It was all very difficult, but at the end of it we established that it was *today*, in fact (we had only slept four hours), and further —that we were not in Ostend—not in Zeebrugge—but in Blankenberghe.

Hammond Innes

OUT OF BOND

THERE are few things in this world that produce a greater sense of satisfaction than to sail your own boat across the sea and into a foreign port. She may be only ten tons, but you have most of the rights—as well as the responsibilities—inherent in captaining the largest ship afloat, including (bureaucracy be praised!) the right to take on tobacco and liquor 'out of bond', in other words free of Customs Duty. To visit Monsieur Henri Ryst's ship-chandling office and see hard liquor, like Scotch and gin, listed at less than a quarter of the price ashore, cognac at a third, cigarettes at a fifth—it is enough to raise the morale of even the tiredest Scotsman; and then to have Monsieur Ryst apologise for not delivering until after five p.m.—because he has to victual the *Queen Mary*! And finally the moment comes when all those beautiful bottles are collected in the dinghy and taken back to the ship to be stored lovingly away against the day they will be drunk, the crew all lending a willing hand amongst a litter of paper and straw.

It is for this that one puts in to Cherbourg. . . . Why else, when close-by are such attractive little ports as Omonville-la-Rogue?

From 'Harvest of Journeys' © *1960*

A E Copping

HOMEWARD IN A HURRICANE

AWAY we went, not tarrying for fresh stores, for time was more valuable than new bread, and what if the water cask were half-empty?

'Why,' exclaimed Gotty, as having curved out of Torbay, we charged the open sea on a strong straight line, 'if the wind keeps in the west'ard, and don't fall away too much, we oughter be in Folkestin' the day arter termorrer. It blows wonderful steady—reg'lar walkin' through the water she is. In by Wednesday mornin' I shouldn't wonder. Yer see, she don't feel the punt now it's aboard. Goes twice as easy, she does, not 'aving all that dead weight ter pull. If the wind don't drop. That's all I'm afraid of.'

On that point he spoke Cole's thoughts and mine. Because perfection seemed too good to last, we feared a diminution of zeal on the part of the wind.

But these timorous misgivings proved without warrant. So far from lessening, the aerial velocity increased. Our mast ofttimes stood at a considerable slant, and the sea came on board at the bow in gurgling mounds of frothy unrest, then streamed down the deck and escaped hissing through the scuppers. Some passed into the hold, where, on going below to consult my chart, I found disconcerting patches of wetness on my books, my clothes, and my bed. But we were going home fast. And faster and faster.

Being well out in the Channel, we had no occasion to concern ourselves with navigation subtleties, and this was just as well, for the pilot did not feel quite himself. He was cold and wet, for one thing, and he was beginning to have a headache, for another.

When day faded, Portland was far astern, and we were south of the Anvil light. All the reefs were taken in. The weather showed no signs of abating its boisterousness.

The question of running for shelter to the Isle of Wight was raised, but only to be unanimously negatived. No one was more prompt than the poor pilot in resisting the suggestion. He now makes frank confession that he would joyfully have gone into harbour if only his swimming brain had been equal to the task of reading up the necessary particulars. The lesser evil was to continue sitting, damp and impassive, on the provision chest, dully wondering if the storm would ever cease.

At midnight he put forth a great effort, and bestirred himself to the extent of thrusting an inquisitive head into the open air. St Catherine's light shone brightly in the north; and no sooner had he made that observation than about a quart of sea water leapt over the dinghy and smote him on the head, icy trickles running down his spine. Stung into a certain amount of life, he fumbled about until he found his lamp, with which, having succeeded in lighting it, he scrutinised his apartment, if haply he might find a dry spot on which to deposit himself. But, with moisture dripping everywhere, the place had rather the look of a grotto than a hold.

My bed was saturated, and a sheet of water was ebbing and flowing across the oilcloth. Boxes and my smaller belongings were passing harshly to and fro, in obedience to the rolling of the vessel. A special lurch deprived me of the support of a chest, and abrupt developments were associated with the extinction and loss of my lamp. Extricating myself from those difficulties, I once more protruded into the open air, just in time to receive about a bucketful of cold sea at the back of my neck.

In oilskins, sea-boots, and sou'westers, Gotty and Cole were encased against those sharp discomforts; my own wardrobe including nothing appropriate to a gale. But I submitted the less rebelliously to the disability on reflecting that my better-clothed companions were doing all the work.

Another subject of my unspoken envy was the way in which, clutching at this and that, Cole succeeded, when occasion arose in traversing the deck without suffering himself to be borne overboard. Fain would I accomplish a gymnastic expedition of the sort; for my inclination lay towards the cabin, which did not leak, and where a fire was burning. Ultimately, and with great circumspection, I essayed and achieved the feat, much as a monkey climbs a tree.

There was no comfort in the cabin. I put coal on the dying embers, and Gotty must have noted the augmented smoke, for Cole struggled to the hatchway, and bade me suffer the fire to die down. Before that could be, the *Betty* indulged in a shuddering spasm which emptied the grate on to the floor, besides working mischief (as the din attested) in our crockery locker.

Afterwards came many upheavals of the sort. Water dripped through the deck, and spray came down the hatchway like rain. I sat or squatted in several situations, but always the lawless lurching of my apartment threw me elsewhere. Lying embedded in a heap of sails, I finally found stable quarters, and I remained there, listening to the roar of wind and water, for many hours.

It was my opinion that the bawley would not founder. Getting into that cold water seemed a thing so pitifully distressing that, by a piece of sublime egotism, I could not believe I should be called upon to do it. And, indeed, physical discomforts apart, there is a sense in which I was, so to speak, enjoying myself. It was drama, bold and spacious. Above, below, and all round, Nature was in a passion—the same Nature which had ofttimes lulled me with rosebuds, blue sky, and linnets. In weak moments, during that awful night, how I longed for the sight and feel of land—if it were only a little in a flower-pot.

At about ten o'clock I came half-way up the hatchway and looked about me. The moist world was tinted in degrees of grey. Swollen masses of water ran towards us in unending succession, and each on drawing near loomed down upon us; but it got underneath the *Betty*, and rolled her about, and hurried on its way. At certain angles of the pitching I saw Beachy Head. We were going home at a pace far outstripping our most hopeful anticipations.

Astern, there were my shipmates, figures of rigid endurance, Gotty still at the helm. At about noon, to get within earshot of them, I clambered across to the hold.

On the previous afternoon we noted a schooner putting back into Portland. Since then the Channel had seemed empty of sailing craft. But we saw many rolling steamers, bravely breasting the weather.

In the early evening we were being hurled towards Dungeness. Suddenly, to the confusion of the helmsman, land was blotted from sight as by a fog. Having been continuously drenched all day by spray, we did not readily recognise that now we were also in a torrent of rain.

On the other side of the headland we encountered our worst weather. The *Betty* only carried her mainsail, storm-reefed, and a small jib. Yet so nearly did she heel over that Gotty perceived the necessity of lowering the former. Tackling his urgent and difficult task with spirit, Cole soon had the gaff on deck. With only a little triangle of canvas over the bowsprit, the *Betty* flew across Dungeness Bay.

Would there be water in Folkestone harbour? Gotty shouted in my ear that I must learn the time of the tide. Somehow I got to the cabin; and, to save me the hazard of a return journey, Cole came crawling to the hatchway for that vital information.

It wanted two hours to high water. With my head out of the cabin opening, I anxiously awaited Gotty's solution of the difficulty. He gave the helm to Cole, and himself came forward and lowered our remaining sail. Then so considerable a volume of water rose from the side and descended upon me that I withdrew into shelter. The next minute our vessel received a blow that sounded like a clap of thunder; a tremor passed through her framework, and I heard an avalanche of water fall on deck.

Amid the howling of the gale, Gotty's agonised shout could not have reached Cole. But the wind carried it back to me, and also I heard the skipper fling himself back to the stern. The less expert hand had held the helm; and to ship two seas of that character in quick succession might have meant disaster. With our dinghy sprawling across the opening, we could not—as now I realised—batten down the hatchways. Cole was slaving at the pump, and, when I judged his strength to be spent, I clambered across and relieved him.

With bare rigging, for an hour and a half the *Betty* staggered in that raging sea. Impatient to the point of pain, with the wind assaulting all my senses, I lived through a long experience of swinging on and on, and still for ever on, in a lost equilibrium of air and water madly mingled. But at last (for the tide bore us towards the shore) I beheld the harbour lights—rigid stars of composure; comfortable reminders that, with good luck, we soon should pass from that quaking realm of boisterous upheaval, and return to the dear old solid land, where roads and kerbstones and houses remained obediently still.

Hoist by Cole, our jib stood against the might of the wind; and, all athrill, we ran for the entrance lights, the tiller in Gotty's tough grip. Then came the sudden relief of sheltered water, and the *Betty*, at peace at last, glided among the multitude of moored luggers in Folkestone harbour. A lifetime had elapsed since we left Torquay—but a lifetime of only thirty-two hours.

Into the public bar of a little inn went Gotty and I—two haggard and dishevelled figures, dripping with salt water and rain. I think it was not the rum we met with, but the reception, that put warmth into my companion. That group of veteran fishermen, sociably assembled under shelter, broke into exclamations of honest astonishment when we went splashing into their midst.

'You've come through it, then!' cried one.

'So that little boat o' yourn,' observed another, with respectful eyebrows raised, 'can stand a bit o' weather!'

'Evenin',' replied Gotty, in friendly greeting to one and all; and not till he had swallowed the first dose of my prescription did he vouchsafe any relief to the curiosity our appearance had excited. Then he casually let fall one crisp, comprehensive sentence:

'We've jest run up from Torky.'

At these tidings the Folkestone men exchanged expressive glances; then bent their eyes anew on the pair of storm-stained mariners.

'Not sorry to be in harbour, I dessay?' one presently ventured.

'Not sorry!' cried Gotty, depositing his tumbler on a table, to be the better able to unlock the inmost chambers of his soul; 'not sorry! Look 'ere, mate! I wouldn't go through that lot again not fer a 'undred pound—nor yet two 'undred; there you are. I've seen a bit o' wind, and I've seen a bit o' weather, at our place sometimes; but talk about larst night! It wasn't water—it was boilin' froth, and all round yer the same! There was times when I thought she was goin' ter shut the door— that's the truth I did. . . . "Where's the Guv'nor?" I says to Joe, fer I 'adnt' set eyes on 'im all day. "Is 'e dead or alive?" I says. "''E was when I see 'im larst," says Joe. "Thank Gawd fer that," I says.'

Next day the storm was over; and on the evening tide we entered upon the last stage of our voyage.

Restored to his delighted family, Cole had exhibited a complacency that rather jarred on Gotty and the Guv'nor. So we scorned to ask his further assistance, particularly as we had no hope that he would concede it. We two took the *Betty* back.

Passing the Foreland next morning, I rolled up my chart. The pilot's work was done. We had re-entered the old familiar estuary—Gotty's world.

Four hours later, with Essex still invisible, I was aghast to feel our keel bumping submerged solidity. As Gotty seized an oar and plunged on both sides for the depth, his face was dark with agony.

'Clumsy old duffer!' I gasped.

'Oh, dear,' he whimpered. 'We ain't goin' ter be pulled up, are we? Shorely—shorely we aint'!' Suddenly his countenance brightened, and he shouted: 'Parst it! Bray-vo!'

'Yes, but—' I began, indignantly.

'I fancied,' he explained in excitement, 'there'd be a fadum over that bank. Not quite there wasn't. But jest enough. That's saved us five miles and charnse it.'

So I forgave him.

They saw us coming. Mrs Gotty stood waiting and waving on the jetty.

'Well, sir,' she exclaimed, as our dinghy touched the stairs, 'I hope he's been behaving himself.'

'Don't talk so silly!' said Gotty.

Grizel Hartley

THE LAUREL AND THE SNOW

WE ran down the hill in the last of the sunset, an apple-green sky cleared for the evening star. We did not speak; James was not, as I thought then, in sympathy with me. He and I were far apart in age (there were twelve years between us). My brother Richard, who came between, had fallen at Falaise, where James himself had been hit in the leg, but I saw that he still ran as lightly as a deer.

Our little ship lay at her moorings below us, seeming as if she were content to lie cradled in the tops of the great ash-trees along the shore, until you looked at the loch running molten silver between the hills, and you saw that she strained towards the open sea. If it had not been to my brother James, I might have quoted —

'She thinks she smells the north-land snow.'

But instead, James said to me —

'Have you got any money?'

'About a fiver.'

'I've got about the same.'

It blew indeed that night, the firtops swaying in the starlight as though the whole sky swung with them, the half-grown moon as suddenly lost as you lose and find a group-flashing lighthouse at sea. We woke to half a gale, and to remorseless rain, cold to the touch; we could not sail that day, and were ill-tempered with one another. We had once called it 'that expedition feeling'; it made me, that day, feel very near to tears, lying on the chart-covered floor, watching the short steep waves and the misty driving rain. I knew, as I said, that James had no sympathy with me, that he neither knew nor cared that he had witnessed the death of all my hopes.

He and Richard, and I, then only a half-grown boy, had sailed together before the war with our two cousins, Randolph and Alex Fane. As the youngest, I had come in for most of the hard words in the ship, and for most of the unspoken kindnesses, the extra blanket roughly thrown over me as I lay dead asleep on the cabin floor after my watch: the peeled orange once put into my hand, after a day and a half of racking sea-sickness, by my brother James. I could think of many more. I thought, too, of our last sail to Norway, and a picture flashed into my eyes of the four young men walking down the main street of Tromsö. They stopped, I can see them now, by the stuffed polar bear that stood outside the shop that sold furs, and lit cigarettes, and laughed in the sunlight. They were dressed, by chance, almost alike, in blue seaman's sweaters, blue reefer coats, once-white blanket trousers and sea-boots; they might almost have been four Elizabethan young men sailing to fight Spain long ago; and I, then half their size and strength, felt my heart swell to know that I belonged to them. Three were fair, and one dark—my brother James. I was walking behind them, I had been left to clean the cockpit. When we got back to the ship James had seen a spent match in the bottom of it, and had said:

'Call that cleaning the cockpit! It looks as though a lot of pigs had been in it.'

'My match, I think,' Richard had said, winking at me, and picking it up he flipped it high in the air, to fall, I remember, exactly where it came from.

That was the year of the war. Randolph, who had been in the Auxiliary Air Force, went down in the Battle of Britain, and Alex only two days before the war ended, in a northern convoy. The cutter, our ewe-lamb, laid up carefully in Norway, 'so that we can go on to Spitzbergen,' was never heard of again. All the ship left to us now was our old sailing-dinghy, with her one sail, and the leak when she was on the port tack that we never quite cured. In her we had all learnt to sail. She was nearly thirty years old; fourteen-foot long, sliding gunter rig; built for racing once, she still wore a faded number seven on her sail. James had cruised in her alone, he understood her ways, and loved her with a passion he did not put into words.

I think Richard's death was the final blow to my grandfather at Ardgillan, where we had spent the enchanted holidays of our youth. He did not live long after that. The house was sold, but James and I had kept a foothold in the gate-house with the old forester and his wife: this was the first time we had been there together since the war.

Once, when my grandfather was still alive, Richard and I, when reading at that time was confined to endless old bound volumes of *Punch*, had turned a page to find James to the life; we had laughed ourselves sick over it, gloated over it, and finally run it to death. I had not thought of it since, but it came back to me on the evening of that stormy day, when the sky cleared, the hills became dark-violet and the water turned to gold.

'Topping sunset, what!' said one exquisite young man to another on a mountainside; and the reply, that might have been James's, 'Well, you needn't rave about it like a bally poet!'

I think, in the end, James had not been amused, and had knocked our heads gently together. He was strangely gentle in his movements, always. It was a treat even to see him lay two pieces of bacon in a frying-pan in the galley.

That night the wind changed; it blew down to the sea, in the morning the sky was pale and clear, the glass steady. We slid away that day, as quietly as if drawn by silver swans, sailing on a broad reach to the sea.

Of the eight days that followed there were no two alike. This is not news to those who know the Western Highlands, where no two days have been alike since the world began. Once out of the loch, we were a leaf in the wind, racing on the long Atlantic rollers that come in from the south-west, that take you, as it were, at one moment up into the battlements, and the next, down to the dark cellars hung with bats and rusty chains. But how we travelled, I shall never forget; sometimes even fifty miles a day, landing as dusk fell, and sleeping, where we could, in farms and cottages: once, in the boiler-room of Duart Castle, whose door we found conveniently open; another time, with the McVanes in Morven. Arriving soaked at half-past ten one night, we were made gloriously welcome, given hot tea and scrambled eggs, whisky and cold apple-pie, and put to sleep in a bedroom full of their boys' clothes and their grandmother's water-colours, with a row of sea-urchins on the mantelpiece. There was, too, an enchanted cottage in Isle Oronsay, where James slept on the floor, and I in the one small bed. The cottage lay three yards from the sea, at the foot of a little green wood, into which, as we waded ashore in the twilight, leapt a roe-deer and her calf; we saw the scut of her tail in the dusk. I did not sleep well at first. I remember how the bed would surge forward, thud down, and I would wake staring into pools of green water, over and over again, till I fell dead asleep when it was time to go, and James had no mercy on me.

The strange mixture of beauty and danger made each more vivid than the last. Racing up the Sound of Mull, on a day of indescribable blue, even the air seemed to sparkle as if full of stars; the hills were gentian-blue, the sea-birds blue-white, and once a porpoise rolled over lazily close to us, showing his turquoise-blue belly, and singing the 104th Psalm.

That evening we sailed round Ardnamurchan Point, the sea rather too big for us, in the setting sun: I bailed, I remember, till my right arm was numb, and a red-hot iron bar lay across my back.

'Get her empty, can't you?' said James. 'Unless you want us to sink.'

I must have looked despairing; he said in a flash, 'Take her, and keep her sailing!'

We changed places with difficulty, shipping a green wave, and James began to bail in a way I could not, with every movement as unerring as a precision instrument: had we not been so near to sinking, it would have been a pleasure to watch him. Within a short time we were nearly empty, and sailing fast in a gold-washed sea, towards Rhum and Eigg, purple on the horizon.

A herring-drifter on her way to Coll, a mile or so closer inshore than we were, and making quite heavy weather as she rounded the lighthouse, had seemed to alter her course a little, as though to stand by us; the sight of her gave me a little comfort. But James said:

'Keep well out to sea, I don't want her to see us bailing; one thing I should hate is to be rescued when I was perfectly safe!'

There was a rush of shadows, and the waves, darkening now, passed us with a low roar, as if to say, 'Did you hear; he said "perfectly safe"!'

A grey wall of water followed us as it grew dark, and hung over our stern so long that once even James said 'Don't look round!' with a ghost of a smile.

He wrote afterwards, in the twopenny notebook that served him for a log: 'The ship was fairly full of water, not entirely owing to the leak'; no more, but enough to conjure up that evening for me for ever.

We got into Arisaig that night, James miraculously steering in in the dark. He knew the channel, but even so it was not easy. As he took the tiller from me, he said kindly—

'You were sailing her very well'; so that I took up my bailing with a lighter heart, and when at last we found a bed I slept soundly for the first time.

I remember a great rainbow on the way to Skye, which stayed with us half the day, fading and renewing itself. The Sound of Sleat was dark blue, with a throng of tossing white horses that reminded you of the Lippizaner stud. The ship was hard to hold in it, we were in danger of broaching to, and I was foolish enough to say to James:

'Are we all right?' I longed to be reassured.

'At least,' he said, 'we could swim to shore now.' I knew I could not have swum it, we were still a good two miles out to sea, but I said no more, and took to my bailing again. I had torn my hand on one of the anchor flukes, the water was red with my blood; I remember thinking that by now all the blood was out of me and that salt water had taken its place; I did not care, I wanted only never to feel again.

We sped on, past the rainbows and castles and the fairy

green of Skye. I was very tired by then, and more than a little hungry; we had hardly eaten, except on shore, it was too difficult to manoeuvre. But I remember that I felt one with the ship as she moved that day! We had to sail behind a precarious little rock for shelter, and reef right down, but even so, in the nine-knot tide of the Kyle of Lochalsh, how she travelled!

Once we sailed on all night; the moon was hidden, the dusk purple-black, then charcoal-black as the blue drained away, the waves curling over gold in the phosphorescent water. The black-pearl sail dripped gold, the rudder sang and throbbed, it was very cold, and it seemed that the dawn would never come. It was not until nearly four in the morning that we could even see our watches; then we saw that the landscape had changed over night; it was now a more northerly, a Norse country; the hills cold crystal-blue as dawn broke, with long white clouds lying stretched in them like snowfields; the sea deep and clear. It was an interminable day that followed, too much wind, and then too little: for a short time we were even becalmed, and, stiff with cold, took to our oars, over which I fell dead asleep, and James cursed me roundly.

Late that evening, our last evening, we turned into Loch Broom, and the little ship was sailing very comfortably and sweetly with her small silver bow-wave, as if she were an aristocratic lady entering the drawing-room, calm and unruffled after a long journey.

James was sailing, and I, dreaming for a moment, sitting with my back to him, when I heard him say very gently:

'We are the only ones left who care about this sort of thing.'

I could not answer him, the words in themselves were nothing, but my heart pounded; it was, to me, the accolade. For I knew, at last, that I was one of them, one of the young men walking up the main street of Tromsö and stopping by the polar bear outside the shop that sold furs, and laughing in the sunlight. There could be no reply, only the bent head and the burning cheek, which fortunately he could not see.

We had sailed on half a mile before I spoke, and were watching the gannets dive by the cliffs, flashing white against the strange dark-green water.

'Extraordinary colour, the sea over there,' I said.

'Yes,' said James; and I could not believe my ears, 'It's a sort of laurel colour. Laurel and snow.'

And a small trill of laughter rose in me, that fought its way to the top and would not be denied, but I kept my face reasonably straight as I turned it over my shoulder, and said to my brother James:

'Well, you needn't rave about it like a bally poet!'

R T McMullen

MR. McMULLEN'S LAST CRUISE

THE following are the entries Mr. McMullen made in his journal after setting out on his last cruise in the *Perseus*, 1891, in the high spirits usual with him when setting out on a single-handed cruise.

June 8.—Went out of dock, and alongside pier (causeway), to scrub the copper and take in water. Hauled off during night to moorings.

June 10.—4 p.m., sailed from Greenhithe; wind high, NE; cool, but sunny. Off Northfleet the breeze freshened, and below Gravesend became strong; weather cloudy and hazy. With no jib, and towing the dinghy, she eventually beat every barge in a long turn to windward. 6.30 p.m., anchored in Mucking Bight.

June 11.—Sunshine. Turned out 4.15; had some trouble with the anchor. 5.30 a.m., set mainsail. 7.40, passed the Nore; weather very gloomy and cold; wind N, puffy. Noon, Reculvers, SW; gladdened by a gleam of sunshine; touched both the Spaniards, but did not stay. 1 to 3, wind very light with swell. 3 p.m., tacked off Westgate; wind fresh, E; large jib set; after rounding the North Foreland, wind fell lighter, with trouble-some swell. 7, anchored with rope on Sandwich Flats; rolled dreadfully all night.

June 12.—Wind NE, fresh and fine. 6 a.m., under way with mainsail only; very much work. Eventually got early tea. Set jib and mizen; washed, and prepared breakfast before reaching Dover. 9 to 10, hove to in Dover Bay, had breakfast, &c., and sailed again. 10.30, set large jib. 11, off Folkestone, going grandly, but the wind soon fell light. 2.30 p.m., passed Dungeness against tide; wind ESE, light. 7 p.m., St Leonards; wind SSW, light; boat making good way, owing to smoother water and the large jib. 8.30 p.m., anchored off Bexhill; night fine. (Bexhill is between St Leonards and Eastbourne.)

In the morning of the 13th, Mr. McMullen landed and posted a letter at Eastbourne. After this he boarded the *Perseus* again, and went on down Channel. The next heard of him was a telegram on June 16, saying he was found dead on the evening of June 15 by some French fishermen. He was sitting in the cockpit, with his face looking towards the sky, and the vessel sailing herself along. The doctor said he had been dead twenty-four hours when his body was found, the cause of death being failure of the heart's action. He must, therefore, have died in mid-Channel on Sunday night, June 14. The weather was fine, the breeze light, and the young moon was shimmering on the placid sea.

Iain Rutherford

SUILVEN'S HARDEST FIGHT

I T was June, 1937, on the West Coast of Ireland, which is about the wildest and most exposed part of the British Isles. With two friends I had sailed from the Clyde down the Irish Sea, round the south coast and had reached a place called Clifden.

It may sound rather odd, but we had spent the night sleeping as best we could in an upstairs sitting-room of a pub. My friend, John Rintoul, had to return to Scotland, and we, Andrew Blaikie and I, felt that it was up to us to see him off. We had arrived late at night after a very hard sail round Slyne Head only to find the railway—although so clearly marked on the chart—had not been running for years; nor could we find an hotel which would open to our knocks. Wandering round the deserted streets of the little town and banging at all the likely-looking doors we finally succeeded in bringing a pub-keeper to his upper window. After listening to our tale of woe he offered his upstairs parlour for the night, and promised to give us an early breakfast, and to arrange for a taxi to be ready at eight o'clock to take Rintoul half-way across Ireland.

It had been blowing hard for several days and throughout the night the wind increased, so that, what with the noise of the wind and the cold, we slept little. John was trying to keep warm under a heap of newspapers on the sofa, while Andrew and I were reduced to walking up and down at intervals, swinging our arms like cabbies.

By the time we got up, the windows were rattling viciously, and branches were breaking off the straining trees. We said 'Good-bye', and made our way down the track that led to the loch, leaning forward into the wind as we walked. I remember we passed a great bank of honeysuckle and I picked a sprig to scent the cabin of the yacht.

As we carried our little dinghy down the shore of the loch, we wondered whether it was going to be possible to row out to *Suilven* at all. The surface of the loch was very dark, but vividly streaked with white, while spindrift was sweeping over in clouds. Somehow we launched our cockleshell after many attempts had failed; the surf had capsized her twice, and we were wet to our waists before we rowed clear, and began the exhausting pull across some hundred yards of water.

When, after quarter of an hour's exertion, we reached *Suilven* I fell on my bunk exhausted, while Andrew switched on the wireless just in time to get the weather forecast: 'A deep depression is approaching the North of Ireland, south-westerly winds of gale force may be expected from Land's End to the Mull of Kintyre; winds will veer to west. . . .'

With such a warning you might ask 'Why anyone should be fool enough to deliberately set out in a small yacht on the west coast of Ireland?' My excuse for such temerity is that Andrew had to be back in Scotland within a week's time, and I didn't fancy being left to sail back single-handed round that exposed coast. Besides we were young and full of confidence in our little ship.

It occurred to me that, if we could but make an offing from the land, we would be able to turn north and run before the gale, making excellent time on this part of our voyage. We had had so much bad weather on the way round, that our one idea was to get home as quickly as possible. Andrew agreed that an hour or two's acute discomfort would be a small price to pay for the advantage of running north before the gale, so without more ado we prepared for sea. Everything movable was carefully stowed away, the dinghy was firmly lashed down, bilges pumped dry, trisail and storm-jib bent on, each reduced to the last reef, and finally our bodies were encased in oilskins, sou'westers, and sea-boots, with towels round our necks.

We hoisted the trisail which banged and cracked so that the mast shook and the sheets whipped about like flails—it was almost frightening as we realised the elemental fury of the wind, but we couldn't give up before we'd even left our anchorage.

As a matter of fact we were nearly wrecked while getting under way. We were beating up to the anchor, tack for tack, getting the cable in bit by bit, when we missed stays and *Suilven* drifted back towards the lee shore, dragging the anchor at a most alarming rate. There wasn't a second to lose. I just had time to hoist the jib so that she filled on the starboard tack, and we sailed our anchor out into deep water—it was a close call.

But there was still the anchor cable to be stowed and the anchor lashed in place, a devil of a job on a wet deck sloping at forty-five degrees and plunging into the seas. A squall heralded by a tower of spindrift would lay us flat, and I would let the chain go and cling on to the forestay with both hands, only to see half the chain rattling over the side—so it went on until at last all was secure.

The beat out of the loch was a laborious business; ten times we had to tack before we made the entrance, and each tack meant luffing while we got the lee runner set up. Then at the shout 'Lee-o' Andrew would put the helm down while I flung the trisail sheet off the winch and feverishly struggled to get a few turns on the other sheet before winding it in, straining with all my strength so that the winch groaned and the rope was as taut as an iron rod.

Then the jib had to be dealt with—a job we always left to the last, for this helped her head round and avoided the possibility of missing stays. This business of putting about in a Force 8 breeze was quite the hardest manual exercise I have experienced, and I sank down exhausted each time we settled on a new tack. It was actually a relief to gain the open water, even though the seas were immensely greater in size, for at least we were able to get a rest from the continual short tacks.

The anemometer had been showing a wind of Force 7, with 8 in the squalls, but now that we were clear of the loch the instrument was registering a steady Force 8—in fact the little vanes were humming round so fast I wondered if it would break up.

Suddenly Andrew shouted out and pointed over the sea—I looked in that direction for quite some time before I caught a fleeting glimpse of a curragh poised on a wave-top with bow and stern both sticking clear out of the sea. It was fantastic—here we were thinking that *Suilven* was doing marvels weathering this sea, while not more than half a mile away a curragh was being rowed out from the land. True, it was in the lee of a small island, but there was little enough protection from the gale, and a curragh is, after all, only an open boat, made of the thinnest framework of wood and covered with tarpaulin. Eighteen feet by four feet, a curragh is probably the most primitive craft still in use round our coasts—the reader may have seen them in that excellent film *Man of Aran*. In the film one saw a curragh weathering prodigious seas, but nowadays one is so used to faking that I never believed it really could do such things.

There were three men rowing, each with a pair of oars, while a fourth sat in the stern-sheets. I don't think we saw her more than ten seconds per minute owing to the size of the intervening seas. It was incredible to watch that long black canoe-like hull breasting those breaking tops, the three rowers straining at their oars in perfect time. I imagine they were rowing out to the nearby island to attend to their lobster pots, but it must have meant a tremendous effort on the part of those men, not to mention the constant baling which seemed to be the job of the fourth man. I was told afterwards that the whole art of curragh handling in bad weather consists in keeping end on to the seas, and that once across the seas all is lost. I can well believe it.

Soon the curragh and the little island were astern, and we settled down to a long board on the starboard tack.

Now that we were in the open sea with no land between us and America, the short steep seas of the loch had become great hills and valleys over which we climbed in an extraordinary way. Down in the trough *Suilven* was almost becalmed, and ahead we looked up to a sort of mountain ridge capped by a white line of breaking fury. It looked quite impossible that we should ever succeed in fighting our way over such a formidable barrier. But then *Suilven* was no ordinary ship; designed by Starling Burgess, the man who designed the American Cup defenders, *Rainbow* and *Enterprise*, and built well and truly by the proud firm of Herreschoff.

So there we were in this wilderness of storm, sitting huddled in the cockpit of a little boat twenty-seven feet by seven feet wondering whether she would perform the impossible as we watched the breaking crest bearing down on us—up, up, we would climb, healing over increasingly as we left the trough, until as we breasted the summit we would be flattened down with the full force of the gale on our sails. Then was the critical moment as the wall of breaking water threatened to overwhelm us; up I'd pull the helm and *Suilven* would turn off from the wind so that the crest hit us very broad on the bow and our buoyancy did the rest. For some horrible seconds we would be carried bodily to leeward, our decks almost out of sight in the smother of foaming sea, and then miraculously we would find ourselves sailing gloriously down the broad back of the retreating sea with nothing more than an extra bucketful of sea water in the cockpit as witness of what we had come through.

The moment when caught in the grip of the breaking crest is a most amazing experience, for the wind picks the sea up in a tearing eddy so that sea and air are indistinguishable, and produces a great roaring which adds to the general furore. I don't mind admitting that we were both genuinely scared. Several times I wondered whether we should turn back, but even that course seemed barred to us for the danger of being pooped as we ran in was a horrible possibility, and so almost willy-nilly we continued on our way. However, after the first awe-inspiring hour, our confidence, which had been wavering so weakly, was strengthened, and I told Andrew that he could go below for a spell after first pumping out the cockpit. Looking back, it seems strange that I should ever have even temporarily lost faith in *Suilven*'s ability to cope with that sea, but the first sight of these mountains of water had undoubtedly been unnerving—they did look so immense.

Presently the sun came out and our spirits rose—the colour of the sea changed, and we saw beauty where before we had only seen danger. The dazzling white of a wave-top contrasted vividly against the dark blue of the sea, while occasionally when climbing towards a crest we saw something I shall never forget; the sun shining through a great wave top so that we were faced by a wall of clear emerald. I was sorely tempted to bring out my Leica and capture something of these seas, but there was so much spray constantly showering over the cockpit that the camera would have been ruined.

Just when I was thinking that all was going well, the jib sheet parted with a bang, and my optimism was pricked like a bubble. Fortunately the weather sheet held, and although our speed was reduced on the starboard tack we were otherwise unaffected. Once one piece of gear has failed, even if only a jib sheet, an owner's mind is likely to be filled with thoughts of further possible failures. The port backstay which you decided would last another season, the storm jib which showed signs of mildew, the very mast itself—all appear horribly doubtful; you curse yourself for having ever been such a fool as to venture out in so frail a craft, and then the cloud of terrible doubts passes and you relax again.

Andrew had gone below and fallen asleep where he sat, still in his oilskins and sou'wester, while I sat in the cockpit, my feet braced against the lee seat, my hands holding the kicking tiller. It's odd how sometimes one feels the necessity of a friend's moral support—not just the presence of someone sleeping a few feet away, but awake and by one's side. We were about to weather a rocky island over which the seas were pounding with a roar which could be heard above the noise of the wind. The spume and spindrift were rising 100 feet in the air and blowing to leeward like smoke from a giant factory chimney; I reckoned I would clear this rather terrifying hazard by about two cables —that is, if nothing carried away. I woke Andrew up and asked him to come up and have a look at a very fine sight—it must have been rather a shock suddenly to see those seas pounding on the rocks close under our lee, but it helped me a lot to have Andrew sharing the experience. Needless to say, everything held and we passed clear with no trouble. I think we both blessed that gear which had not let us down during those critical moments.

I am afraid our resolution to run north before the gale had been weakened—we now had only one idea—to find shelter, and it was fortunate that a safe refuge was not far distant. In the lee side of a little island called Inishbofin there is a harbour completely sheltered from the westerly gales which so frequently afflict that coast, so to this we made our way. It was a wonderful experience to sail in through the narrow entrance so close to the rocks on the starboard hand that we could almost have jumped ashore, and then to find ourselves in calm water surrounded by protecting land. It was a barren-looking island with white-washed cottages dotted here and there, each surrounded by pathetic little patches of cultivation, while in the foreground one or two curraghs lay to their moorings.

As we rounded up to anchor beside one of these quaint craft Andrew very solemnly quoted Stevenson's lines: 'Home is the sailor home from the sea and the hunter home from the hill' and then we both laughed for the tension was over and we were able to relax.

We could see people hurrying down to the beach from all over the island as we were blown ashore in our dinghy, and stepping out we were greeted by a crowd of islanders. 'We watched you coming in from the top of the hill,' said one, 'she was all mast and no boat at all', and another added, 'even a two-engined boat couldn't have done it'.

Never had our stock been so high; we were the heroes all right and they welcomed us accordingly. We were led in a procession to the finest farmhouse on the island to be given food and lodging for the night. The living-room into which we were shown was also the kitchen, having a stone-flagged floor and a great peat fire burning in an open hearth. There were four generations assembled in that room, not to mention an odd hen which occasionally wandered in, and we felt very privileged to be accepted into this family circle.

Andrew and I shared a bed, and although wedged back to back in the hollow of the mattress, we slept the sleep of the dead.

From 'At the Tiller' 1945

Part IV

RACING IN YACHTS

As soon as the race was over the trouble began.
Was the trapeze legal or was it not?

Peter Scott: *The Eye of the Wind*   181

Carleton Mitchell

NO ONE TO SEE

I AM still grinning. A few minutes ago Frank posted our day's run as 183 miles, only slightly less than three times as much as we made the preceding twenty-four hours. And things still hold the same—improving, if anything. Now the barograph is catching up to the action of the wind, showing a gradual but steady descent. It stands at 30.35. At ten a.m. Dick logged the breeze at south-south-west fifteen knots; at noon south-west by south eighteen knots; and at the moment we call it south-west eighteen knots. So for the first time we have the wind we should have enjoyed ever since crossing 40° north latitude: Force 5, south-west.

This is close to our fastest and most satisfactory point of sailing. Every reaching sail is hard at work: parachute spinnaker, balloon fore-staysail, main, mizzen staysail, mizzen—everything on board is flying except Henry's tablecloth, and as soon as the port watch can be persuaded to stop eating, we'll hang it up, too. The sea is beginning to build: the wave forms have lengthened and are well sprinkled with the white foam of breaking whitecaps. But steering is still easy, so we tear along reeling off the miles with no effort at all. For once the wind does the work, and we poor slaves do nothing but ride along.

It is clear, warm, and sparkling. The sun shines brightly most of the time, but occasionally ducks under small cumulus clouds, the fat puffy clouds I always associate with fair weather. Oddly, however, even during the brightest periods the sea is never really blue; it has a cold greyish tone, a steely metallic quality, somehow carrying a feeling of the lonely expanses to the north.

At lunch Bobby bet me Frank's tomorrow's dinner dessert we would top 200 miles in the next twenty-four hours, and I came back by betting him Jack's dessert we would break 210. We are very sporting and wager their desserts on the slightest provocation, which shows what good-natured watchmates they are, but I am afraid it would take a riot squad to enable either of us to collect our winnings. So far neither has tried. But our bet was the first time any of us had dared assume out loud this wind would hold; that it is not another of those streaks which start by looking like a super-highway and end as a blind ally. To use an old Bahamian expression, until now all of us have been 'afraid to put mouth on it' for fear the wind would vanish.

Little wayfaring Chicken, little blue eyes, don't leave us now!

3.05 p.m.: The sleigh-ride continues. Now we are logging the wind at twenty-two knots, while the direction remains south-west. There has been no change in sails, and only slight modifications in trim, during the last two hours.

But everything else has changed, a most astonishing demonstration of how swiftly things can alter at sea. This has become a real grey North Atlantic day. The sun is completely hidden by a solid blanket of low stratus, ragged at the bottom. A fine drizzling rain falls, barely heavier than thick mist, yet raw and penetrating. The wind has a new edge of chill. Astern the seas roll up longer and higher, and breaking crests are frequent; when one slaps aboard it seems to have more weight, just as this colder air seems to have more drive against the sails.

Square pole, ease sheet; let pole forward, trim sheet: the spinnaker rides high and round, head nearly lost in the mist above. Seas running up under counter, lifting stern; a momentary hang and shoot; seas passing forward with a roar under the bow. Roll and go: 9 knots, 9½, 10 knots. This is it: again this is what we came for.

Occasionally the main boom dips deeply into a passing crest, throwing a wide fan of spray. I remember when bathing in the lee scuppers it was impossible to hold a leg out rigidly against the rush of water, and suddenly have some comprehension of the strains involved: in the mast and halyard carrying the spinnaker, in the sheets and guys taking the thrust of the wind, in the preventers holding the main boom, in the rudder, in the steering-gear fittings. And am thankful for the engineering that computed the strains, and the honest craftsmanship that fashioned the materials to withstand them. As civilisation advances, man is increasingly dependent upon the integrity and ability of his fellows: driving an automobile, travelling in a train, flying an aircraft. And especially sailing a boat across the Atlantic.

5.10 p.m.: My last wheel trick was something of a work-out. The sea is now large and long enough to make *Caribbee* sheer as the stern rises and the bow buries. And again there is no such thing as a satisfactory combination of clothes. Oilskins out here are like the ancient crack about women: you can't live with them, and you can't live without them. If you're dressed warmly enough to be comfortable on deck, after fifteen minutes of wrestling with the helm you're steaming, and at the end of a half-hour trick are thoroughly parboiled.

But we're not complaining. During the last hour we averaged 9·2 knots, and on shoots down unusually big waves the Kenyon needle climbs to 10·5 and above. As Frank noted in the log at 5 a.m.: 'Going well—downhill, and less than a thousand to go.' It is odd, but we almost have the feeling of being in coastal waters. Yet at the moment we are about the greatest distance from land of any part of the passage—Newfoundland, Greenland, Iceland, Azores, and British Isles. We really are in the middle of the deep blue sea in a very literal sense.

As I wrote that, the spinnaker broke. I heard Frank call urgently from the bow: 'Curling, curling! Go down! Go down!' Then on a lower note: 'It's broken.' I look up and see the leading edge folded in against the rest of the sail; the huge expanse of nylon is aback, pressed against the headstay. At the wheel Jack grinds as hard as he can, while amidships Bobby heaves on the jerking line. The rudder takes effect. *Caribbee* swings sharply to port and we come almost before the wind. The sensation of rushing speed vanishes. It seems as though the wind has died, and the sea magically smoothed. Then the spinnaker fills with a crash, a sudden lift of hundreds upon hundreds of square feet of sail that shakes the whole boat. We come back up to course. Again the wind is heavy; *Caribbee* heels and water begins to rush past to leeward.

7.50. p.m.: My watchmates have already turned in. I sit alone in the cabin, feeling under me the alternating lift and fall of a boat being driven hard before a gradually freshening wind and rising sea. Along the hull is the swish of water, a sound not unlike the babbling of a brook running swiftly between narrow banks. It is a good sound. I hear calls from deck, the occasional thump of a block, the slap of breaking crests. To use another simile, a somewhat hackneyed one because it is so perfectly descriptive as to be inescapable, the hum of wind in the rigging makes *Caribbee* reverberate like a huge violin, a resonant and vibrant song of many pitches, as many notes as there are lengths of wire and rope aloft. It too is a good sound, for in it there is no note of malice, none of the deep-throated roar of the gale, the demoniac shriek of the squall.

It is raining. Visibility is poor. We now average 9.5 knots and shoot the seas at eleven. The wind has gone a fraction west of southwest, and has freshened to twenty-five knots—a good solid Force 6 on the Beaufort Scale, where according to Bowditch, 'Smacks double-reef gaff mainsail'. Yet while fishing vessels larger and far more heavily constructed than *Caribbee* would theoretically shorten sail, we carry everything that can be hung from the masts; in Harbour, fishermen from those same trawlers, lying alongside, would probably study the weight of our gear, our comparative lack of freeboard, our towering masts and gossamer rigging, and consider *Caribbee* a very pretty toy; they would most likely think her slippery, handy for afternoon sailing, but for the open sea—no. I can almost picture a grizzled old character spitting in the water as he shakes his head.

Which again makes me consider the somewhat fantastic nature of ocean racing. Here we are, nine men, driving a fragile complex of wood, metal, and cloth through driving rain and building sea, a thousand miles from the nearest harbour; no one to see or admire or applaud; no one to help if our temerity ends in disaster. We exceed the bounds of discretion, even go beyond what we know is good seamanship —those basic lessons passed down through generations of men who have fought the oceans. In us all there is a devotion to the somewhat formless and unspoken ideal of simply keeping the boat going at her maximum speed, a dedication which carries us beyond considerations of personal comfort and even safety.

Our attitude is not even wholly based on the competitive aspect of racing. It is that we all feel there is just one way to do things, one standard, one code, and we live up to it for our own satisfaction. We are driven by our own compulsions, each personal and secret, so nebulous we probably could not express them to our mates if we tried. But in our own way we are about as dedicated as it is possible for men to be.

Peter Scott

THE TRAPEZE

As the summer of 1938 approached I began to think of our new sailing plans. John Winter and I had long had a theory which we had now decided to put to the test.

We believed that the crew rather than the helmsmen should be responsible for the tactics of a dinghy race. The helmsmen's attention should be exclusively occupied with watching the luff of the jib and sailing the boat, especially to windward. The crew was in a very much better position to look all round at the other competitors, assess the tactical situation and decide when to tack. Neither of us had ever had a crew we could entirely trust to do this, so we had sailed our boats by feel while we ourselves looked around to see how the tactical situation was developing.

There was the additional advantage in the new idea that, in sitting out, the helmsman uses rather different muscles from the crew; if we sailed one round each of a long and gruelling race, by changing over we should be much fresher, and therefore much less likely to make mistakes or to be clumsy in our exhaustion. Some years before we had planned to join forces — become joint owners of a boat in which we could put our theory to the test. Until this year there had been one difficulty about the plan. I was unwilling to join forces with John until I had won a Prince of Wales's Cup on my own account. My pride demanded first a success without John, the winner of 1934, to show me how. But having finally won the Big Race in *Thunder* at Lowestoft the way was now clear, and we had commissioned Uffa Fox to build us a new boat. In order to make it quite plain what the new boat was and how the system would work she was called *Thunder & Lightning*. John planned to retain *Lightning* and I retained *Thunder*. If the idea did not work we had our escape routes ready.

We had also had another idea—the device which is now universally known as the trapeze. Some years before I had crewed Beecher Moore in his Thames Rater at Surbiton to which he had fitted 'Bell rope' attached to the mast at the 'hounds' and one member of the crew hung on to this and was thereby enabled to lean much further out than without it. Uffa, Charles Curry, John and I had discussed taking the invention a stage further by the use of a harness to be worn by the crew which could be hooked on to a wire hanging from the 'hounds', that is to say from the point of attachment of the main shrouds to the mast. In this way the crew would lean or even sit in the harness with his feet on the gunwale and his body horizontally stretched outboard. If it really worked this device would give enormously greater driving power to the boat than had ever been possible with toe-straps in the middle of the boat and the crew leaning out just as far and as long as his belly muscles would sustain him. The Canadian dinghies had also used a method of belaying the jib sheet to a cleat on a sort of breast plate strapped to the crew. Our harness would combine the two.

As well as this trapeze, we felt that the very light wooden centreboard, which I had tried out in *Daybreak* but which I had not dared to use in heavy weather, might be operated in combination with the new trapeze method of keeping the boat upright. We hoped to keep her up with the trapeze and at the same time have the advantage of the greatly reduced all-up weight off the wind. *Thunder & Lightning* was completed only very shortly before the Prince of Wales's Cup Week, which that year was at Falmouth. As a result there was no chance to try out the trapeze in realistic conditions. First, it had to be kept secret, or moderately so, and secondly, during the early races of the week the winds were quite light.

On the evening before the big race John and I sailed out from Falmouth Harbour, round the corner into Carrick Roads and there, safely out of sight of all our competitors we tried out our new device in a very light wind. If I sat out to leeward and pulled the sheet in tight, it was just possible for John to go out to windward on the wire. The device seemed practical. How would it affect our performance? Of this we still had no clue.

There was in our minds no doubt that the trapeze was legal. Outriggers were not allowed, but nothing solid protruded from the boat in this system, and a wire hanging from the mast could not possibly be described as an outrigger. However, so that there should be no doubt of the legality if we used it, on the night before the race, when it was too late for anyone else to apply the system to their own masts, we leaked the information in the bar. There were cries of derision. We even showed them the harness and breast plate, which had been made for us. It brought loud and ironical laughter, and the cry, 'No big race has ever yet been won by a gadget'.

The day of the race again dawned utterly calm. We had to consider whether or not we should put in our light centreboard. The trapeze, its concomitant, could be used at will, but the selected centreboard had to be fitted before launching the boat.

Was it to be the one made entirely of wood, or the one ballasted with fifty pounds of metal? We dashed by car up to the headland and looked out over Falmouth Bay. The race was to be held in the open sea and there was the merest cat's paw of a breeze lying across the face of the water. Sitting on a seat overlooking the bay was an old man in a navy blue jersey and peaked cap. 'What do you make of the weather?' we asked. 'How much wind will there be by midday?'

'Well,' said he, 'I think that'll blow. You wait till the sea breeze sets in and you'll find you've got all you want out there.' This was a most encouraging prophecy, but how good was the prophet? We were disposed to be convinced that none was better.

We hurtled down the hill, put in the wooden centreboard and were towed out of the harbour, through Carrick Roads and round the headland into Falmouth Bay eating our sandwich lunch as we went. By the time we reached the Committee boat a light breeze was blowing and it was evidently freshening all the time.

There was a big fleet—more than fifty boats—and the usual build-up of dry-mouthed tension. Just before the start it had become a planing breeze. We were carrying *Lightning*'s old mainsail, a famous sail which had been borrowed by Stewart Morris for one of his wins in *R.I.P.* and used by John for his win in 1934. A sail which had won two Prince of Wales's Cups already, and been second in two more, had a certain magical quality quite apart from its proven excellence as a power unit. It was getting old now, and perhaps more suitable for heavy weather; through stretching it was flatter than it had been, but it seemed just right for a good whole-sail planing breeze.

I was to sail the first half of the race and I did not make a very good start. Immediately to windward of us and slightly ahead was Robert Hichens in his latest home-made dinghy *Venture II*. We were both on the starboard tack and in a matter of moments John had belayed the jib on a cleat and was out on the trapeze. Standing horizontally out from the boat with his feet on the gunwale, he was a startling sight even to me. To the other competitors the spectacle was irresistible. At an important time a great many of them gave their attention to our trapeze at the expense of sailing their own boats. Robert Hichens was now almost directly ahead; his crew looked at John with amazement, drew Robert's attention to him and for a critical ten seconds Robert sailed his boat 'off the wind', which allowed us to luff across his wake and get our wind clear. At one stroke we had escaped the consequences of my bad start and with John's weight keeping the boat much more vertical, with much less effort than any of the others, we forged ahead and rounded the weather mark first by thirty seconds. But what about the jinx? Still in all the history of the Prince of Wales's Cup no one had ever won the race who had been first at the first mark. I said something about this to John, whose sharp reply was, 'There's got to be a first time.' Stewart was lying second for a while, until he was overtaken by Colin Ratsey, sailing brilliantly in a very broad-beamed ugly-looking dinghy called *Hawk*.

We finally finished nearly four minutes ahead of him, with Stewart third. Although it was satisfactory to win and as a race it was exciting in the extreme, it could not quite compare with the thrill of my first success in *Thunder*, the year before. The holder of a Championship has more to lose than to gain. If he wins, so he should; if he does not, eyebrows are raised.

But as soon as the race was over the trouble began. Was the trapeze legal or was it not? When it was pointed out that the rest of the fleet had had an opportunity to say whether or not they thought it illegal before the race and had not done so, nobody was ready to enter a protest against it after we had won. All that was left was to say that in future it must be banned and, on the principle of setting a thief to catch a thief, I was asked by the Yacht Racing Association's Dinghy Committee (of which as a Cup-winner I had now become a member) to draft the wording of a rule which would ban our exciting new invention.

I am still sorry about this decision. It may be that it would have radically changed the fourteen-footers, yet here was a system of keeping a small dinghy upright in strong winds which was eminently enjoyable, required no very great skill, but looked spectacular, appeared to have no danger, and reduced the compression strain on the mast. Most important of all it made the body weight of the crew a little less critical, because it enabled a light crew, for example a girl, on a trapeze to compete on even terms with a heavy man in wind strengths up to fifteen knots, whereas previously the light ones had been at a disadvantage in any wind above ten knots. All these advantages were there for the taking, but because of a prejudice against what appeared to be too difficult and acrobatic and what was imagined to be dangerous, and perhaps most of all because we had won the Prince of Wales's Cup by its use, it was outlawed and did not in fact return until the design of the Flying Dutchman seventeen years later. Now it is also carried in the 505 class and one or two others as well, and greatly enhances the enjoyment of sailing on a hard day. It is tremendously exhilarating to stand out, comfortably supported by the trapeze, almost horizontal and skimming low over the waves.

It is sad that a handful of people who did not have the vision to see this should have outlawed the trapeze for so long.

From 'The Eye of the Wind' © *1961*

D R Collins

THE OSTEND RACE

THE race was due to start on Saturday before August Bank holiday, as it does, or did, every year. We motored down on Friday morning and met George Brentnall at Brightlingsea. His family kindly asked us to dinner that night.

I think George's father experienced some qualms about allowing his son to sail in the race with anyone whose experience was as limited as my own. To find out how much I knew he kept on asking me questions as to what I should do in imaginary difficulties. We were all in much too good form to be able to cope seriously with this, and Bill and I claimed complete ignorance of all things nautical — swore by the infallibility of the Lonsdale Library book on yacht-cruising, and said that in the event of any difficulty we would consult this oracle as to the proper procedure. As a final shot Dr Brentnall asked me what the recognised distress signals were, and Bill replied that the best thing to do was to tie a knot in a bucket and hoist it to the truck. Serious probing was abandoned after this in favour of roulette, at which we spent an amusing evening. Mrs Brentnall more sensibly suggested that as Bill and I had sailed *Helen* round from Portsmouth we could presumably get her to Ostend, and even if we proved incapable, George knew enough to take over.

The race is started with all competing yachts at anchor and sails stowed. As zero hour was to be during the first hour of the ebb tide, we decided to lie to a kedge from the bows, to lead the line aft, and swing *Helen* round on it just before the first gun, so that she would be heading the right way for a fair tide start. We were all very excited to see if any of the other competitors had thought of this dodge, which we hoped would give us a good advantage at the beginning of the race.

Unfortunately, in our eagerness to swing stern to tide, and our anxiety not to leave the manoeuvre until the first gun went, we swung too soon, and allowed four of five other competitors to spot the idea and follow suit.

Our organisation was that Bill and George Brentnall should

dash forward at the gun, and start hoisting sails, George Fairly-Clark should pull the kedge in over the stern, whilst I steered. At the explosion the three dashed into action, and I gripped the tiller with what I imagined was a Bookstall Smith 'J'-class touch. The start did not proceed exactly to plan, as we had had to veer quite a lot of kedge warp to prevent the anchor from dragging and allowing us to pass the line before the start. George Fairly-Clark was hauling in manfully, and as there was no point in steering until we were under way, I abandoned my attitudes and gave him a hand. Together we hauled in so quickly that *Helen* gathered appreciably sternway, and went tearing backwards through the water, whilst our more able competitors were proceeding in the opposite and correct direction.

In spite of this our start was not bad—we crossed the line about fifth out of seventeen. We held this position for a few minutes, before the faint fair wind slowly veered from north to south-east and our run down Colne was changed to a beat. The faster, closer-winded boats were able to round the first turning point without tacking, but I tried to sail *Helen* too close to the wind, and we sagged away to leeward, necessitating two short boards on the port tack before we were clear of the lower Colne. By this time we had dropped back to last but one, where we remained whilst our competitors disappeared, one after another, in the haze ahead of us.

The course from the mouth of the Colne is north-eastward for about twenty miles to the Long Sand Head buoy, and for this reach we had a freshening wind from just abaft the starboard beam. It was a delightful sail; for once I had an adequate, able and willing crew. George Brentnall had succeeded in borrowing from someone in Brightlingsea a barge's staysail which we set as a reaching jib. The old boat tore along and even overhauled *Silver Fox*, our next ahead. As the rest of the fleet had disappeared we were not tantalised into undue effort, and spent a pleasant afternoon—everyone was keen to steer, and as I get bored by holding the tiller and normally spend most of my time trying to make *Helen* sail herself, I was able to settle down comfortably on cushions aft and criticise other people's efforts.

It was getting dark by the time we had reached the Long Sand Head buoy, and as the direction of the wind made it impossible to lay the course from there to Ostend there was some argument as to which tack we should start off on. As it happened we correctly anticipated that the wind would veer from south-east to the westward, and so started on the starboard tack. As the wind gradually veered we were able to lay the direct course, and eventually arrived at Ostend at six o'clock the following morning without having had to tack at all. The wind freshened considerably just after dark, and we took in the barge's staysail and our own topsail. It eased off again later, but by then we were feeling too sick to be very enthusiastic about the race, and no doubt lost time, as we did not re-set the topsail. In spite of this our luck in starting off the final leg on the starboard tack allowed us to pass two more competitors during the night, and we finished up thirteenth.

Iain Rutherford

RUNNING BACK TO THE FINISH

THROUGH the night the wind eased somewhat and after getting back to the small spinnaker we set the large blue nylon one at 0400 hours by which time our speed had dropped to $5\frac{1}{2}$ knots. Wednesday morning gave us some quiet peaceful yacthing with speeds as low as $1\frac{3}{4}$ knots, peaceful that is, apart from one rather exasperating trick which the spinnaker played upon us. For this piece of devilry it was necessary to have the combination of a momentary lull in the wind combined with a leeward roll. In these circumstances, the spinnaker would fall abaft the top-mast forestay and then swing round it, so that in less time than it takes to tell, it had one or more complete turns around that innocent piece of rigging. Very easily done, but exceed-ingly difficult to undo; as often as not the spinnaker had to be lowered altogether and then re-set. I was told that to avoid this Rod Stevens uses a jib made of fishing net and such a gadget would have undoubtedly saved us a lot of trouble.

By 1430 hours we had rounded the Bishop and as the after-noon wore on the wind increased, the sky becoming overcast with rain. The wind dogs I had noticed in the sky earlier had not been there for nothing and although my forecast of strong winds had been received with a certain amount of good-natured scorn, that night brought us all we wanted. The sea was, of course, quite calm at first, and with the large blue nylon drawing well, each hour saw an increase in our speed as darkness closed in. By 2300 hours we were doing 7 knots, by midnight 8 knots, by 0100 hours, 9 knots and by 0200 hours, 10 knots!

That was quite the most fantastic piece of sailing I have ever experienced in my life and all the members of the crew said the same thing. The visibility was only about one mile, it was as dark as pitch without any horizon or stars or lights to be seen, so that the helmsman only had the glowing compass card to steer by. We were tearing over the water, leaving a wake like that of a destroyer, the water fanning up from the bow as if we were being towed at twice our maximum speed. As each wave came up from astern we started to plane and remained for long periods (fifteen seconds or more), poised on the top almost as if we had developed wings. You could feel the ship quivering and vibrating under the strain and we blessed the stout double mast-head preventers which took the enormous pull of the spinnaker. How the nylon stood it I don't know, for we were being drawn through the water far in excess of our theoretical maximum speed—there was something awe-inspiring, almost frightening, about the whole thing.

The job of helmsman had become exacting, to say the least, and we took it in quarter-hour tricks. Gradually the wind veered and we eased the spinnaker boom guy to the bitter end (it had been led round the large centre line winch in addition to the smaller side one, for the strain on that rope was immense). In spite of this there was a tendency for the spinnaker to get partially aback as we yawed to weather and at such times the danger of broaching-to was very real. At last it became impossible to hold our course. I was at the helm, and to counter a luff, I managed with every ounce of my strength to force the tiller behind my back, until it was hard up against the cockpit side. In this position the *Myth* did not respond, and for an agonisingly long time she held her course not quite decided whether to broach-to or not, before eventually falling back on to her proper course. When this happened a second time, I shouted to the skipper that I couldn't hold her safely on her course and he told me to bear away as far as I considered necessary and to report my new course.

I see from the log that the time was 0257 hours and it was soon after that we had a rather unpleasant experience. A fishing trawler on our port hand was steaming on a broadly converging course and, as her relative bearing never altered, we realised that something would have to be done about it. It was almost impossible for us to alter our course to any large extent nor could we alter our speed. Our navigation lights which rather surprisingly had been working satisfactorily throughout the race, had at last given up the struggle, so it was a case of sail illumination. Pete was at the helm and a more reliable cool-headed helmsman I have yet to meet. I asked him to try and edge off to leeward as far as he could and at the same time shone a powerful torch on our mainsail. The trawler's coxswain must have been asleep for she took not the slightest notice of our presence, but proceeded relentlessly as if determined to run us down. Feeling rather desperate I shouted for the skipper, advising those below of our danger, but Pete, in spite of imminent risk of gybing, was holding the *Myth* so far off that the trawler's bearing was slowly drawing aft. I suppose we crossed her bows with about half a cable to spare, but it was too close for peace of mind.

In a surprisingly short time we were off the entrance to Plymouth and all hands were called on deck for the handing of the spinnaker, a job I had been inwardly dreading. However, with the drill carefully planned in advance, we had no trouble at all and, with the billowing mass of blue nylon out of the way, the order was given to set the staysail. As we luffed up for the Plymouth breakwater light, the real strength of the wind could be felt, and I marvelled at the toughness of that spinnaker which was now safely below. No sooner had we got the staysail drawing and with only, perhaps, three cables to go, the skipper ordered us to set the jib. It was pitch dark with driving rain shutting down visibility and we were already travelling at about eight knots, but up went the jib for those last few yards to the breakwater. 'And this,' I said to myself, 'is how ocean races are won.'

Pete from the after cockpit was hurriedly striking at damp flares until one spluttered into life and we were dazzled by the brilliance which lit up the *Myth* like some weird theatrical set with a backcloth of the blackest night. The time was 0446.16 hours on Thursday morning and we were told by the watch-keeper on the Breakwater that *Latifa* had crossed at 1725 hours and *Bloodhound* at 2335 hours on Wednesday night.

We sailed quietly into the outer harbour and the grey light of dawn brought with it a mixture of many conflicting feelings, elation, satisfaction and, at the same time, a sad feeling of anti-climax. After so many hours with a purpose there was now nothing more to do. That night I left for Scotland and said good-bye to a truly remarkable skipper, and a truly remarkable ship.

Erroll Bruce

STORM NEAR ROCKALL

THROUGH the night we sailed on across Rockall Bank with six rolls in the main and forward the heavy-weather jib set; not once did she drop below 6·4 knots, hard on the wind, so we were certainly not laggardly in setting more sail. Below, sleep cannot be called impossible, because George achieved it when he was off watch, but no one else managed better than short periods broken by some change in the violent rhythm of the motion. We also had to pump each hour, and every part of the yacht was as soggy as a peat bog.

With trawlers sighted and Rockall estimated twenty miles off our track, extra care was needed over the lookout, although even a glance to windward in those conditions was painful. The trawlers, each time, were sighted in the dark at least a couple of miles away, but a yacht might well remain unseen at half a mile off or less.

Perhaps one came as close as this to *Belmore* that night, as some time during the five hours of darkness we overtook *Delight*, hove-to on the same tack.

We knew nothing of this at the time, nor that at noon she was twenty-eight miles astern, after having led us for 2,660 miles from Bermuda. At dawn the seas were more regular, but having seen that she would carry no more sail without loss of speed, I tried to dry up some of the bog below. We were safely past Rockall itself, but navigation was still important with our landfall likely within twenty-four hours. Sights were impossible in heavy rain, and radio bearings little use until a chart could be made dry enough to draw pencil lines. I lit the cooking-stove, hooked on the cook's steadying belt round my waist, and, a few square inches at a time, dried out part of the chart over the gas ring. Inside the cabin the temperature was just under fifty degrees, but with a northerly blow it was very much colder outside, so condensed drops dripped even if waves no longer washed over the deck to send jets under the edge of the hatch, or dollops each time it was opened.

I found George's favourite chamois leather and wiped off the moisture from the deckhead; but by the time I had worked forward to the mast beam the drops were as large as ever in the dog-house aft. Everything was wet. I started the whole thing over again, then stopped half-way; here was the gale, the tough gale for which we had prepared for so long, and the best I could do about it was to fuss about in the cabin like a broody old Mrs Mop. The deck was the place I ought to be, keeping up the offensive, stirring up enthusiasm to race harder.

Reluctantly I dragged on oilskins, then heaved myself up the fore-hatch, as we had not been using the main hatch for twelve hours due to the amount of water it let straight down into the galley. It was still raining, and spray beat over the deck; she could not quite make the course we wanted, but was probably averaging about ten degrees from it. 'There's no point in any more sail until we can ease the sheets,' I said to Mike, then added to myself: 'As it is, I think she's really sailing too fast to be sensible.'

I went below for the 07.45 shipping forecast. There were gale warnings for our area and many others to the east and south, but annoyingly there was none for Orkney, where I expected the leading yachts of Class B to be about that time. The storm centre was still reported to be near us, moving east-north-east and filling slowly; for Rockall area the gales would die, with wind backing to the north-west. 'Splendid,' I thought, 'Good running conditions, weather clearing, an odd sun-sight this morning, clothes hung on deck to dry this afternoon; star-sights this evening. All perfect for a good landfall tomorrow morning on the Flannan Isles; perhaps even the Butt of Lewis a bit later if the visibility is not too good.'

Yet by 8 a.m. the rain was heavier. 'Wind freshening, I think,' said Mike, opening the hatch for a second. Then I noticed that the barometer had stopped its upward climb. I could see only one explanation after that radio forecast: we were sailing as fast as the depression and perhaps getting even a trifle nearer the centre once more.

'Going to moderate, sir?' asked Barry, when he saw my dictated shipping forecast on the chart-table.

'Probably not yet,' I answered. 'This may hold up until the afternoon.'

'No, oh no,' said Roy, putting aside breakfast which Barry had prepared punctually in spite of the weather. 'Not more. We've had quite enough.'

'You might just as well eat your breakfast before it spills,' suggested Barry.

Turning over the watch took a long time in that weather and it was nearing nine a.m. when Mike slumped down the fore-hatch on to the wet sails. He lay there too exhausted to take off his oilskins for some minutes, and then took little interest in breakfast. I offered him a warming tot, but he declined it. Still uppermost in my mind was the easing after the blow, and always it had been my plan to have Mike on the fore-deck hanking on bigger genoas; if he was as tired as this none of us would have the strength to force on sail. There were some sleeping-pills in my locker, and they had proved fairly strong when used for easing down after the race in Bermuda; I found a couple and put them in Mike's cup of coffee; his mouth would be too full of salt water to taste them, and I did not want to waste effort arguing about it. Mike needed some real sleep if he was to take this leading part several hours ahead.

The pills worked well, and Mike was soon fast asleep; if I took his two-hour watch from 10.30 to 12.30 there would be no more need for him until 16.30, and I felt it was likely that the blow would continue until then. In my watch there was a slight freshening, although the rain stopped and she actually speeded up to log 13·9 miles in the two hours; it was impressive the way *Belmore* sailed into the great seas, but rather awesome at times to see big ones charging down on her from to windward.

Within a few minutes under these conditions the mind was dulled; there was the compass card, the sails, and the waves to windward. All else was lost.

A wave piling to windward might seem due to break just as it reached us, but she had ample speed for a heave on the tiller in good time to let her swerve clear to leeward of the curling cataract.

At first I regularly searched the whole arc of bearings every few minutes, turning in the deep cockpit to sweep my eyes through the weather quarter behind me, and pausing each time she dropped in the trough of a wave; but nearly every time I turned round for this careful look-out search the reward was a heavy slap from a wave that curled over her unnoticed. Soon I gave up the look-out astern and was content to watch only the sea to windward, the tiny area of sails, and the compass card.

It was when I went below again I noticed the shriek in the rigging had pitched higher as it fought with a gale. She was soon dragging the feet of the sails through the water, and there was nothing for it but another change down; first we went down to the spitfire jib whose high-cut foot keeps it clear of the water, but a couple of hours later waves were sweeping right over the yacht once more, and we took in a couple more rolls in the main.

'So much for easing and backing to north-west,' I said as we came below. 'It hasn't moved a quarter point from north-by-east, and now it's blowing force eight.'

'I'll tell them. I'll bloddy well tell them, if we get home.' George was getting quite angry. 'I'll see no one volunteers for one of these larks again. This is bloddy hell.'

'Tea or coffee, George?' asked Barry.

Whether it was just the sea and the gale, or whether it was the judgement of a tired man, but things seemed worse then than at any time before, with the waves more vicious as they pounded on the deck above. Mike woke from his sleep indignant but perhaps a little rested, and no one else seemed to have much left. She was still sailing to windward into a gale at six knots, and we were just being hammered to pieces.

'Second and third hand coming on deck,' I told Mike at the tiller. 'I want the spitfire hauled up to windward and a dodger rigged to weather of the cockpit. I want the speed down to five and a half knots on the log.'

Half a knot less speed felt as though we'd put on the brakes. Gone was that wild plunging into the waves, and by comparison she seemed almost comfortable; but if a man did not secure himself down below he was still liable to crack into the deckhead from time to time.

William F Buckley, Jr

THE PANIC

HILAIRE BELLOC was driven to a rage at the very thought of racing a cruising boat. It was never very hard to drive Belloc into a rage, but in this case he surely had a point, and if he had participated in some of today's races, he'd have felt fully justified. Cruising boats, offshore boats of varying design, are made for cruising; and to race them, Belloc seems to feel, is like seeing how fast you can play a symphony: the very point is lost.

I disagree, obviously, for I race; and will race again and again, in all likelihood. But I do believe that the dangers that most horrified Belloc are preeminently there, that one has only to go down to a yacht club, survey the ministrations tendered to a 12-foot racing dinghy, extrapolate, and you have an idea of the way you may find yourself spending your life if you race a 40-footer to win. I can understand an amateur's mothering a dinghy, or a Comet, or a Star—or even an International 12-Meter—with the kind of loving care necessary to eliminate those marginal seconds and half-seconds; but I do not understand why such a thing is done when disparate boats race each other, under the colossal, though conscientious, hoax that is The Rule—I do not understand, because the contest, multiplications, square roots, and long divisions notwithstanding, is essentially a phoney.

I have witnessed cases where the obsession with high fidelity has displaced the appreciation of the music. I have known one or two persons of essentially bright disposition develop into crashing bores, as they transmute ocean racing into a neo-Spartan and never-ending ordeal that, even when it gives pleasure, gives a pleasure that is totally unrelated to the generic source of pleasure in sailing, which is the sea and the wind. I have a notion that the inertia of our age, the perfect expression of which is the Western paralysis in international affairs during the past half century, has had the effect of extravasating the natural physical and moral energies of some people into athletic channels. I can understand the lure of the total workout, expressed in sailing by the devotion of twenty hours a week, thirty weeks a year, toward the perfection of one's yachts, and the forwarding of one's competitive position; but I say such as they threaten the sport as surely as some of the new critics threaten the art of poetry. And I say to the beginner, don't let them tyrannize over you, or you may never recapture your romance.

I am solidly for amateurism in ocean sailing. I have lost faith in the very existence of the expertise before which, even did I know it to exist, I should not be disposed to humble myself in quite the manner that some deem appropriate. I am quite serious in saying that I idolize Carleton Mitchell, because he is an expert who, one can tell by reading what he writes, derives an amateur's pleasure out of his trade. (Has anyone noticed that there is no rasp in Mitchell's writing? That is the sign.) He would never, I think, stultify the sport by discouraging its discovery by beginners—as so many people are likely to do. Of the eight or ten people who regularly race *The Panic* nowadays, it is fair to say that by contrast with the gold platers, our boat is crewed by rank beginners; and before the comment gets made that this is all too visible to any boat a half mile away from *The Panic*, let me say, brother: think what you like. Let us go, amiably, our amiable ways. Just rescue me if I fall overboard, as I would you, and get out of my way when I'm on a starboard tack. I make no other demands.

Do I have advice for a beginner? Yes. If you intend to race, buy a racing boat. They are just as comfortable nowadays; but remember, they are much, much more expensive. If you buy a boat that is afflicted with an unviable rating, and then race it, you will—unless you exercise a solipsist's self-discipline—fret, and be unhappy. Do you know about the Law of Rusher's Lag? Well, it especially applies to ocean racers. Rusher's Lag is the lag *beyond* the lag that one normally anticipates. Apply it generously in your calculation of costs. Assume your upkeep will be five times what you first anticipated—especially the first year or two. Assume no one has yet invented a radio telephone. Take four extra turnbuckles everywhere you go, and a hundred cable clamps, to say nothing of course, of a complete hardware store. Have your drink (singular) before dinner. The first couple of days out, take a sedative when your turn comes to go off watch, and take a stimulant when you get up. That will catapult you, rather than drag you slowly by the hair, into the new and very different rhythm of life aboard an ocean racer. Wear an eyeshade when trying to sleep during the day. Do not assume it is possible to stay dry when you go forward in a heavy sea. Race your boat hard. And pay no attention to the results.

From Morris and Coulson's 'Racing at Sea'
© *1959 D. Van Nostrand Company Inc. Princeton N.J.*

Keith Shackleton

WHISPER

It came about one Easter that we had three days of hot sun, with scarcely a hint of wind, and by the end of it I felt as if all my life had been spent sailing boats on glass mirrors, watching sails corrugated with creases and inert against a blue haze, and basking under a sun that might have shone on Sorrento.

Whisper was there and in the fleet were *Thunder, Fly, Thor, Stardust, Eagle, Martlet* and *Tern*—who had just been painted cream and blue for the first time and thereby set a fashion— and *Afterthought*, which was another of the boats not quite in the picture! A neap tide was ebbing, and apart from one boat which had re-crossed the line stern first none of us had yet reached it, though we had been 'racing' for fifty minutes. *Whisper* had acquired a lead at one stage by being the first to slip her kedge over the side, and though firmly anchored she had passed each boat with serenity as they came towards her borne on the tide. In this way we had all clustered in a tight little bunch almost within touching distance, and there we waited and talked and enjoyed being alive, and in many cases forgot about boats and the winds of Heaven.

Several cruisers were moored in the channel and some were still finishing their spring fitting-out. There were the racing class keel boats off the Club and the line of Sharpies, and beyond them the green marsh lost in a shimmering haze that was born of the heat. A man in a boatswain's chair reaving a new halyard in the top of an eight-metre's mast looked for all the world like an insect crouched on a reed. Right across the anchorage a small dinghy with a substantial woman in the stern jerked hen-like from the jetty to a big white schooner; a small man rowed, and dipping sculls broke up reflections as they went. The voice came clearly across three hundred yards between us—'Left, pull with your left, dear—your left—' a pause and then a little intolerant snort merging with the crisp thud of the pram against the unyielding hull of an interspersed vessel. I looked away as my heart went out to the man at the oars.

In our dinghies we all sat still, as one does in these restful conditions; half-heartedly we considered trimming the boat to leeward to let the sails fall into a contour receptive to the wind, but there was no leeward because there was no wind, and there was a difference of opinion about which way to lean, and from which quarter to anticipate the arrival of a breeze. Somebody aboard *Stardust* was saying that it would be possible to sail on days like this just after an appendix operation. A large bee droned heavily past my ear and plopped into the white glare of the mainsail, then it fell down on to the centre thwart where it careered about describing small circles and ineffectually whirring its wings—the year was too young for aviation.

I remember sitting on *Whisper*'s floorboards with forearms on her gunwale and my chin on my hands; from here I could see her plate hanging below her, changing its shape each second like something in a distorting mirror. The kedge warp stretched away down into the gloom and some little rose-coloured jellyfish marked by four rings on their backs went slowly by with that strange lethargic pulse they have, reminding one that they must enjoy a form of life, though their worries are probably somewhat restricted. Then I noticed again the rich dark mahogany of *Whisper*'s sides, and mauve colour of their reversed image in the water, and I saw my own reflection looking back like the Chad on the wall with an inverted sky behind—it might have said, 'Wot, no wind?' The Chad was wobbling too in the almost imperceptible movement of the water like a jelly struck by a stick.

A movement caught my eye, and I looked up to see that a herring gull had settled; it appeared silently like a vision without warning cry, as buoyant as the dinghies, and stemming the tide with an occasional stroke of a webbed paddle beneath. I looked into its cold uncompromising eye and wondered how a bird could be so pristine and spotless when it lived on such filth. The gull stretched its neck and with jaws agape laughed that great laugh which is the music of the sea itself, and when the laugh was over I noticed for the first time in my life that one could see right through a gull's bill—in one nostril and out the other. The bird had been so absorbing that with attention attracted for several minutes I hadn't noticed a young girl in a cruising yacht moored a few feet beyond the gull, and she too was watching it. She was in the steering well of her boat, leaning on the combing, and in some way our common interest, and indeed physical positions, seemed to cry out for some sort of comment.

'You can see right through its bill,' I said, anxious to pass on the new discovery.

'How?' she asked.

'Right through its nostrils,' I replied. There was a long pause and then she said, 'Well I'll be darned.' It seemed to end the matter there—I felt it was going too far to explain that if her head were also ten inches from the water, like mine, instead of four feet, she too could see through the gull's bill. And then all at once it struck me that this was not very important anyway, and perhaps I'd had too much sun. I turned over and sat up in the boat and then lay back with head on one gunwale, heels on the other, to survey the fleet.

All the boats were as they had been since the starting gun. They were kedged and still, with the tide sliding under them. Hidden behind their light weather jibs the crews of *Thor* and *Eagle* were talking; intriguing and distinctly-said passages of random conversation on the subject of psychic phenomena came across the water from the direction of their boats — 'Perfectly friendly, oh yes, perfectly friendly, simply a presence, but that pub outside Royston, I've never struck anything like it in my life. I wouldn't go in there again for all the rice in China.'

Every now and then interest would be drawn back into the boat, one would lie back and look up the mast to check its straightness, push out the boom with a foot and retrieve it on the mainsheet, rejoicing in its smooth running and silence, and noticing with satisfaction that the 'creeping oil' put on the sheet blocks earlier on had, in fact, crept. A search for the sponge and a tiny drop of water along the centreboard trunk would be dried up and replaced over the side. The painter would be coiled down as if an Admiral of the Fleet were due to be piped aboard. Finally, a survey of one's own toenails would reveal irregularities due to too much shoe-wearing and they would be suitably pruned with a clasp knife. All the while the sun shone down warm on the shoulders, giving a sense of the most supreme well-being and peace, and still not a breath of wind stirred.

The girl reappeared in the cockpit of the cruiser and leaning over scraped some ends off an enamel plate into the water. The herring gull which had allowed itself to drift some distance astern saw and heard all and with a cry of anticipation came gracefully back into our small circle for the promise of kipper bones. For a fearful moment I thought I would find myself talking about its transparent beak again — perhaps the girl feared this too because she suddenly said: 'Would you like some ginger beer?'

We sat up like eager children and *Whisper* rocked, spreading water rings, slapping her empty sails. We were anxious to accept because auto-suggestion has given us a sudden and unendurable thirst, as if we had crossed Arabia dragging a handcart.

'I'll give her a sheer,' said the girl, and untying the lashings of the tiller she put her hip against it and pushed the helm over. With a sheer the other way we moved over to meet her, and the two boats came together with enough momentum for the girl to be able to reach out and put the little bottles into our hands. With rudders centralised again the two boats slowly parted and we lay back as before, a great gulf between us positioned by our own anchors. The bottles of ginger beer then seemed to have come to us from another world. Our friend waved and went below, and as the cruiser was gone from her borrowed mooring on the next tide, she went out of our lives.

Whisper's bronze hatchet plate was perfect for opening crown cork bottles and we hauled it up wet and dripping into its case and opened them on its hard edge. Later we played U-boats with the empties over the side and finally watched their drunken wobbling course downwards into the depths to join a seabed which in this locality I have discovered, through diving for lost gear, to be almost entirely carpeted with empties.

So we sat and waited, and the sun shone down, and minute by minute the hour grew nearer lunchtime. Conversation had germinated, developed, and died while the scene remained unaltered, and only the sun's angle and the gentle ebb off the marsh showed any change, with supremacy gradually moving from blue water to green grass.

Then came the thin line on the water, a dark blue horizon line no thicker than a hair and geometrically straight. It grew slowly darker as its size increased and its near edge became irregular like a series of opening fans. The warm air stirred slightly in the faint precursors of the breeze, and the boats moved ahead as their kedges were hastily recovered and stowed. Concentration began on the flags at the mast-heads and sheets were held lightly feeling for the true direction of the newly-born breeze. The boats had become alive like white butterflies stretching first crumpled wings. That forward movement was enough to stem the tide, yet it varied so that their positions changed one with the other in this first fitful few seconds. A catspaw ruffled the water up to *Whisper's* bow, and as it found her sails she heeled gently and moved away. Her sheets came in close-hauled and her sails smoothed out as she gathered way, and when we came up on to the gunwale to hold her against the increasing weight her mast creaked slightly and her rigging began to hum.

She chuckled through the water, freshly ruffled and sparkling now, where it had lain so long as under a film of oil. There was a perfect balance in her and a quality of response and keenness to go unsurpassed by any other boat. The sight of her and the sound she made, and the responses that came through her sheet and tiller, provided one of those sensations of immeasurable enjoyment that draw so many people to small boats and having drawn them keep them content. The wind had come.

Part V

DESPERATE MOMENTS

Never did a cockpit seem so empty.
Ten years have done nothing to fade the memory of that tiller swinging idly,
naked; horrified, it seemed, at the terrible part it must have played.

Peter Haward: *All Seasons' Yachtsman*

Peter Combe

THE LAST HOURS OF WINDSTAR

THE yacht *Windstar*, R.Y.S. 29 tons T.M., with an overall length of 55 feet, registered Poole, built 1937 at Mevagissey for Mr. Philip Ionides—sold 1938 to Sir Philip Hunloke, G.C.V.O.—served in the war as an anchor to a barrage balloon—and bought by Captain Bertram Currie in 1948—was a Bermuda-rigged auxiliary cutter, powered by a four-stroke Thorneycroft engine.

She had just returned from a three weeks' Scandinavian tour from Cowes, via the Kiel Canal to Copenhagen, Gotenburg and Oslo, carrying with Captain Currie, myself, a skipper and two other crew, and—as far as Copenhagen—General Evelyn Fanshawe.

On Saturday night, July 28th, 1956, we took her out of Lowestoft, and failed to bring her again to port.

Captain Currie was still an invalid from recent illness and a diabetic. He had, I believe, been greatly disappointed in his youth at being forbidden the Navy by his father and was only allowed by his doctors—under protest—to take this sailing trip—which he enjoyed, I think, more than anything else—so long as he did not 'overdo it'. A man of astounding imperturbability and apparent nonchalance, with complete disregard for the possibility of hazard, he seemed sublimely and blithely content to sail on indefinitely so long as there seemed to be water under his keel. We motored out of the harbour with the jib furled and bent on ready to hoist and the main sail uncovered, and took the inside passage south from the harbour mouth before heading to sea. At 2200 hours the first gale warning had been broadcast. Neither of us had heard it.

After two miles we had cleared the coastal shallows and set course to southward. 'Well, chum,' said Bertram, 'we're going to be pretty sleepy by the time we get to Cowes. You'd better turn in for a while.'

The situation then, if not too attractive, presented no cause for anxiety. We knew where we were, the night was clear, and the journey, which should have taken about eighty hours, well marked and lit all the way. We had enough oil to motor the entire distance, if necessary, and I was confident of being able to hoist the mainsail alone, even if with no great rapidity, if we had a fair wind in daylight.

I did not foresee getting much sleep, as he had said. After we had started I had also some qualms about abetting him in undertaking this tiring run at the end of his holiday; but he was determined to go, and eager to get the boat back to Cowes for the regatta week. There was something of an anticlimax about the run home at the end of the tour, and since leaving Oslo, the nearer we approached England, the colder and wetter and drearier had the weather become. The challenge and amusement of taking the boat home alone did, in fact, enliven what would otherwise have been a rather flat finale.

After sleeping a while I found we were quite a bit to shoreward of our course, due to confusion about lights, and while Bertram took a spell below I ran out to Shipwash Light Vessel from which I had laid the course for a clear run down to Kentish Knock.

At 0700 hours we passed Sunk Light Vessel the tide having carried us eastwards towards the Thames Estuary, and I laid a new course for Kentish Knock. It was not worth the effort of trying to hoist any sail to hold us steady, as the wind was only a few points off our starboard bow. By now it was as rough as the North Sea passage had been, and even a little more choppy. Apart from the lack of Calor gas it was impossible to do anything in the galley, so we lived that day, on some chocolate and biscuits and hard liquor. In any case, I was now feeling far from well, tired, a headache, slightly sick, and sorry that we had let ourselves in for another beating. I had hoped that by the time we reached Dover Bertram would be tired enough to agree to put in there to sleep. As the prospect of a hot, dry lunch in Dover receded I became anxious about Bertram's being able to go on without making himself ill, or taking a bad fall. He had managed to give himself his daily injection of insulin—no mean feat in that weather—but there seemed little chance of his eating his accustomed fill to balance it. By midday the gale was at its height, the seas growing very big, breaking at the tops, and the surface streaked with foam. Visibility grew poorer as the volume of wind-driven spray increased. It was now becoming difficult to steer. Our course fortunately lay into the wind, but we could only hold it spasmodically. There was no question now of a sail holding us steady. We could steer fairly steady about fifteen degrees either side of the wind until a strong gust blew her head away, when she would take a long while to come back up again.

At 1245 hours we passed Kentish Knock Light Vessel very slowly, making possibly two knots had our course been less erratic, and for a moment it looked as though we would be carried down on to her, the tide or the weather taking us still to the eastward. Dover seemed a very long way off. It was now a question of holding our head into the weather and riding out the gale, which was so freakish for the time of year as to seem incapable of lasting. By now it was only possible to hold our head against the wind with the wheel hard over and watching for the ticklish moment when the wind was more or less dead ahead, when, if we were carried off to starboard, it had now become impossible to bring her up again into the wind—the propeller being on the starboard side and the thrust being weaker from that side. Each time she fell away to starboard and kept falling with the weather abeam we now had to wear her right round and start again. Fortunately, we were never badly pooped doing this, but each long lapse to starboard brought us nearer to the Goodwins.

We had the canvas cockpit cover rigged, inside which whichever of us was not steering could shelter from the attentions of the wind, although the water was everywhere coming through it. Whoever was at the wheel, sitting abaft this cover, was obliged to sit up quite high to peer over it—which occasionally seemed a good idea in case one could see anything into which we might be running—getting what cover one could, hunching oneself forward into its lee and steering most of the time by compass. In fact, it became almost impossible to watch the seas ahead, as every time one raised one's head one received at once with uncanny precision a discouraging blast of salt shot in the eyes. In spite of the fact that one shivered more, I then found it more agreeable to steer, as it occupied my mind and distracted it from the disagreeable state of my head and stomach. Facing thus fore and aft with my hands on the wheel, I seemed in a better position to balance. As in the North Sea passage, it was a rather exhilarating sensation, like riding a big high-mettled hunter, as *Windstar* plunged and reared, occasionally taking the seas with a sharp leap like a dolphin. Bertram took one or two crashing falls during the course of the day. In fact, on our return his doctor discovered three fractured ribs.

A day or two before, I had been reading about the forces and symptoms tabled in the Beaufort wind scale, and remarking this to Bertram—shouting conversationally at the top of my lungs—added that, as far as I could see, this bore all the characteristics of a hurricane. 'It very likely is,' he replied calmly, and we lapsed again into silence for another half-hour or so. We later learned that hurricane Force 10 had, in fact, been registered.

At this period we were still holding our head more or less into the weather and, I think, making some way through the water. We were able, with care, to keep most of the time on the starboard tack and away from the direction of the Goodwins.

The engine was well able to keep pumping out any water we were making, and we were riding the seas well, only occasionally shipping a big sea on to the decks at more than a minute's interval which only slightly splashed into the cockpit and drained overboard before the next. My only anxiety was that we should be able to have some indication where to turn westward up channel as soon as possible, to try to make Dover. I had little faith in the good fortune of seeing the East Goodwin Light Vessel on our present course, and hoped that we would see the coast of France before being run on to it. Presumably it would be dark by then and lights visible. The radio D/F receiver was not operative with the engine running, and it was impossible to hold steady into the weather without this.

I was also growing a little anxious about our ability to hold on indefinitely without rest, or something sensible to put inside us, if this wearying, weakening, utterly dreary grind continued without a single glimmer of hopeful change.

But though anxiety had grown, my feeling was chiefly of frustration and impatience, with the apparently indefinite uncomfortable antic unpleasantness of our situation.

About 1400 hours came a radical change in our situation, though far from welcome. Three things happened almost simultaneously. First, the engine failed. A moment later—and I presume it to have been later, as we swung out of the wind without steerage way though I cannot swear to it—a really big sea broke over our starboard side, and for a while I looked through a pale green world of pouring water, such as one is treated to sometimes in the cinema from uptipped water tanks. I was at the wheel, and held on confidently for the boat to lift, and the sky to reappear, for what seemed some time. When the water stopped I saw the cockpit quite full of it, and Bertram, who had been carried from the starboard side together with the cockpit cover, clear through the cover on the port side, perched between the metal struts, like a bird in a bush, with his behind on the deck. I helped him back, apparently unhurt, and we set about fetching back the lengths of main and jib sheet that were trailing outboard, and cleared away the mess of the cockpit cover.

Although the engine still started and ran, it stalled when we tried to coax it into gear, even astern. While we were still shaken at all this, the jib, which I had earlier doubly secured to keep it quiet in the gale, flung off both its lashings and hoisted itself. Presumably the changed direction of the gale's attack enabled it to get a better purchase. The canvas ran practically to its full and correct height, and promptly blew to bits, with a flapping and crackling most painful to the yachtsman's ear, while I watched fascinated. It would have been madness to try to catch hold of any part of it under those conditions, so we just waited, hoping that it would destroy itself as soon as possible. In doing this it managed to carry away, by the flailing of its sheets and the attached block, the lowest port-side main-stay (a half-inch wire hawser), the for'ard portion of the port side deck rail, together with two stanchions—the next one remaining was bent double over the side as if it had been made of tin—and also the spinnaker boom, which had been secured there.

'There goes the spinnaker boom,' I shouted at Bertram as it floated past us. Rather as one might point out a porpoise to one's Mum on a trip round the lighthouse in the *Skylark*. He treated this excited comment with the contempt it deserved. There being no possible enjoinder, except perhaps that we probably would not require it this trip. The yacht now, with these first wounds, began to look sorry and unship-shape.

So strong was the gale that she sailed, to my wonder, for ten minutes steady upwind on the few tattered ribbons of jib, but not close enough, so that the seas were dangerously abeam.

'What do we do now?' I said to Bertram after pointing out this interesting phenomenon. 'Run before the wind under bare poles,' he replied, and I heard the ring of trumpets in his voice. This thrilling phrase, often read in the books of sea adventure which I had devoured as a boy, made me chuckle with surprised delight, yet it seemed quite reasonable. I did not feel disposed to secure the loose stay which was waving about crackling things with the wooden sleeve it wore. Eventually I think it fouled something below the mast and stayed quiet; and I was certainly not eager to try to construct a sea anchor. Later we were told we should have done this, but even had the ship's company been more up to it, the gear easy of access, and conditions more sympathetic to efficient and seamanlike movements, I think it would have been an error. There is something so very helpless about being at the mercy of a sea anchor, and our hull would have taken a worse beating holding into the seas. As it was, we were driven along at an astonishing speed, which we later calculated to have been about six knots. We could thus steer quite well, sustaining less strain on the hull, as we were carried along with the weather, sometimes like a surf-board on the crests.

We expected to be badly pooped, but only twice do I remember really big waves breaking in over the stern, which rose wonderfully to each oncoming sea. These did not come in exactly parallel waves, but after a while I found it less tiring and unnerving to steer in the general direction of the weather than to look over my shoulders and try to line up our stern to receive each approaching sea. I am prepared to swear that they varied from thirty to forty foot high at their worst—there are few witnesses to contradict me. One of the advantages of running like this was that we could keep a fairly steady course, which was about north-east, and from where I thought we had been when we turned. We had plenty of sea ahead until we reached the north-west coast of Denmark, or missing it, find ourselves back in Norway—by which time we could only hope that the gale would have blown itself out.

The weather was now less vicious in our faces, but we were fully exposed to the following wind, and I noticed both of us shivered violently all the time we were at the wheel. Earlier in the day I had changed once, but was now quite drenched again. Over blue jean trousers and a thick cotton naval rating's shirt, I wore a sweater and a light ski-ing anorak—chiefly because of its hood which protected my ears—and on top of this an oilskin, more to keep the wind out than the wet. On my feet I had a pair of fleece-lined snow-boots, also completely soaked but nevertheless quite cosy. Strangely enough, the sea and the wind were not very cold; it was only the force of the latter which chilled us, driving right through our backs. We were quite pleased to take a spell below, where everything was now wet and disordered with books, clothes and cushions and other gear all over the floor of the cabin and the saloon. The crew space for'ard was even wetter, and the galley a fine jumble of smashed crockery, tins and pots which had broken loose. When I went below to drag, without much success, at a damp cigarette, and find a little peace, I kept throwing things back off the deck, but eventually gave up. Whoever went below shut the door from the cockpit after him to keep out the splashes, and the man at the wheel was left alone in the water. Occasionally we bailed for each other with biscuit tins—chiefly for the sake of morale. The cockpit was quite isolated, in the watertight sense, from the rest of the craft, but the self-draining part of it had some sort of valve trouble. Having effectively removed the water, it had the habit of belching back as much again with a merry gurgle. We had accordingly settled its hash with a champagne cork some days before. I found the large glass binnacle cover more useful for bailing the cockpit, and developed a handy technique of holding it in the corner with my foot while steering, and after a good roll hoisting it up full of water, with my spare hand. I had already discovered the uselessness of putting a quick temporary lashing on the wheel while I left it for a moment to do anything. She just kicked it off in about three sharp jolts.

At some time after 1500 hours—I do not remember looking at my watch at any time after we started running north-east—the situation became timeless and immediate, I began to check the well when I went below. It was showing a good deal of water, but as I had not had occasion to look into it myself since leaving Oslo, I had no idea what would be considered normal. On a previous occasion, when water had been showing on the lower part of the deck by the galley door on a return trip from Deauville, it caused little alarm as I remember, and this was not yet apparent. This time, however, we could not pump it out with the engine, the drive being off the shaft. I pumped a while by hand, but it was difficult to tell how much difference I was making—if any. I told Bertram that we had a good deal of water inboard, and he was naturally not surprised. I pumped some more, and later, when it seemed to me that the hand pump was achieving very little, I told him this. Later, when he took a spell below himself, and had been through similar motions, he confirmed my fears that we were gradually making water.

The situation then, although we did not discuss it, took on a more doleful aspect. It became colder as the day faded, and we were both quite eager to take a turn below pumping. It seemed to me from the bore and the feel of the pump's action that it might be able to hold the water we were making in various ways above water-level as it filtered down into the bilges; but what was happening below the water-line one could only guess.

At about 1600 hours, while I was at the wheel, I suddenly saw a trawler off to port on a parallel course up weather about three hundred yards, and yelled at the top of my lungs, to Bertram, 'Do you want to signal her?' 'Oh, I don't think that's necessary,' he replied, and disappeared again below.

It seemed to me, since we were alone and helpless, that we might have asked for a tow, or at least through her made our presence known to the outside world, but although I waved wildly with my spare hand I saw no answering sign. In fact, I believe that she would have been unable to turn out of the wind and come to us without getting into difficulties herself. It would have been a good idea to have been wearing a signal to say at least that our engines had failed, and were under no control, if anyone could have noticed and read our tiny signal flags. The only other thing I had seen that afternoon was a large dolphin which came gambolling down the side of a big sea to meet us like a puppy, and apparently quite undismayed by the weather.

It gradually became clear that we were making water much faster than we could pump, if, indeed, the pump was achieving anything. I selfishly took long spells at the pump, believing that I could pump a great deal faster than Bertram.

It was strange below, comparatively quiet, comparatively dry and warm, and gave one a strange sense of security, while the movement of the ship itself seemed less violent. It seemed so remote, I kept wondering whether I would open the doors of the cockpit and find Bertram had disappeared over the side without my knowing, and as I looked at them, bolted to keep them shut, it was hard to realise how easily a really big sea coming over the stern could stave in their frail wood like cardboard.

I arranged the cockpit cushions on the deck by the pump, and pumped hard and long with my right arm stiff, rolling my body back and forth, which seemed a less tiring method, for an indefinite period. There was no comparable method possible with the left hand, the pump being hard against the port side of the engine space, but I used my left arm on occasions to save fatigue. I did not fancy having my arms too tired to pump before the rest of my body was too exhausted to care.

I kept thinking petulantly, 'This is such an utterly dreary and stupid way to die', as I lay there damply rocking, confronted with a confined prospect of darkly swirling bilgewater and the stink of diesel oil.

Towards 1900 hours I thought of putting on the wireless, which since the engine was no longer working would receive without interference, and enjoyed complete unreality for a while from the unctuous smugness and patronising *bonhomie* of the B.B.C. until the news bulletin. 'Unprecedented gales in the Channel,' the announcer tritely enunciated—at least we were authenticated. The *Moyana*, returning triumphantly from winning the Torbay to Lisbon race, had sunk in the early morning—80-mile-an-hour gusts registered in Cornwall. A steamer had capsized with the loss of one life. Out of twenty-four yachts in the Channel Race, only ten had been accounted for. Lifeboats and distress calls all along the Channel. I began to feel proud of ourselves for being afloat. Apples had been flying off the trees in Kent (too bad), and a dozen people had been killed ashore by falling or flying objects. Perhaps we were safer here!

With this happy news I relieved Bertram at the wheel. I asked him if he knew where the distress flares were, and suggested that we should have them handy. He agreed. I also asked him to switch the navigation lights on while he was below, so that we were ready and visible when it got dark, and we started the engine, running it slowly, to keep the batteries charged. It was somehow heartening that Bertram now seemed prepared to admit that we were sinking, and should make the fact known if we met anyone who was interested.

I had hitherto always been sustained by a sort of metaphysical confidence that it was not yet my time to die, believing in a kind of eternal rhyme and reason or poetic balance—whereby there was something for me in this short life before my card was full and ready to hand in, even though there might be a lot more balance yet to be made in other existences. Taking account of the futility of my life to date and my lack of conviction for the future, I realise that this confidence in my own purpose and capacity had of late faded. Bertram, who seemed to have lost all zest for life since his son died, and seemed to show little will to live, would have been rather happy, I think, to have gone down in *Windstar* which he loved. It did in fact seem devastatingly right—or at least agreeable to sublime rhyme and reason—that 'finis' should be written here.

As sands ran out and the water in, it occurred to me that this was my last opportunity to make the acquaintance of God

Almighty. I felt a natural desire to complain to some eternal authority about the futility of our predicament without knowing where I should address myself; it seemed a perfect opportunity for the Almighty to show His hand and fill me with faith—not faith in deliverance, that would be too much to ask of any deity at first acquaintance; nor could I reasonably hope for the vision of Jesus Christ drawing up alongside in Simon Peter's fishing smack to come striding across the waves to take my hand or pass us a celestial tow, but almost everyone, when age, disease or sorrows strike him, inclines to think there is a God or something very like him. I remember learning these words at school and this rather stark state of affairs seemed well designed to edge me into a cosy state of belief. Perhaps he was waiting for the final moments; in any case, I took a few sharp pulls of the brandy bottle instead, which imparted a more direct, if temporary, glow before I took over the wheel as dusk was falling.

I was quite looking forward to a little more dark, as it would increase the chances of seeing a light, or having ours seen, at greater range. I did not want to burn our few flares until we definitely saw something to show them to, after which I planned to let the pump take a position of secondary importance while I made a distress signal with the masthead light, and kept on making it until something happened.

When we got low enough in the water for the seas to start breaking inboard seriously, and accelerate matters, I could not somehow see us making brave and stirring valedictory gestures to each other. Should I suggest putting a note in a bottle to keep the records straight and say 'good-bye' to our friends? We would have to drain a bottle first. Happy thought!

About 2100 hours I suddenly saw for a moment a large vessel bearing green 130 about three miles off, and yelled for the flares. Bertram, after a short argument with the cabin doors, leant out on to the seat with a red tin which had a screw cap on one side, and seemed to take an age to unscrew. He then tried to get out a flare through a small hole, and after a great deal of probing and pulling, produced a piece of rumpled newspaper packing. This went on for some time until he had fished out quite a few newspaper scraps with some difficulty. At last a flare permitted itself to emerge. We then had to discover what to do with them. 'They are self-igniting,' said Bertram. But how, neither of us knew, hoping faintly they would burst into flames when they understood what we wanted. Neither of us could see very well by this time, yet when I found light and spectacles I could make out the far from striking printing, which said, 'Tear off cap, and rub inside smartly against head of flare.' This produced absolutely no result, and as it seemed to smack rather of Aladdin's cave I tried it several other ways, even pulling one flare entirely to pieces. Eventually I went to the galley and found a packet of matches which did work, and striking a whole box at a time held the exploding heads against the wretched things. One flare, at length, did give a slight sizzle, and I kept working at in the shelter of the cabin — to absolutely no purpose.

Under the stress of these exercises I remember my language grew unregrettably unparliamentary, and I even spoke quite sharply to Bertram. It was curious though, as we remarked afterwards, that throughout this entire adventure we remained ridiculously polite to each other, if a little curt, without any of the, 'For heaven's sake, grab that you bloody fool' kind of dialogue, usual in such emergencies.

I then soaked a strip of the driest piece of cloth I could find with a can of lighter fuel, and wrapped it round a flare. This also was too damp, and wouldn't burn. I gave up the flares, briefly thinking of starting a bonfire with them somehow on the deck.

Our ship seemed to have disappeared. I went for the Aldis lamp, which I plugged into the masthead light socket at the foot of the mast, there being no other place for it. It didn't work. When I told him, Bertram said, 'It worked the other day,' and I put the masthead fitting back. No masthead light either. This, anyway, had been suffering from mysterious fits of failure which the electricians had been unable to cure, I checked the other navigation lights. None of them was burning — nor would they.

All this time I was moving very fast about the deck, and below, slipping and bumping in my hurry, and increasing the mess in the galley looking for matches, and in the saloon looking for the lighter fuel, and something to burn. The inside of the yacht was now a terrible mess. Even the bottom boards had been thrown out of the bunks, and the decks were a mad jumble of clothes, cushions, books, charts, and tins and pots of food, two food lockers having burst open to pour their contents into the muddle, and the water was now splashing up out of the bilges as she rolled. In the middle of it all the swinging Tantalus attached to the saloon table ticked happily back and forth with its cargo of bottles, as though nothing were amiss. I took the hint and some more brandy, and found a wet biscuit on the deck.

Looking again for our ship, I eventually found her a little for'ard of our beam. Her lights were now showing clearly and it was getting darker. A little later I realised she was another craft. I could then also see what I took to be the original ship in about the same position as before.

While below I had put on every inside light we had as I passed to show as much of us as we could. And then, to my amazement, when I switched on the stern light it lit — although it had been unshipped by the seas, and had lain banging about the deck at the end of its flex for most of the day. I got up on the deck aft and seized it. With one hand on the back stay I stood holding it as high off the deck as I could, and began to flash S.O.S. in a wide arc between the two ships. The light had flickered out once or twice rather sickeningly, and, not knowing how far above the water the batteries were, I started looking for some other light. Our rubber torch had gone to ground among the rubble on the cabin floor, but Bertram told me where to find an old army pattern map reading and signalling torch in a leather cover, which he had carried in the First World War. With this spare light between my teeth, I went on flashing. It seemed that the smaller vessel was approaching, and at last she quite definitely flashed back to us.

It was a wonderful moment to be in contact at last with someone else in the world. Time and space had returned to focus.

I was now anxious not to lose them. It was strange how, as rescue became more tangible a possibility, and the odds calculable, I became more anxious and impressed with the problems involved. I feared for our battery system and that we might lose each other, playing hide and seek among the troughs of the sea. I kept flashing to her to dispel any doubt they might have about our signals, and to keep our position well in view. The East Gabbard Light Vessel, now visible to them thirteen miles off beyond us, did in fact confuse them for a moment.

Now that they were definitely coming in to us I rested my right arm with the stern light, and kept on flashing with the torch which had a morse button. As the urgency eased a little, I began to grow ridiculously self-conscious, and wondered if it might not be more professional to send a proper message. I sent our signal letters a few times in between the S.O.S.s, so that they could relay our identity in case of mishap.

We found we could steer towards the ship fairly comfortably, and eventually I saw she was a small vessel about 100 tons register coming in quite slowly with a nice big Aldis lamp on the bridge searching amongst the waves for us. I began to realise the difficulties ahead, of getting from a comparatively helpless yacht on to a steamship, in the dark, in a hurricane.

I asked Bertram—who, by this time, had been continuously at the wheel since I started playing with the distress flares— whether he wanted to try to take a tow, or whether I should try to board her as soon as possible, and organise some means of transit for himself. This was my gravest worry, as I did not see how he could be expected to perform any violent gymnastics.

'Yes,' he said, 'you had better do that.'

As she got closer I went below, found my brief-case among the rubble, and put my address book in the pocket of my oilskin, ignoring my passport and wallet which were next to it. This was a completely superstitious gesture. It seemed that I would be lucky to get my body out of it alive; what else could I not dispense with in the circumstances? It seemed to be tempting fate to put anything else in my pockets, but to lose an address book, as I had done before, breaks a great number of human contacts, cutting off some for ever, so I had decided to go and fetch this.

While I was below, Bertram shouted that she was flashing to us. Let her flash, I thought, this is no time for conversation and, in any case, I would probably no be able to understand. I expected her to be a French or Belgian, or even a Dutch coaster, and only hoped that we would understand each other when we got within range for yelling instructions.

She came round very slowly and carefully astern of us. I tried to wave her on in the direction of the weather, since that was the only way we could steer, and shouted to Bertram to hold her there. He replied that he couldn't see. The cabin lights dazzled him, and as all this time he had sat very quiet, I thought he was pretty tired out. I think now, considering this eye trouble, that he was probably suffering from an overdose of insulin as well as everything else. I directed him from the stern as well as I could until the ship came in alongside.

It was a most admirable piece of seamanship. She came in very slowly, carefully and deliberately, in that appalling weather, and laid herself alongside us as though we were a pier on a fine day instead of an erratically bobbing yacht.

They began to throw us lines, and eventually we were close enough for them to land aboard, I cannot exactly remember everything which took place from this moment in fast frenzied succession. I leaped and clawed my way about *Windstar's* deck as swiftly as I could, trying to secure and make ropes fast. They threw me the heaviest hawsers they had, which made it even more difficult to find anywhere to belay them effectively on such a craft.

It was difficult to see in the dark punctuated by the dazzling glare of her searchlight. They had thrown oil on the water, which covered the hawsers and splashed aboard, so that I slipped and slithered more than ever, and at one moment heard myself sobbing with the effort like a wounded cowboy in an action-packed western—a dramatic exercise in which I had never before believed.

'Put a line round the mast,' someone yelled, and I thought vaguely how clever of them to have noticed our ensign and taken the trouble to speak English. I led one hawser round the mast which jammed somewhere before I could get enough rope round and make more than a half-hitch with a bight. I dropped the eye of another round the anchor winch for'ard, and then found that we were moving forward. In fact, the steamship had sternway and was slipping back. We had taken some violent bumps against her side already, but moving forward under the sheer of her bows was even more alarming. I expected to be pounded under at any moment as we both plunged up and down.

To complicate matters, two wire stays caught behind her

anchor, where they began to saw up and down, making a horrible noise like a mad violin. The bo'sun told me afterwards that I swung myself up and wrenched these free, kicking against her plates, but I really don't remember. I was too preoccupied with the urgency and concern of having made only one line properly fast for'ard, and nothing aft to stop us sliding away like this. Her bow looked very sharp and vicious, glistening black and silver in the dark and wet as she chopped up and down. Imagine being a mouse on the block at Tower Hill, whom a drunken executioner is trying to behead, at night, during a thunderstorm and an earthquake.

We moved apart quite quickly, while I tried to make fast the hawser, which had pulled free of the mast and was now running out over the stern. I got it through the fairlead, but couldn't hold it, nor find anything strong enough to suddenly jump it on to. I considered the binnacle for a moment, but it wasn't stout enough. It would have been useless to damage the boat any more, ripping out stanchions, or stays, or the binnacle, in the hope that it would check our flight. The bar on which the main sheet block ran would have been ideal, but the hawser was too thick to push through it easily as it ran out like a live thing, and the block itself slamming from side to side as we rolled could have removed my fingers very easily. I watched the rope snake away overboard.

We were driven forward and across the steamer's bows while she slid backwards and round our stern until she seemed to be about a hundred yards off or more, over our starboard quarter, and still holding us on the remaining hawser like a badly harpooned whale. Her rope was thus around all the standing rigging from just for'ard of the mast on the port side to just for'ard of the cockpit on the starboard side. As the strain increased it seemed impossible that she could reel us back in, or fail to bring down rigging, boom and mast on top of us. The hawser stood between us in a stiff, straight line. There was a sharp series of vicious cracks, whangs and creaks, and eventually the hawser parted with a snap. I think only two stays had carried away, but I didn't bother to check.

I was now afraid that after the beating we had taken against the steel hull we must be filling with water even faster, and for a while feared that the steamer would or could not return to us again. For an unreasonable moment I even thought perhaps she might be more interested in salvage, and wiggled the stern light at her again in what I hoped was a winsome fashion. As she eventually came in again I made ready multiple loops from the tangle of sheets, made fast at several points to bend her next hawser on to. Bertram, I noticed, had finally left the wheel and was sitting in the cockpit looking rather dazed. 'The steering's jammed,' he said, and went below to collect ship's papers and one or two valuables. I tried to shift the wheel, and after a hard heave it spun out of my hand like a catherine wheel.

Something had either broken or jumped out of gear as we bumped against the steamship. We were now completely helpless.

I stood on the stern again with the stern light in my hand to watch how the ship came in again. As we swung helplessly about I tried, ineffectually, to keep the ensign from flapping in my face, and then caught hold of the jackstaff to put it out and clear it overboard. This suddenly seemed not the thing to do, apart from looking like an unlucky gesture of despair.

As I had plenty of time to indulge in romantic gestures, I went and searched for my knife in the cabin, and then climbed aft again to cut the ensign down, stuff it into the collar of my oilskin like a scarf, and jettison the jackstaff. I wonder if I would have made this quaint gesture had it not been for a nostalgic respect for the white variety of ensign.

As the steamer approached I yelled that we could not now steer to help in any way.

A voice shouted back, 'Do you want to come aboard?'

'Yes,' I shrieked in amazement.

Apparently they had noticed Bertram sitting at the wheel in an attitude of such unconcern that they were in some doubt that we wished to leave!

A few moments later we struck her side head on, smashing in the stem and carrying away the forestay. As we rocked crazily alongside again I heard them yelling on deck to look out for the mast as it swung over her deck. I managed to secure another hawser around all the winches for'ard, and it then seemed high time to leave.

Bertram was now on deck, wearing a spare cap (we had both lost ours overboard during the day), and seemed ready to abandon ship. I had noticed the previous time, as the two vessels soared up and down alongside like a pair of demented elevators, that her deck rail for'ard came within reach now and again. This time I did not intend to let the opportunity slip, and made my way for'ard to wait until we were scraping along-side again in the same position. For a pessimistic moment I wondered if I still had the strength to pull myself aboard; everything felt numb and weak. I stood for a while trying to take a deep steady breath and relax, hopefully looking at my hands as I flexed my aching fingers. I needn't have worried. When her deck ducked within reach I found myself up and over before I had time to think about making any effort.

As I picked myself off the steel deck I heard someone cry out, 'There's one of them aboard', and then repeat it again to the bridge in such a wild tone of voice that I felt for a moment they were going to throw me back! I joined three of four of them by the rail below the bridge and explained at the top of my voice that Bertram could not be expected to do anything violent.

'He's sick', I bellowed, which seemed the simplest formula to inspire a more complicated plan of rescue.

Meanwhile they had thrown several lines down to him, and were shouting at him to tie one round him. Luckily the line I had secured for'ard was well fast and fortunately placed so that *Windstar* towed alongside very nicely as the steamer moved forward just enough to keep her there.

I watched from the dark deck of the steamer and an entirely new viewpoint. I was now safe—so small a phrase and so minute a difference of time and place to denote so vast a change of state—like a spectator watching the brightly lit stage of *Windstar*'s deck from which I had now stepped.

Bertram stood upright with difficulty on the slippery, heaving deck. Luckily the remaining section of portside rail was in front of him as he tried to hold his balance and secure a rope at the same time. Three times the boom swung over and caught him on the back of the neck a sharp blow which looked as though it could fell an ox. He lost his spare cap overboard too, while tying the rope round his middle. He seemed to make, as best he could, a sort of half-hitch with the end which none of us who were watching believed to be really secured. Another line he held in his hand taking a turn around his arm, and we tried to catch his hands as the two decks rose and dipped towards each other. Twice we nearly had his hands, and then as *Windstar* plunged down and away the lines jerked him overboard and he fell between the two hulls.

It was a quite sickening moment, and I think I tried not to see. I know that for some moments I didn't dare to pull on the rope to prove to myself that he was not on the end of it. The bo'sun, who was on the rope with me, deliberately let as much slack go as he could, so that Bertram could either duck below the hulls as they came together or, if not attached, try to secure more line. The gap, however, widened for a moment, and we eased in the line. There was a weight at the end and, expecting any moment to lose our prize, we pulled him aboard in about three heaves, suspended by the middle like a sheep being loaded, and caplessly lacking all the dignity of a captain leaving his sinking ship. When we bundled him over the rail and said, 'Thank God—we never thought the rope was fast', he replied at once, 'Nonsense—tied it myself', and after he had been dragged across the deck and into the saloon before he could catch his breath he at once began to make quips about knowing how a walnut felt in a cracker, and remarking that he had no need to be a frogman to know what a ship's bottom looked like. He had no right to be capable of either speech or movement at all.

Five minutes later *Windstar*'s mast snapped off about 10 foot above the deck and vanished over the side, but we never went to look at her again. The captain asked Bertram if he should try to tow her, but he told him to let her go. This he did, with great regret.

The ship, we found, called herself M.V. *Alouette* of the

General Steamship Navigation Company, and had only been passing because she had been unable to hold her anchorage while sheltering in Margate Roads.

The ship's company were extremely kind and, I think, thoroughly enjoyed the whole business. The captain, Captain F. Baker, a youngish man who had the air of a P. & O. liner captain, and sucked a curved pipe in a stately way, had a great time talking to us. The second night, when we had docked in Harlingen, the crew wanted me to drink with them in the fo'c'sle, which I did with considerable glee, got thoroughly drunk very quickly, and began to relax a bit for the first time. They were a splendid bunch of humorous, irreverent ruffians, like my shipmates had been on the lower deck, although they were a curious mixture of nationalities. I always thought this sort of cynical, boisterous roguery was due to the ephemeral uncertainty of wartime services. It seems, though, to be a common quality of seamen. I was almost sorry to depart.

Our trek across the dykes to Amsterdam, through the kind assistance of the shipping company's agent in Harlingen, was fairly comic, though frustrating to my impatience to get home. We looked like a pair of brigands in our salt-caked clothes. Bertram wore his inflatable blue jacket from which a long rubber nozzle (for inflating) reared itself under his right ear.

On the various buses, trains and trams we took, people tittered all the way to Amsterdam — which seemed a picturesque old city, full of waterways, trees and hump-backed bridges.

We startled two young ladies at the British Consul's office considerably, but were very ably and sympathetically supplied with identity papers, money and air tickets to London at Consular speed.

We made a splendid entry into the reception hall of London Airport, first and alone, being without baggage, except for the tattered ensign I still carried bundled round a small piece of *Windstar* which had been found the morning after, jammed in one of *Alouette*'s hawsers, while the customs officers glared sullenly at our retreating backs. A small party of friends and relations burst into a welcoming sound more like guffaws than the brave and resounding cheers more appropriate to this momentous occasion, but we saw their point.

At another large dinner at Bertram's flat we regaled the company with salty, stirring yarns, while the chandeliers rocked in sympathy, and as the first bottle followed the coffee round the table the final curtain line was provided by a young gentleman who, apparently having found nothing better to do the following week-end, telephoned to say that he would be very pleased to accept the invitation to race in *Windstar* at Cowes. Xandra, who answered the telephone, laughed immoderately for some time before the caller or ourselves could discover what was the matter.

Claud Worth

TERN IN THE GALE OF 1896

WE had not been able to visit *Tern* since Anderson and Bennet left her at Falmouth. Anderson and I had arranged to go to Falmouth on Saturday, September 19th, to sail her home to the Thames. At the last moment Anderson was prevented, by the sudden death of his father, from joining. Bennet could not come, so I decided to hire a man at Falmouth to help me bring the yacht home. There were probably plenty of good men to be had if I had known where to find them. After much inquiring on Saturday night, I found in a public house an obese, alcoholic-looking person who rated himself able-seaman and assured me that he had 'used the sea man and boy these thirty years'. I was not favourably impressed, but could not afford to wait, so hired him.

I had a week for the trip. After that there was no possibility of my joining the yacht, even for a day, until the following April. I was therefore prepared, if necessary, to put up with rather more than I usually care for in the matter of weather, in order to get the vessel home. But, it need scarcely be said, If I had foreseen what was coming, she would have had to remain at Falmouth. Having fortunately come safely out of it, I am glad to have had this experience of what a small vessel can live through. In its prolonged violence and in the havoc which it wrought at sea, I think that this gale must be the worst which has occurred in the 'yachting season' within the memory of most of us.

The following account is copied verbatim from the log. The style is abrupt, and, in places, inelegant. But, being written while the impressions were fresh and vivid, it probably gives a truer picture than a more polished narrative written years afterwards.

Monday, September 21st. —SSW, moderate. Started with whole mainsail. Wind freshened off Dodman. Tied up one reef and furled staysail. My A.B. turned out to be no sailor and was quite useless to me. So put into Plymouth and anchored in Catwater at 6.30 p.m. Fired out my 'A.B.' Much wind and rain in night.

Tuesday, September 22nd. —Fine and strong wind. Single-handed, got topmast on deck and coiled away topmast gear; reefed bowsprit. Bought sixteen small mutton chops and had them cooked ashore, as I do not expect to have much time for cooking.

Got away at about midday. Two reefs in mainsail, reefed staysail and third jib. Wind strong WSW. Very heavy sea between Bolt Tail and Start. Three or four heavy seas broke over the starboard quarter, and once she nearly broached-to, but no harm was done. Brought up in south-west corner of Torbay, off a little sandy beach. Bower and about forty fathoms chain. It took about twenty minutes' pumping to clear ship of water. Blowing hard, so tied up third reef in case of a shift of wind.

Wednesday, September 23rd. —Wind and rain in night, but slept securely knowing that I was prepared. Wind W, breezing up again harder than yesterday. Must be back by Monday, and cannot leave the ship anywhere, as I shall not be able to fetch her; so shall start this afternoon, so as to get to Needles in daylight tomorrow.

By the afternoon it was blowing a gale, W, and I felt like staying where I was until the weather improved, but time is short. So I read a few pages of 'Sirius' and hardened my heart.

Lit binnacle lamps and tied canvas round. Lit riding light and put it in well. Started with three reefs in mainsail, single reef in staysail, and spitfire jib, at about 6 p.m. Wind W, blowing hard, with rain. Determined to get well to southward while I could, as if I found sea very bad I might have to run her off before it very often. (This turned out to be fortunate.) Course SE, therefore. As I drew away from the land I found the sea very heavy and as much wind as I wanted for my three reefs. Binnacle lamps went out, but I had the Start light and an occasional look at compass to guide me, as riding light burned all right. About an hour after dark wind increased so much that she would not have any more, so watched my chance and hove her to on starboard tack and hauled down my fourth reef—very heavy work. Wind inclined to back. Stood away on course again, very often dead before it, but getting to southward when I could. Rain. No lights visible.

Thursday, September 24th. —She dished up several small seas with her long low counter, but soon after midnight sea was so heavy and irregular that she was almost out of hand. While I was waiting for a chance to heave her to, a great sea came over the taffrail, completely burying the vessel. I was nearly taken overboard, and the cockpit was filled to the coamings. She broached-to, and I expected that the next sea would finish her. But luckily it only partly broke on board, and then there was a smooth during which I got in the slack of the mainsheet and all fast before she began to pay off again. Headsails were already aback, so I lashed helm a-lee, and she lay fairly quiet. Pumped ship. Had brandy, bread and a chop, and felt better for it. About 3.30 a.m. crawled along deck and furled staysail. The steering and pumping had kept me warm, but now, sitting in the well—of course, soaked to the skin—the cold wind seemed to blow clean through me.

Just as the first streaks of dawn began to appear wind backed SW and blew harder than ever, and she would not lie any more, at one moment all shaking, next fell off and lay over, until I thought sometimes that the mast would go. Sea-anchor and warp were all ready, so led warp through hawsepipe, bent on drogue, and put it over. Tried to take in jib, but it flogged itself to rags as soon as I started the halyard. Let go throat halyard and got throat down, so that gaff was nearly up-and-down the mast. Got boom amidships. Slacked peak halyards, and sail flogged horribly. Paid out drogue warp as she gathered stern-way, slacked topping-lifts, and got boom on deck and mainsheet fast. Then gradually got sail off without accident. Slowly paid out the whole forty fathoms of warp.

After she was once fairly astream of her drogue she shipped no more heavy water. She stood first on one end, then on the other, but climbed each sea safely. The wind tore off the tops of the seas, and the spray came in sheets, everything white as far as one could see. Daylight; no land visible. At about 11 a.m. wind suddenly veered to W. and blew—I don't want to pile on superlatives, but I have been in a pampero off the Plate, and a heavy gale of wind in the South Pacific, and I have never known the wind so strong or the seas so steep and so near breaking. A large barque, the *Rose Ellen* of Wilmington, passed quite close, running up Channel under bare poles. Managed to change my clothes and to feed. About 2 p.m. wind moderated a little. By 6 p.m. blowing only a moderate gale, but still too much wind and sea for me to make sail single-handed.

Tried to fix riding light to runner, but finally gave it up as it would not keep alight. About 9.30 p.m. lay down on cabin floor and slept until midnight.

Friday, September 25th.—Less wind and sea now, but judged it best to ride to my drogue a few hours longer. Several times from the top of the sea caught sight of Portland lights bearing about NNE, distant perhaps ten miles (?). Glad to know approximately my position. At dawn blowing a hard breeze only, and less sea. Shook out close reef, hoisted treble-reefed mainsail, got drogue on board, hoisted reefed staysail, and away. Very difficult getting drogue aboard, as in hurry of getting it over I had omitted to bend tripping line. Nothing in sight. Course E½S, which I guessed would clear St. Catherine's, as I did not fancy the Needles with the sea that was running.

After three or four hours' sailing it suddenly cleared and showed me the Isle of Wight from the Needles to St. Catherine's. Passed about two miles south of St. Catherine's. Brought up in St. Helen's Roads at about 3.30 p.m., with bower and thirty fathoms chain.

Very cold; lit coke stove. Had tea—pints of it—but could not eat. Turned in at about 6.30 and slept the clock round.

Saturday, September 26th.—Very cold. Fine overhead. Wind WNW, a nice breeze; glass risen nearly half an inch in the night—now 29·55. Lit stove. Had a great breakfast at 10 a.m. Cleared up, and am now writing log. Very fit after my twelve hours' sleep.

If weather continues as at present shall start this afternoon, so as probably to arrive at Dungeness in daylight.

Got away at 4.30. One reef, whole staysail, and third jib. Owers about 7.30 p.m.

Sunday, September 27th.—Beachy Head 4 a.m.; 7 a.m. hove-to and shook out reef. Lit coke stove, had breakfast, and stood away on course again. Nice breeze, W. About 11 a.m. passed Dungeness. About 4.30 p.m. anchored about a mile north of Deal pier.

Monday, September 28th.—A slice of luck. Wind at first WSW. After I rounded the Longnose it backed SSW, and allowed me to lay all through overland channel. A nice whole-sail breeze. Some showers. Moored off Queenborough about 2 p.m.

Joshua Slocum

MILKY WAY

I WAS exultant over the prospect of once more entering the Strait of Magellan and beating through again into the Pacific, for it was more than rough on the outside coast of Tierra del Fuego. It was indeed a mountainous sea. When the sloop was in the fiercest squalls, with only the reefed forestaysail set, even that small sail shook her from keelson to truck when it shivered by the leech. Had I harboured the shadow of a doubt for her safety, it would have been that she might spring a leak in the garboard at the heel of the mast; but she never called me once to the pump. Under pressure of the smallest sail I could set she made for the land like a race-horse, and steering her over the crests of the waves so that she might not trip was nice work. I stood at the helm now and made the most of it.

Night closed in before the sloop reached the land, leaving her feeling the way in pitchy darkness. I saw breakers ahead before long. At this I wore ship and stood offshore, but was immediately startled by the tremendous roaring of breakers again ahead and on the lee bow. This puzzled me, for there should have been no broken water where I supposed myself to be. I kept off a good bit, then wore round, but finding broken water also there, threw her head again offshore. In this way, among dangers, I spent the rest of the night. Hail and sleet in the fierce squalls cut my flesh till the blood trickled over my face; but what of that? It was daylight, and the sloop was in the midst of the Milky Way of the sea, which is north-west of Cape Horn, and it was the white breakers of a huge sea over sunken rocks which had threatened to engulf her through the night. It was Fury Island I had sighted and steered for, and what a panorama was before me now and all around! It was not the time to complain of a broken skin. What could I do but fill away among the breakers and find a channel between them, now that it was day? Since she had escaped the rocks through the night, surely she would find her way by daylight. This was the greatest sea adventure of my life. God knows how my vessel escaped.

The sloop at last reached inside of small islands that sheltered her in smooth water. Then I climbed the mast to survey the wild scene astern. The great naturalist Darwin looked over this seascape from the deck of the *Beagle*, and wrote in his journal, 'Any landsman seeing the Milky Way would have nightmare for a week.' He might have added, 'or seaman' as well.

The *Spray*'s good luck followed fast. I discovered, as she sailed along through a labyrinth of islands, that she was in the Cockburn Channel, which leads into the Straight of Magellan at a point opposite Cape Froward, and that she was already passing Thieves' Bay, suggestively named. And at night, March 8th, behold, she was at anchor in a snug cove at the Turn! Every heartbeat on the *Spray* now counted thanks.

Peter Haward

TRAGEDY

THE mate poked his head from the quarter-berth and shouted to the watchkeeper:

'You're all right!'

Gruffly spoken for a youngster of 20 years, the remark punched out reassurance tinged with contempt. The third hand was fussing as the ex-German 22-ton auxiliary sloop *Marianna* lay over to the rising wind. Spray over the cockpit was becoming more and more frequent. Raw to the business of yacht voyaging, he felt his plight was unfairly remote from the delightful photographs of sparkling seas and pretty yachts which had led him from the magazines to this wild night in the Wash.

I was delivering *Marianna* from Southampton in the south of England to Sunderland on the north-east coast. The yacht was in need of a refit but, after restitching the mainsail and awaiting a break in the foul weather, we had made a good passage along the English Channel and round past Suffolk. Then it was light airs and power to head across the Wash — that aptly named area of shoals stretching north from the chilly Norfolk coast. Good motoring weather had been wasted while the magneto was overhauled and, by the time our auxiliary was earning its keep again, the wind had veered west by north and was freshening.

I had worked all the afternoon on the engine and wanted an hour or so in my bunk before relieving the third hand. Before turning in I rolled a stiff reef into the main. We were snugly rigged: even so, the man on watch had the jitters and continuously resorted to calling the skipper — just for the companionship. It provided only jaundiced company but he settled even for that. I was most grateful for the mate's stolid support.

The snow came as I finally gave up all ideas of sleep. I began to don as much out of my seabag as would fit on at once. Then I sent the third hand below. The wind was still veering. The north-east Docking Shoal Buoy was astern and, close-hauled, we could only just lie for the Humber Light Vessel. The remainder of the passage was going to be tough: a true December voyage.

Snow can create that worst of all situations: strong winds coupled with foul visibility. Sitting in an open cockpit, it seemed as if the flakes against the eyes and face were blocks of ice. It was impossible to look where we were going for more than an instant and no amount of vision could penetrate much beyond the forestay. The vicious steep sea, typical of the tide-charged Wash, was rising steadily and the yacht crashed into it like a thoroughbred. *Marianna* has two interesting characteristics. Her low freeboard has stipulated a shallow cockpit, the self-draining variety being the requisite, and her helm kicks violently as she dives over the waves. Two sizes of tiller were provided and even the larger, which we had now shipped, was sometimes hard to hold. A tiller lashing was a sensible idea but it had to be adjusted continuously and this sometimes required both hands. I discarded the idea because, precariously astride the cockpit, I preferred to hang on to a coaming cleat with one hand, allocating only the other to the helm. On several occasions during the next wild three hours, when the yacht reared up and over extra big ones, I let the helm go to vent its mule-like kick on thin air.

Just before 2300 the snow cleared and the flash of the Humber Light Vessel was sighted some five miles ahead. The wind remained strong and it was a relief to have our position confirmed. I handed over to the mate, mentioning the trials and hazards of the prevailing weather, and, after rolling down three more turns of mainsail, dived thankfully into the comparative warmth below.

Cloudbanks, storm-brewed and bulbous, hinted only a brief respite from snow. I knew the north-west wind would be blowing on shore beyond Flamborough Head, forty miles distant. As it was, the short fetch out of the Humber Estuary was giving *Marianna* a wild ride. Studying the chart, the tidal harbour of Bridlington, tucked under the shelter of Flamborough, looked good. As a port of refuge it satisfied all my honourable senses. I reckoned we had earned a day's rest: the last seventy miles from there could be polished off later, possibly after the dead muzzler had shifted, yet giving us time to be home for Christmas.

As I prepared to turn in, the yacht struck a big one. You knew just how deep the hole by the way she reared upwards before until, levelling out, the thrust against gravity gradually diminished to leave a feeling of suspended animation. Then she crashed down into the hollow and I was hurled against the leeward settee. I shouted to the mate.

'I'm all right!' the reply came back.

Calm, stolid, the best that Yorkshire breeds, he and I had been shipmates in yachts for over a 1,000 sea miles. A keen novice had changed into a competent, self-reliant sailor. I could not have wanted a better man in charge of our little vessel as she thrashed into the teeth of the wintry weather. Equally strong had grown our bond of comradeship.

Three minutes later he was gone.

Again *Marianna* crashed into the trough, doubtless her tiller tugging viciously at the helmsman. His cry of surprise and annoyance came clearly above the wild conglomeration of noise as the broken sea drove over the yacht. Then silence.

I hurled myself on deck.

Never did a cockpit seem so empty.

Ten years have done nothing to fade the memory of that tiller swinging idly, naked; horrified, it seemed, at the terrible part it must have played.

Without time to find oilies, I pushed the helm up and yelled to the third hand. We were in irons now and the stock 'man overboard drill' of gybing would not fill the bill. I gathered way on the other tack, the runners a shambles, the jib aback; then freeing the sheets to run down the reciprocal course. Suddenly in the darkness came an unflurried shout.

'Here I am!'

We were doing seven knots on a board reach and he was out of reach on the beam. A lifebuoy was thrown but the self-igniting calcium flare failed to burn. Now: gybe. Helm up, we took ages to come round, far too long I thought, to bring up at the crucial point. Therefore, having travelled what I considered was the proper distance, I swung her round into the wind. Everything a-shake she came to a halt.

We shouted into the darkness and out of the pitch-black the reply showed him way beyond the starboard bow. I got way on again but it was impossible, in the black night, to know how our relative positions were changing. His next shout, weaker, came from the other quarter. Unable to see, relying on a position inaccurately estimated by a single sound, rendered the problems of manoeuvring under sail guess work. The water was bitterly cold and the man in it was heavily clothed including seaboots and oilskins. Speed was essential and this dissuaded me from starting the engine — a lengthy business of reaching a barely accessible fuel tap and flooding the carburettor under the floorboards.

We turned too soon after the next run back. He was dead astern when he shouted again. This time a gybe was the answer. She swung off the strong wind, both runners cast off. Then the boom slammed over and the mainsail split from leech to luff.

Now no shout came from the sea. We dragged in a mess of canvas, yelling again and again. The tragedy was sealed.

We lay in the trough and worked at the engine routine. It always took some time to start. When it came to life we cruised the area for the best part of an hour, seeing nothing. Finally all hope was abandoned, but it was difficult to comprehend that we two left must take *Marianna* away from this awful place. The mate was gone: snatched away as quickly as happens in a nightmare. We had parted company: the unimportant, wretched story of two survivors was all that could be known from that point.

I suddenly realised I was soaked, frozen and with hardly any clothes.

The beat under foresail and power towards the Humber Estuary halted after the first tack. The engine seized because a rope that had been placed on deck during the emergency was trailing astern and fouled the propeller.

Brand new and unpacked, the heavy trysail was dragged from the eyes of the ship. Trysail sheets of hard hemp were rigged and finally this canvas was set. More snow and bitter weather slowed our sail drill. Then started a hellish struggle into the teeth of the rising gale. At dawn we entered Grimsby in blizzard conditions.

My vow never to go to sea again quickly changed to a promise to learn from this tragic accident. Never again would a crew of mine be on deck or in the cockpit in bad weather or at night without a safety belt. I set about designing a suitable one for yachtsmen and the development from it, which has now been in general use for eight years. In 1957 the R.O.R.C. recommended that safety belts be carried aboard all yachts entering offshore events and in the same year the Cruising Club of America stipulated a safety belt for each crew member in the Bermuda race.

From 'All Seasons' Yachtsman' © *1961*

Edward Allcard

MARATHON RUN

HOUR after hour went by, but there was no sign of easing. Great seas thundered down with endless repetition; *Temptress* performed her seemingly impossible feat of keeping afloat. Time and time again she was buried by pooping seas; each time the fear struck me that the hatches had gone, for I was only assured that they had resisted the impact, when they once again rose clear. At other times the mass of water stayed so long covering us that I thought surely the boat must be breached, and was already being dragged down to her doom.

All sense of time was lost. Daylight had given way to darkness, so it may have been five, six or seven hours after the start of this nightmare run, when another of those monstrous waves caught up the yawl and, like an arrow, hurtled her through the air, wave-riding perilously on the edge of this world and the next — but she steered straight and true.

During that reign of terror there were four waves in all which forced *Temptress* to fly along at a speed out of all proportion to her length; but times out of number she was smothered temporarily by those frightful seas.

It became bitterly cold and I was becoming weaker as the hours ground by, for I had started the run already exhausted. The only respite from the cold was when the warm seas swept up above my waist; but when the water receded the icy blast froze me to the bone.

Shivering fits become more and more frequent. My muscles ached and racked me through and through. I was bruised and sore, with only the one position possible, lashed down as I was by two stout ropes. These ropes themselves were grazing and cutting into my skin.

Quick judgement and concentration were necessary at the helm to keep the boat dead before the seas, and an added complication came after about ten hours, when my eyes got so encrusted with salt that I became completely blind. This could only be cleared by sucking my fingers and rubbing in spittle. My eyes were soon raw and painful.

Still the wind battered, roared and slapped as I watched fearfully the approach of my unrelenting enemies.

Always to windward was a hateful white 'V' in the clouds; always in the same place; always mocking me in my grave distress. I shouted and swore with every obscenity known to me towards this 'V'; but the hours passed and still there was not the slightest sign of improvement. *Temptress* and the gale appeared to be irrevocably locked in embrace by an occult superimposition of two 'Vs'—the one in the clouds astern and the other cut in the air by the mast swaying to the rampant roll.

I had no idea of the time except that it was dark. Surely night could not last so long?

'I cannot go on,' I cried; but I went on—there was nothing else to do. To stop was death. And I wanted to live.

The pain from my whole body became worse and worse; the strength of my arms was weakening. Time and time again that heavy tiller had to be pushed as hard over as it would go, and with anxiety I would watch the slowness with which the boat would straighten in her course. And all the time to leeward somewhere, perhaps one mile away, perhaps twenty miles away, was that shoal line, right across my path. I could pass over one side of it, but could never come out on the other.

Then a time came when I was so exhausted that I shouted out aloud: 'I am going to stop now—no, not now, five minutes more, and I must stop.' Five minutes passed, and another five minutes, and still another. Where was the dawn that always brings renewed strength? I knew the light alone would give me added power could I but endure.

The skin was beginning to tear off my white and wrinkled hands which had long before lost all sense of feeling. My bare feet pressing hard on the cockpit grating were swollen and caused me agony at every lurch; my back, continually scraping the deck coaming, was bleeding and raw; and over all, that searching, bitter cold. I had reached and passed the limit of my physical endurance; but there remained the will not to fail.

Looking down from a height at those ranges of snow-capped mountains, *Temptress* would scarcely be seen; just her mast oscillating wildly in snowdrifts of heavy foam. The dark hull would occasionally leap upwards out of the water, showing the deck—a mass of broken and splintered wreckage. In your imagination the boat would be unreal, non-existent, like a phantom of the ocean; the helmsman would seem to be a ghoulish apparition—the great wind tearing at his long, wild, matted hair surmounting a gaunt salt-encrusted face and sunken eyes, and as far as you could see there would be only that fearful unutterable sight that filled those painful eyes.

At last it came. My dulled senses were sharpened by a change —the grey light of day, and as the last smudge of darkness was obliterated, that 'V' of cloud to windward melted away as if in defeat.

Looking around me I realised that the seas had grown so enormous that it was no longer possible for the existing wind to build up the water in overhanging crests.

It then became apparent that the wind itself had undoubtedly abated. The flying spindrift was no longer everywhere. Peering as far as I could to windward, there was not one crushing pinnacle of water. It was safe, but only just, to end the hell and lie to. And down to leeward, somewhere, was still that dreaded shoal.

With some trepidation I lashed the helm half down, and waited to see what would happen. *Temptress* slewed drunkenly round and took up a position beam on to the seas. She passed over one, then another, then another; in safety. I could go below.

Casting off the double lashing round my waist, I crept on hands and knees to the hatch and climbed below.

My glazed eyes blinked at the clock — five minutes past six. On top of all the previous days exertions, I had been fifteen hours at the helm. The barometer had only risen a little over two-tenths in all this time, showing that the tropical cyclone was barely moving.

Peeling off my sodden clothes, and making an ineffectual attempt to dry myself down with a wet towel, I collapsed into my bunk. As I lay on my back and dragged the cold wet blankets up to my chin, I felt my lips crack into a self-satisfied smile. Ah, the luxury! All things are a matter of comparison, and to me this was heaven — to be in shelter out of that terrible wind.

After a few moments of this mental bliss, I tried to turn over on my side; but it was impossible to move; my muscles had given their all; even the uttermost reserve had been drained away.

Miles Smeeton

SURVIVAL TRAINING

THE glass has dropped steadily and it is now blowing gale force with a big following sea. 1,150 miles to the Horn.

Early in the morning of February 14th it was obvious that we would have to hand the headsails, and we all went on deck to take in sail. A very big sea was running but *Tzu Hang* was surging along, the automatic steering, worked from the staysail sheets to the tiller, in perfect control. Beryl slipped into the cockpit to take over as we let got the halyards, and John and I went forward to hand the sails. After bundling them down the forehatch and securing the two poles to the lifelines, we went aft and took in the log and let go the big rope coiled in the stern. We hoped that it would check our way and help break combing crests. I took over from Beryl and the others went below.

The wind seemed to increase rapidly and the seas were most impressive. A wave top boarded us over the stern and hit me with surprising force, bursting the canvas dodger in doing so. The dodger was made of old sail and soon blew away. I was glad of my lifeline snapped to the shroud. This was the biggest sea and the strongest wind that we had yet experienced, but I was so confident in *Tzu Hang* that I had no fear that she would be unable to cope with it. There was such a weight in some of the crests that I felt that we would be less likely to sustain damage by running than by lying a hull. There seemed to be no reason to think that we might broach-to; *Tzu Hang* was steering reasonably well and her speed was by no means excessive. She would waddle and shrug as the waves passed, sometimes leaving her a little crooked, but she always answered to the helm and was straight for the next one. Perhaps her speed was about four knots. We had no log out and the water was very confused, but from the way she was steering it felt a little less. With a wind like this it must have been around four knots anyway.

Beryl took over after breakfast and she thought that there was a still further increase in the wind. She said that she had no trouble in the steering. She is a very careful helmsman and her worst enemy would never describe her as a bad witness.

John had been filming the seas, and had just gone down into the after-cabin below the bridge deck, to change his film, and was sitting on the bench alongside his bunk on the starboard side. I was lying on my back on the port bunk in the saloon, with the cat on my stomach and reading *Harry Black*.

Beryl looked astern and saw an exceptional wave coming up very high and steep. *Tzu Hang* was dead stern on to it. She did not see how *Tzu Hang* could surmount it. It did not appear to be breaking or about to break, but it was the height and the steepness that made a lasting impression on her mind. The next thing that she knew was that she was being thrown head first out of the cockpit, thrown out and not washed out, and then she knew no more until she found herself in the water, the snap hook of her bodyline providentially broken, and with *Tzu Hang* lying, swept clean and dismasted, 30 yards away. She had sustained a good cut on the top of her head in spite of the woollen hat and oilskin hood that she was wearing, which probably accounts for the momentary blackout.

John was conscious of being thrown forward and to port as the water rushed in on him, and I of being ground into the side and end of my bunk, on the port side, but we were both immediately engulfed in darkness and raging water, and John eventually emerged by the galley, as I struggled out of the saloon.

Beryl was able to swim to the wreckage and we soon had her on board again, and meanwhile John had realised that if he could get the gaping holes covered, we still had a chance of saving *Tzu Hang*. Beryl's shoulder was injured and her head bleeding. She dived below for the spare buckets and John followed her for materials for repair. I was able to look at *Tzu Hang*. From the stern to the main mast she had been swept as clear as a board.

The mizzen mast was gone and the boom was lying in several pieces under the lee of the stern. The tiller was gone and later we were to find that the rudder had gone too. The cockpit coaming had been ripped off and the dog-house taken off at deck level. The two skylight hatches over the saloon had gone and the two dinghies had disappeared without trace. The mainmast had gone and the main boom and these were also in several pieces in the lee of the ship. The anchor was gone off the deck and the bowsprit was broken off short, and the fore-stay fitting and the staysail boom traveller were smashed. The twin forestays had both been set up, and were fastened to 5/8 eye bolts, which secured the after-end of the anchor winch, and bolted through a deck boom. One of these bolts had stripped its thread and pulled free but the other had held, and the stay now led over the bow to the broken mast. Later on when we had time to let the rigging go so that the mass of broken spars would act as a sea anchor, it was all left attached to this stay, but unfortunately the strain was too great, the mast fitting broke, and we lost the whole lot, including the sails on the booms. The deck beam, through which these two bolts passed, had cracked and the deck had lifted momentarily, before the mast broke and relieved the strain.

It was soon obvious that John could manage without my aid. He was working in a fury of energy, sure and certain of what he had to do. I went below to get on with the bailing for it was really touch and go whether she would sink or swim. With my head and shoulders out of the weather hatch, which I tried to fill with my body as best as I could, when the seas broke on board, I hauled up and emptied the buckets which Beryl filled below. We had two small pumps but neither of them were designed or placed to deal with this sort of thing.

By nightfall we had *Tzu Hang* empty and the gaping holes were covered, and we felt that at least for that night we were safe. We huddled together trying to warm ourselves and the cat, which had been washed up into the forepeak, and didn't seem to think that life was worth all the trouble any more. It seemed to us then, when we began to think of how the accident had occurred, that we had been stood upon end, and then plunged over sideways in one motion. Beryl was insistent on the size of the wave, the fact that we were straight, and the belief that she was thrown out and not washed out. Some weeks later, when we were safely in Talcahuano, I wrote to a friend in Australia, a yachtsman, writer, and aeronautical engineer, and I received a very interesting reply.

He pointed out that in the case of a ship running before a big sea and pitching steeply, there are two additional forces acting through the centre of gravity. One is a rotational force, because as the ship pitches, it is rotating about its centre of buoyancy, and as the ship pitches steeply the centre of buoyancy shifts towards the bow. The other is the force of inertia, for as the bow goes down the centre of gravity is still trying to go forward, and it is opposed by the friction of the water at the bow. If the pitch is so steep that the combination of these two forces and the force of gravity is at an angle or direction which lies above the centre of buoyancy, the ship is in a highly unstable state and tending to somersault. If she does so and as she comes over the vertical the weight of the keel will pull her over on one side or the other, and she will fall over sideways. We all believe that that is exactly what happened to us. Two factors which I had not spoken of in my letter, seem to prove it.

Lashed alongside the starboard bunk in the after-cabin was a heavy toolbox, full of tools. This broke its lashings, smashed the starboard doorpost of the after-cabin, and fell into the sink on the starboard side of the saloon entrance, where it jammed. It would only have done this if the ship had been standing vertically or over the vertical on her bow, as the sink is ten feet farther forward, and a foot higher than the place where the tool box was lashed. If we had broached, the tool box must have been thrown over on to the port side. But to corroborate this, we found, some time after our arrival, wedged between the bulkhead and the deckbeam which lifted when the forestay pulled, a small powder compact. It is there now and we cannot get it out unless we lift the deck again. This powder compact is immediately above the position it was lying in on a shelf at the head of Beryl's bunk. If a giant had picked up *Tzu Hang* and held her just over the vertical, so that the powder compact had slid from its shelf down the bulkhead to the deck beam, and at that moment he had broken the mast so that the deck lifted, he could have caught the compact in this position, and in no other way. It is as if someone had taken an instantaneous snapshot, and caught the ship in this incredible position. Of course, we were all aware of the danger of broaching-to. Most of us have done it in a dinghy in the surf, and know how it takes place, and what is the cause of it. As far as I am concerned this is something new and I have written it in detail so that it may be of some benefit to others, and it is that a ship, running before a very high following sea, may be in danger of somersaulting, when there appears to be no danger of her broaching-to. But of course it all depends on the size of the ship and the relative size of the wave, and it is not often that the contrast is so great as on this occasion. But it is possible that it accounts for many disappearances, of which there have been no trace.

We had many things to be thankful for, but chiefly that we were still afloat, for when we started baling there was over three feet of water in the saloon. And although many books and all charts had been washed out of their shelves and destroyed, the navigational books, the instruments, the chronometer, and one of the radio sets were more or less intact. The radio set had been screwed right up under the deckhead, but the chronometer had been submerged, and in spite of its double case, we found water under the glass. We dried it off and it never faltered.

Although we had lost as much as a ship could reasonably be expected to lose and survive, we had resources sufficient to make an adequate jury rig, and sufficient food and water for another 100 days.

BOATS SOMETIMES LEAK

Being very aged, *Smew*, according to her owners, made a great deal of water and generally when they were sailing the cabin floor was awash.

George Millar:*A White Boat from England*   243

E F Knight

THE NEW BOAT LEAKS

IT was high water the next morning at seven o'clock; so we turned out of our snug berths, rather unwillingly I remember, to get under weigh. The strong north-east wind was still blowing and it was uncomfortably cold; the sky was heavy with snow-clouds, and a few flakes did fall in the afternoon. It was a strange day for mid-May, but we were destined to meet with plenty more or less foul weather in the course of this cruise.

It was the very day to test the yacht and reveal her faults. The wind was fresh, the lee-scuppers were generally under water, and there was a choppy sea in the lower reaches of the river. The boat behaved splendidly; she evidently turned to windward in a much smarter manner than she had done the previous year, and we felt that we had the right sort of craft under us.

We had reached the Lower Hope and were talking in rather a sanguine spirit, and congratulating ourselves on the improvement that had been effected in the vessel, when Wright happened to go below and light his pipe. As soon as he was in the cabin I heard him utter what may be politely called an exclamation of surprise, and one of anything but pleased surprise.

Leaving the tiller for a moment, I looked into the cabin, and, to my dismay, beheld the water high above the floor, washing backwards and forwards over our beds, while the blankets and mattresses were floating to leeward. We were evidently leaking at a very great rate. Now the boat was quite tight when we left Hammersmith, so we could come to but one conclusion.

'She must be straining badly, Wright.'

'I am afraid so, sir.'

'And after all these timbers have been put into her, too; what can it mean?'

We did not say much, but across both our minds flashed the horrible suspicion that the boat in which we had placed such confidence might be too rickety to stand much tumbling about in a sea-way and be quite unfit to cross the North Sea. It was strange, however, that she had shown no signs of this weakness before.

Then we set to work to pump her out. After some half-dozen strokes the pump choked. We pulled up the small hatch in the cabin floor that covers the pump-well and made a curious discovery. It would have been strange, indeed, had the pump worked properly, for the well was full of deal-shavings! That lazy scoundrel the Hammersmith self-called ship carpenter had evidently, after completing some work in the cabin, stowed away his shavings here to save himself the trouble of throwing them overboard.

If we had had that carpenter on board I think we should have first compelled him to eat his shavings and then have cast him into the sea to find his way to the nearest shore as he best could. Surely such a punishment would not have been too severe for a man who, out of sheer indolence, risks the lives of others in this fashion. I think Mr Plimsoll would agree with me.

At last we succeeded in clearing the pump, and, as it was luckily a far more powerful one than is generally put into yachts of our size, we soon had the water out of her.

We were now in Sea Reach, and as the ebb was nearly done we ran into the little creek of Holy Haven in Canvey Island for the night, not feeling by any means so sanguine about the sea-worthiness of our boat as we had done on starting.

We let go our anchor opposite the coast-guard station, and proceeded to wring some of the water out of our mattresses and blankets and to hang them out to dry; but our beds, to put it mildly, were somewhat damp that night, as they were very often afterwards during this cruise.

We found that it was necessary to pump the boat out every four hours or so in order to keep the water from rising above the cabin floor; but it must be remembered that ours was a very shallow vessel and that our floorcloth would be wet (and the lee-bunk under water if we were sailing) when there were but a few gallons on board. Very uncomfortable is a leaky vessel, and, above all others, a shallow boat should be perfectly water-tight.

We remained in Holy Haven for the night, and on the following morning I decided to take the *Falcon* to Rochester, where I could run her ashore and discover what was amiss with her.

So after breakfast we again put to sea in our sieve and sailed across the broad estuary of the Thames to the Medway. It was still cold, but constant exercise at the pump kept us warm.

In the Medway we overtook several barges bound for Rochester. Wright, who has sailed these seas before, recognised some of his old friends, and he saluted them in proper bargee fashion. Carried away by his pride at seeing our vessel leave one rather smart barge astern, he held up a rope's end to her skipper—a delicate way of bragging of one's own speed, understood by all mariners.

'So you've come down to shipping on board of a Dutch galliot at last, eh, Jack?' sang out the skipper by way of repartee, between two whiffs of his pipe.

There was, indeed, something Dutch in the *Falcon*'s appearance, and a remark of this nature was often passed on us by facetious strangers.

We reached Rochester early in the afternoon and anchored among some other yachts not far below the bridge.

On the following morning we brought the *Falcon* alongside a boatbuilder's yard at high tide, and at low water, when she was high and dry, we proceeded to examine her minutely. The usual crowd of yacht-sailors, carpenters, and nondescript nautical loafers that hangs about a shipbuilder's yard was soon around us, ready to proffer gratuitous advice of more or less value—much of it of no value—advice, however, in all cases driven into the poor landlubber of an amateur sailor by these learned professionals with language deliberate and dogmatic.

Each had a different infallible opinion of his own as to the cause of our vessel's leaking, but all agreed that she was not strained; she showed no signs of that serious fault. My own idea was that the tar, which had kept the water out of her during her last year's cruise, having been burnt off, and the varnish which had been put on in its place being insufficient to keep her tight, she was leaking all over her skin. It was easy to account for her not having taken in water at Hammersmith; for, while lying there, the mud had got into her seams and given her what sailors call a Blackwall caulking—very efficacious as long as a vessel remains stationary, but apt to wash out after half an hour's sailing.

Some of the wiseacres on the yard suggested that we should have her caulked throughout, but we knew better than that, for a diagonally-built boat—tightest of all boats when she is tight—is the most difficult to deal with when she is leaky. It is impossible to caulk her even in the most delicate manner without damaging her and forcing the two skins apart. Again, so beautifully constructed was our vessel, that it would have been impossible to insert even the smallest penknife between her close planking, far less a clumsy caulking tool.

At last the master shipwright of the yard, who had spoken little and listened less during the consultation over the invalid, but who had been employed in scientifically sounding with a mallet and closely examining every portion of the *Falcon*'s bottom, as he crawled under her in the mud, gave his opinion.

'It's the old story,' he said. 'The boat isn't strained at all. She's as strong as when she was built. It's only along the garboard strake she leaks. She hasn't been caulked there for years. See here'—and he pulled out a bit of oakum that was decidedly rotten—'when they scraped the tow off this boat's bottom they scraped the caulking out too. It's just a little bit of stuff along her keel she wants, and I'll guarantee that she'll then be as dry as a drum's inside.'

On hearing this the crew of the *Falcon* felt happy and sanguine again, his explanation seemed so probable a one. The garboard strake, I must explain for the benefit of some readers, is the range of planks along a vessel's keel. In a diagonally-built boat this seam only is caulked.

So, having confidence in this wise man, I delivered the *Falcon* over to his care and took train to London, in perfect faith that I should return to find my vessel as tight as the tightest drum that was ever beat upon.

Business detained me in town until the 19th, when I bade London a final farewell and returned to Rochester. I found that our shipwright had completed his work and was confident that the leak was stopped. Wright, who had been living on board all the while, was not so confident.

'You see, sir,' he said, 'we can't tell how she is yet. Lying here she's only afloat an hour each tide, so she hasn't time to leak much. I have had to pump her out, though, each day; but that may have been the rain-water that gets into her through the well, and it has been raining ever since you've been away.'

Oh, this Jubilee spring! A heavy gale of wind that commenced at south-west and shifted right round the compass now detained us at Rochester for four days. Not only did it blow, but it rained and hailed and snowed in turns, and for twenty-four hours the wind attained hurricane force. The papers were full of accounts of disasters at sea and on land.

Being thus weather-bound, and having nothing else to do, we anxiously observed the yacht's behaviour each day when the water was round her, and soon convinced ourselves that she leaked as much as ever.

Our shipwright, puzzled but energetic, determined not to be beaten, set to work again. Coming to the conclusion that some of the planking along the bilges had worked loose he screwed them up, and once more informed us that it was 'impossible for the yacht to leak now'.

On the 24th the weather improved somewhat and the wind shifted to the north. We sailed from Rochester in the afternoon and anchored off Port Victoria for the night.

Even as a man who receives a letter which he knows contains news of vital importance fears to open it and hesitates awhile, so were we for a long time afraid to break our suspense by looking into the cabin and learning the progress of our leak. We dared not hope that the shipwright had indeed been successful this time.

But after we had let go the anchor and stowed the sails I summoned sufficient courage, not indeed to look myself, but to ask Wright to do so.

He went below, and then I heard his voice declare the fatal news.

'The water is above the floor, sir. She leaks as much as ever.'

But I am afraid that some of my readers will get very weary of reading about that leak. It was the great feature of the cruise, and one we would willingly have dispensed with. I have much to write yet concerning the many and fruitless attempts to cure it, until that happy day when, being hundreds of miles from home, with no professional by to doctor the poor vessel, we two amateurs took her in hand ourselves, with the result that we succeeded gloriously in effecting a complete and permanent cure of what seemed a hopelessly chronic complaint.

To stop a leak is easy enough when you have found your leak, but to find it is not always so easy as some would imagine. It is the diagnosis that distinguishes the great doctor. I think Wright and myself could now do a good business as quack leak-finders.

George Millar

NEON AND SMEW

FROM raking bow to equally satisfying canoe stern *Neon* was exquisite, and we learned much of practical value from our observations of such beauty. The teakwork gleamed with the deep lustre of coat upon coat of good varnish skilfully laid on, daily washed with fresh water, and polished. Her stainless-steel (not a metal that appeals to me) deck fittings were covered with an invisible film of preserving gun oil. Her blue topsides were meticulously washed and cosseted with sponge and chamois leather. There was a lovely thick white cotton mat for your feet before you ventured in awe to set them on the still lovelier white teak deck. This superlative condition was maintained by the owners, Lieut.-Commander Nicholl and his wife, and Ponsonby, who was with them on that cruise. It is true that attaining such perfection left them little time for anything else, but at least they had more to show for their labours than most of us. *Neon*'s layout below was all that I could desire: a big forecastle with one pipe cot, roomy, simple, and with good stowage space; a normal saloon (possibly rather dark, but *Neon* is flush-decked, and you can't have everything); a vestibule with oil-skin locker on one side, the washroom on the other, and the companion mounting to the deck; the owners' state-room, large and comfortable; and aft the small engine-room, entered separately from the cockpit. For her displacement *Neon* carried less canvas than *Serica*, and I should say that of the two on deck *Neon* would be the easier to handle, although *Serica* would be considerably faster, even, I believe (though many would not agree with me), in heavy weather.

Another interesting, and very different, yacht was *Smew I*, which sailed into Benodet while we were there, a boxy, extremely ancient, shallow-draft, gaff cutter, clinker-built and rough. Two Jerricans and two old tyres (fenders) lay on her narrow painted deck. Her owner and master, Brigadier Nott-Bower, tall, active, was at the tiller, and Mrs Nott-Bower, an equally well-balanced and handsome figure, was forward by the anchor. (Most married couples who go sailing seem to reverse the duties that Isabel and I assume, but I think we have reason on our side, for I have more strength to deal with the ground gear, while she has the lighter touch and better judgement with the tiller and, if it be needed, the engine.) The Brigadier had bought *Smew* during the war when he had for a time to work in the War Office. He bought her as a 'floating home' on the river at Richmond. When peace had been proclaimed (everybody was quite enthusiastic about peace for a time, you may recall) he and his wife set off on their first cruise, to the Channel Islands, possibly the most difficult waters in the world. They next sailed from England across the Bay of Biscay, down to Gibraltar, up the Mediterranean to Sète, through the Canal du Midi to Bordeaux, and back to England again (most of this with an auxiliary engine that would not work).

By contrast with *Neon* and *Serica*, *Smew*'s accommodation was of the roughest, consisting only of a saloon into which you had to crawl backwards, a small lavatory, and a forecastle without piped fresh water. But it was a delightful interior, painted white, and filled with books and the apparatus of living. The cabin is low, but roomy enough, for it has a wide floor that almost corresponds to the underwater shape of the hull. Being very aged, *Smew*, according to her owners, made a great deal of water, and generally when they were sailing the cabin floor was awash, and sea water slopped into the lee bunk. They had fitted a new bilge pump, the most modern thing on the boat, but the pump functioned much better with *Smew* on one tack than on the other. The Nott-Bowers on this occasion had left England when we did, and had intended to sail to Ireland, but they ran into heavy weather and sailing for Ireland put them on the wrong tack with regard to the pump. Accordingly they made for Finisterre, and we had the good fortune to meet them.

Smew's stumpy 'legs' were carried on deck. At Audierne *she* had squatted comfortably on the sand by the quay, and the Nott-Bowers had walked ashore over a plank stretched from the bows. They liked to take the ground frequently, for then they could pump plastic glue into the old boat's seams.

Which, then, is the best type of cruising yacht? An adaptation of the racing machine, like *Serica*, lively at sea, giving subtle pleasure by her balance and speed, yet comfortable and convenient below? The more solid *Neon*, still more comfortable, perfectly constructed in every detail and a creation of real beauty? Or *Smew*, the haystack, old, tarry, and lovable, able with her shallow draft to venture up almost any creek, to squat on the sand when the tide recedes, to find shelter when the faster yachts must roll outside, the kind of craft that scorns a few bumps, on which a mark or a graze does not matter, into which nails may be driven without spoiling the work of craftsmen, the sheen of paint and varnish?

Arnold Bennett

VOYAGING ON THE CANALS

IT was at Middelburg that the leak proved its existence. Middelburg is an architecturally delightful town even in heavy, persevering rain and a north-west gale. It lies on the canal from Flushing to Veere, and its belfry had been a beacon to us nearly all the way down the Schelde from Terneuzen. We went forth into the rain and into the town, skirting canals covered with timber-rafts, suffering the lively brutishness of Dutch infants, and gazing at the bare-armed young women under their umbrellas. We also found a goodish restaurant.

When we returned at 9 p.m., the deck-hand, a fatalistic philosopher, was pumping. He made a sinister figure in the dark. And there was the sound of the rain on our umbrellas, and the sound of the pumped water pouring off our decks down into the unseen canal. I asked him why he was pumping at that hour. He answered that the ship leaked. It did. The forecastle floor was under an inch of water, and water was pushing up the carpet of the starboard sleeping-cabin, and all the clean linen in the linen-locker was drenched. In a miraculous and terrifying vision, which changed the whole aspect of yachting as a recreation, I saw the yacht at the bottom of the canal. I should not have had this vision had the skipper been aboard; but the skipper was ashore, unfolding the beauties of Holland to the cook. I knew the skipper would explain and cure the leak in an instant. A remarkable man, Dutch only by the accident of birth and parentage, active as a fox-terrier, indefatigable as a camel, adventurous as Columbus, and as prudent as J. Pierpont Morgan, he had never failed me. Half his life had been spent on that yacht, and the other half on the paternal barge. He had never lived regularly in a house. Consequently he was an expert of the very first order on the behaviour of Dutch barges under all conceivable conditions. While the ship deliberately sank and sank, the pumping monotonously continued, and I waited in the saloon for him to come back. Dostoyevsky had no hold on me whatever. The skipper would not come back; he declined utterly to come back; he was lost in the mazy vastness of Middelburg.

Then I heard his voice forward. He had arrived in silence. 'I hear our little ship has got a leak, sir,' he said when I joined the group of professional mariners on the forward deck, in the thick rain that veiled even gas-lamps. I was disappointed. The skipper was depressed, sentimentally depressed, and he was quite at a loss. Was the leak caused by the buffetings of the Schelde, by the caprices of the piano, by the stress of working through crowded locks? He knew not. But he would swear that the leak was not in the bottom, because the bottom was double. The one thing to do was to go to Veere, and put the ship on a grid that he was aware of in the creek there, and find the leak. And, further, there were a lot of other matters needing immediate attention. The bobstay was all to pieces, both pumps were defective, and the horn for rousing lethargic bridge-men would not have roused a rabbit. All which meant for him an expedition to Flushing, that bustling port!

The ship was pumped dry. But the linen was not dry. I wanted to spread it out in the saloon; but the skipper would not permit such an outrage on the sanctity of the saloon, he would not even let the linen rest in the saloon lavatory (some times called the bath-room). It must be hidden like a shame in the forecastle. So the crew retired for the night to the sodden, small forecastle amid soaked linen, while I reposed in dry and comfortable spaciousness, but worried by those sociological considerations which are the mosquitoes of a luxurious age — and which ought to be. None but a tyrant convinced of the divine rights of riches could be always at ease on board a small yacht; on board a large one, as in a house, the contrasts are less point-blank. And yet must small yachts be abolished? Absurd idea! Civilisation is not so simple an affair as it seems to politicians perorating before immense audiences.

Owing to the obstinacy of water in finding its own level, we went to bed more than once during that night, and I thought of selling the ship and giving to the poor. What a declension from the glory of the original embarkation!

The next afternoon, through tempests and an eternal downpour, we reached Veere, at the other end of the canal. Veere is full of Scotch history and of beauty; it has a cathedral whose interior is used by children as a field, a gem of a town-hall, and various attractions less striking; but for us it existed simply as a place where there was a grid, to serve the purpose of a dry-dock. On the following morning we got the yacht on to the grid, and then began to wait for the tide to recede. During its interminable recession, we sat under a shed of the shipyard, partly sheltered from the constant rain, and laboured to produce abominable water-colours of the yacht, with the quay and the cathedral and the town-hall as a background. And then some one paddling around the yacht in the dinghy perceived a trickle out of a seam. The leak! It was nought but the slight starting of a seam! No trace of other damage. In an hour it had been repaired with oakum and hammers, and covered with a plaster of copper. The steering-gear was repaired. The pumps were repaired. The bobstay was repaired. The water-colour looked less abominable in the discreet, kindly light of the saloon. The state of human society seemed less volcanically dangerous. God was in His heaven. 'I suppose you'd like to start early tomorrow morning, sir,' said the skipper, whose one desire in life is to go somewhere else. I said I should.

J D Sleightholme

SLURRUP CLONK

I HEARD a good phrase from Bob Roberts, skipper of the sailing barge *Cambria*, the other day. Speaking of a leak, he said, 'Then she started makin' a drop o' tea. . . .'

Now, I thought, that's good. My ship makes tea like a Church Army mobile canteen on manoeuvres or a plater's mate on night shift. Your boots float every half-hour down below and she's the only ship with a caulked and coppered cabin sole. The row all that water makes when she rolls puts you in mind of Shepperton weir in spate and if you stop her suddenly there's a tidal bore sweeps for'ard and lifts the lid off the heads.

When I bought her, I said to the man that she seemed to make a drop, but he said that it was in there to put a bit of nature back in the timber, 'synthetic sap' he called it. First night aboard I woke and found my shoes coming alongside the settee. I called out to the wife that it was only the sap, but she said to get baling.

She said there were more sorts of sap than one and how much had I paid for this gaff-rigged truffle-bed? I had wondered why the owner had insisted on demonstrating how the pump worked all the time he was talking to us. Now a leak like that can make men nervous. It's a leaky butt and it opens and shuts like it was trying to pluck up courage to ask a question after a lecture. It bit Harry. You can crack nuts in it. They talk about boats 'chewing their caulking'; ours spits it at you.

When she's sailing hard with that butt opening and closing and all her seams gnashing away it's like standing behind a snack bar. The only time I saw a death-watch beetle in gum boots was on that ship. I've known Harry to wring a mug of water out of the tail of his fleecy lined pants, after a short watch below. If we hadn't got THE PUMP we might get a bit edgy about it.

There are yachts with pumps made of chromium that are about as much use as a nasal spray. I could bale out with my cap faster than they pump. We have a pump that sucks like a minute to closing time and delivers a flood of bilge water over the deck that floats the dinghy off the skylight. It consists of a barrel and a plunger and looks like a Lake Maracaibo oil rig. You stand on a couple of bricks we keep handy and you work the handle up and down. It shudders and then goes 'slurrup clonk, slurrup clonk'. Sometimes it has to be primed with a bucket, but usually it would suck juice out a Board of Trade sponge cake.

At sea we give her a jerk out at the change of watch. That way a man can turn in with his boots off. She's got a lot of cement in her and a little water shows up a lot, but when it fills your footwear and you get up and ease your flats into them and they're awash it sets you back a bit.

We were in the trots during Cowes Week once. We had tiddled her up a bit yachty for it—fresh gas-house tar and a fortune in linseed oil and tallow. Harry had a new serving on his pipe-stem and he'd snipped all the long ends off his pullover sleeves. We had a diesel yacht one side and an ocean racer moored to the other. We wore them down. They thought it funny at first and they were 'Yeok, yeok, yeoking,' away fit to burst the first time we rigged pump.

Now we all have our ideal. Mine is a strong-faced silent character who crinkles his eyes. I tried it in the mirror and my wife caught me at it, said if they hurt me that bad I should bathe them, so I had to go through with it and dribble Optrex down me hop-sack. Nor am I strong-faced any more than Bambi. Nor am I silent. If I'm in trouble with a mooring you'd think there was a circus in town.

Well, it made me vexed to be laughed at. There they were in yachting caps like angled flight decks and enough Breton Red trouser to make sails for the sardine fleet. I forgot about crinkling and gave them a blast that sent their shirts up their backs like roller blinds. Then Harry and I went ashore for the night. When we came back fresh and dewy there they were slurrup-clonking away like pecking hens. They thought she would sink they said. That was because they didn't know what she drew. She's so long-legged we've got to take soundings anywhere inside the Continental ledge.

There is a dignity about 'rigging the pump', as we say, which any amount of small-time wig-wagging behind the gas bottle or fidgeting with little handles under the companion seems to lack. Give me that great gaunt gallows of wrought iron standing crookedly in its socket by the pump barrel, looking like an old heron peering down a well—something I can spit on my hands for and settle down to pump all night if needs be. A *man's* pump and not a confectioner's icing pump like some of them.

The whole ship thuds and shudders when we pump. There's a whirlpool under the saloon where the well is and you can hear it gulp. I pity any poor devil who fell in there. He'd be sucked in and spat out quick as a professional ale-taster finding a hop.

Guests sailing aboard for the first time (they rarely sail a second time) wake and think we've been hit.

They come on deck in lifejackets, packed, dressed and praying. There was a man who was noble. He wanted to save the women and children. My wife, awakened by this Grace Darling in gumboots, crowned him with a candlelamp and Harry's lad, who is hulking and two foot between the eyes, resisted rescue by butting him in the teeth.

What that pump sucks up is a treat. We gather around to watch. First you get clean water like tea, then you get to the diesel and sump oil and finally hunks of ship come up along with lost socks and things. Finally she sucks dry and that is horrible. It sounds like an old horse with a bucket or the row you make in a silent theatre trying to suck 'Coke' through a bent straw.

When it's not in use, when she's dried out alongside that is, there is a screw-plug that goes in the hole in the deck. It is the size of a dinner plate and brass. If you don't get it square the threads cross, then it has to be hit. If you leave it off, people look down it and wish. It looks like a commemoration plaque and people take their hats off thinking somebody must have fallen at that spot during an engagement.

Harry is sensitive and highly strung. His nervous system would make London telephone exchange look like a book of string games. He went home after a cruise when she'd been making a lot of tea and he was properly shaken up. We have a system of sleeping with one hand out of bed so the rising water will wake you in time to pump. It got him a bit nervy.

Now, at home he keeps his teeth under the bed ready for answering the phone—he's a vet—his hand fell out of bed into the mug with the teeth in. He woke up and screamed, 'Out, out, she's sinking. On deck, quick!' and threw his wife's reticule through the window to break the glass. She thought he was having a fit and tried to shove a pencil between his teeth, but it went up his nose and he looked like *Cutty Sark*, Harry never got over it.

Part VII

SHORT BOARDS

– the man in the exhibition-shop-window boat hailed me, and shouted through a horn, as he stood up and steered with his knee, 'Are those the Needles?'

Hilaire Belloc: *The Cruise of the* Nona

Aubrey de Selincourt

FITTING OUT

I HAVE a photograph in my pocket-book, and sometimes I take a look at it to improve my spirits. The photograph shows a yawl yacht, painted black, lying alongside a wooden jetty. Her bows are towards the camera—a half-front view which flatters her. There is no mainsail bent; her boom is bare. On the jetty I can see Bob. He is pushing a handcart towards me. He is very small in the picture, but I am pretty sure there is a grin on his face—a grin of contentment.

He is engaged in fitting out.

There is no accounting for a man's pleasures. A friend of mine passionately loves railway engines, heaven knows why. I myself find railway engines convenient, but I don't love them; my friend, who cares nothing for boats, doesn't find them even convenient. Indeed, nor do I; but I love them. I await the brave new world as eagerly as most people; but if it turned out to be so brave and new that it did not provide me with a boat in which I might quite often escape from it, I should like it less.

My photograph is an old one. I don't remember exactly when it was taken, or even who took it. It is a good photograph —not good, perhaps, from the point of view of those who like *photographs*, but good from the point of view of those who like boats, especially this particular boat, *Sybil*. It is evocative. I can see the four bow warps, two over each bow, curved and slackish. A bit of weed is caught in one of the pair on the farther side—the starboard side, away from the jetty. The water is crinkled, and there is a breeze from the westward. I know that because the burgee is up (the Little Ship Club burgee). I am sure Bob is grinning, as I said before, though his face in the photograph is very small and dark and distant; but one can recognise a grin not only by the face, but by something else besides in the general outline and carriage of the whole person, even from quite a long way off.

I think myself that Bob has just put the mainsail aboard. It is much too heavy to carry; that is why he has got the handcart. And now he is bringing the cart back for another load. There's a lot of stuff still left in the store.

Evidently it is early in the season; the first week in April, I should say; for most of the moorings in the river astern of *Sybil* are empty. Moreover, Bob (I think) has more than one sweater on, busy though he is.

Sybil herself has just been painted black. When we bought her —years and years ago—she was grey, like a battleship, and she had lain on the mud of the Medina river for longer than was good for her. Some might have thought she looked a wreck; but we knew better. The borings which a shipwright took in her stem and rudder trunk came out clean, and the keel bolt he removed was sound. As for the rest, it is wonderful what paint and black varnish can do—and just a bit of stopping here and there in a seam. But in my photograph *Sybil* is black; and that, now I come to think of it, helps me to remember when the photograph was taken; for it was just after we changed her colour that we made our first voyage west of Portland. But that is another story.

Happy people do all their fitting out themselves. These, however, are few; for few have either the time or the skill. I myself have neither, though I should like to have both. I should never, for instance, trust a wire splice of my own making; and as for time, it seems more sensible to spend the little I have in sailing than only in preparing for it. Nevertheless, the happy man does both; and both are equally delightful—almost.

However, there is my photograph, and in it Bob is fitting out. Perhaps I took the photograph myself, and that would mean — obviously—that I was helping him. For though neither Bob nor I can do it all, we can at least do some. And that is better than nothing.

What landsmen don't understand is the pleasure of pottering. In the same way, I suppose, an illiterate (or severely practical) person doesn't understand the pleasure of spending an hour in a second-hand bookshop without buying anything—or even intending to. I do not mean that fitting out consists of pottering. Indeed no. Apart from certain tasks which even the happy people I referred to would probably leave to the yard (shifting ballast, for instance) there are a great many things to be done which bear no resemblance to pottering at all. For one thing, there is that mainsail which Bob has just got off the handcart. I expect I helped him; for though Bob is extremely strong, and could easily lift *me* on board, the mainsail would have been too much for him.

If Bob were with me at this moment, I would ask him if he remembered putting that coat of anti-fouling on *Tessa*'s bottom. Probably he'd answer, 'Which coat?' For we've put many. But I'd soon make him understand which one I had in mind. (I said, by the way, that that photograph was evocative; I can't help it if the things which it evokes are not strictly consequent.)

It was one Easter—a sunny day about the middle of April. We put *Tessa* ashore (it was *Tessa* then, not *Sybil*) opposite the Jolly Sailor. I've not invented that name. The Jolly Sailor is an inn, built of red brick, and a hard gravelly beach runs down from it to the river. That beach is a favourite place for a scrub.

Now scrubbing and anti-fouling a yacht's bottom, even of so small a yacht as *Tessa*, who is only five tons or so, is hard work. It has to be done against time, to get the paint on before the tide is up again. The composition works extremely stiff, and certain parts of the boat's bottom are difficult to reach. The work gives one a crick in the neck, an aching back and a numbed wrist.

But the paint—the anti-fouling composition—smells delicious. There may be two or three other smells which come near it; tarred rope, for instance, roasting coffee beans, or a hot June hayfield. But they don't beat it. Just as certain sounds connected with things we take pleasure in are more expressive than others—as the cry of a seagull, for instance, or the intermittent purr of the blocks on a still morning when somebody is getting his mainsail up, suggest, to me at least, more of what I know of the sea than any other sounds; so the smell of this paint (of the red kind especially) is for me the most expressive of all sea-smells. It makes a nucleus for me, when I remember it, for all sorts of other things, not smells but sights and sounds and feelings, to cluster round. I don't know why this should be; but it is so.

There was a cold wind that April afternoon, but the sun was shining. There was a place under *Tessa*'s quarters where you could not feel the wind; I was working there, stooping forward to reach an awkward place, and already standing in a foot of water. I felt the sun hot on the back of my neck—hot and benignant. Bob's brush was going steadily—slap and slide—round the corner. I caught a whiff from his pipe. Old Tovell was having a rest. I had forgotten to mention Tovell. We had borrowed him for the day. Bob and I might possibly have finished the job by ourselves; between tides; but it was better to have a third. So we borrowed Tovell.

Tovell was skipper of *Arlette*, a yacht of our acquaintance, but not (if I may so put it) quite in our class. *Arlette* made me think of Cowes week more than I usually do; and whenever I sailed in her I was apt to feel uncomfortable about my clothes. Tovell was a little old man like a benevolent monkey, with a face like pale parchment, pale blue eyes, a pale drooping moustache, and a sorrowful manner. He said to me once in confidence that if he were caught in a blow he would rather it were in *Sybil* than in *Arlette*. I loved him for this. But he was very proud of *Arlette* none the less, and kept her like a new pin.

The beer at the Jolly Sailor tasted good when the job was done. We could see *Tessa* while we were drinking it—propped on her legs but now nearly afloat again—and behind her the bend in the river and the big black beacons.

Pottering? I suppose you think that now I've got to the beer, I have explained what I meant when I talked about pottering. Not at all. The pottering for that day was finished before we began to scrape *Tessa's* bottom. When we put her ashore by the Jolly Sailor it was high water; the second ebb—there are two in our river—was just about to begin. It would be at least three hours before we could begin work. Three hours on a fine April morning! Now I maintain that those three hours were spent in fitting out, in spite even of the fact that most of the work had been done for us at the yard weeks before, just as truly as the subsequent three when we were scraping and painting. And it is not only laziness which makes me add that they were every bit as pleasant.

I don't remember what we did, exactly, any more than I remember what I read when I last spent an hour in a second-hand bookshop. But I was busy. If anyone had asked me to spend the morning, while the tide was ebbing, somewhere else, I should undoubtedly have refused.

'Certainly not,' I should have said. 'I'm busy—I'm painting the bottom.'

For the point is that it takes two tides—ebb and flood—to paint the bottom. The fact that the actual work with scraper and brush takes only one, doesn't signify. After all, when the legs were out, and lashed to the rigging, one had to see that the yacht took the ground properly; and one can't do that in five minutes, for the ebb can be very dilatory on a fine April morning. Moreover there was a fishing boat close alongside (a first cousin of *Tessa's*) whose owner, in thigh boots and blue jersey, had put her ashore for the same purpose as ourselves, and he had a number of things to say which we wanted to hear —including some chaff for his friend Tovell. He wanted to know if he had changed owners. And there was a trip or two in the dinghy to make, across to the yard on the other side of the river, for some whipping twine probably, or a shackle, or something of that sort—nothing much, but enough to make the trip necessary. There is something satisfying about rowing a dinghy across a river which is pretty thick with mooring buoys, and boats moored to them, on a sunny morning when you are not in a hurry, especially when your destination is the yard. I won't say anything about the yard now; if I began I might become garrulous. But it's a wonderful place for an idle half-hour, which is about the least you'll need to buy a shackle in.

E E Nott-Bower

THE ENGINE

THE history of the next part of the voyage, from Gibraltar to Bordeaux, cannot be recorded without frequent references to a somewhat sordid subject—that of our auxiliary engine, Henry. Had it not been that an engine was essential for navigating canals, I am fairly certain it would have been accorded a sea burial quite early in the voyage. I must hasten to explain that no reflection whatever is cast on the designer or maker of the engine, a Mr Ford—I have had much carefree use of his products on the road—nor on the various well-meaning individuals who have contributed to its conversion for marine use, but this particular one laboured under two severe handicaps. It had lain idle in the boat for most of the war, to the detriment of almost every working part, and it lacked many of those loving little attentions from a devoted hand which every engine expects. I do not attempt to absolve myself from blame, but I can plead in extenuation that, in addition to being engineer, I was also skipper, navigator, half-time helmsman, diplomat, interpreter and scrounger. To avoid constant references and explanations I will once for all describe Henry and detail some of his characteristics. Readers who are easily nauseated are advised to skip the following paragraphs.

First, the method of approach. One stands on the cockpit floor, facing aft, just forward of the cabin entrance. One drops on the right knee on a small damp cushion specially placed for the purpose. The left foot can now reach the cabin floor level, between the wardrobe and the w.c. The right knee is then withdrawn, leaving the head and shoulders bending over the cockpit floor at the cabin entrance. From now on, one cannot stand erect. A hatch-cover is now removed from the cockpit floor, and the dreadful spectacle of Henry's upperworks is exposed. Next a heavy wooden horizontal cross-piece, which had supported the forward end of the hatch-cover, is wrenched upwards from its guides. In wet weather a hammer or mallet has to be found to assist this operation. Next a square vertical board, cutting off Henry from the cabin, is withdrawn and thrown backwards into the cabin. Henry is now fully exposed and the starting-handle may, though it is really much too early to do so, be attached to the cranking shaft. If it is raining, either Henry gets very wet, or the cockpit cover is slid over, which effectively shuts out the light and makes any further contemplation of him impossible. We will assume, however, that it is a sunny day.

We will now proceed to start the engine and get under way. The petrol is turned on and the two screws securing the float-chamber removed. This is necessary in order to fill the float-chamber with petrol from a bottle. Many people have told me how to avoid this operation, but so far they have all been wrong. The screws are then replaced, assuming that one of them has not fallen into the bilges under the engine, in which case the engine has to be removed before further action is possible. The choke wire is now wedged out with a special spanner kept for the purpose, and the engine turned over four times. During this operation the skin of the knuckles is lacerated against the too-adjacent bulkhead. The switch, situated high up on the cockpit coaming, behind the door connecting with the cabin, is now turned on by means of pulling it out with a pair of pliers, the screw-on knob of the switch having long since come off. The body has to be bent round behind the door for this operation, the weight being supported by one hand on No. 2 cylinder, if cool. One more pull up on the crank and the engine starts. The operator then springs up over the engine (left knee on the dynamo, right foot just missing the coil, and then a press-up on the coaming) and peers over the transom to see if the water is circulating.

Let us assume that it is. Returning briskly to cabin level, the operator removes the starting-handle, replaces the vertical board, the horizontal cross-piece, the hatch-cover, the screw-driver, the special spanner, the pliers. The bottle of petrol and the small damp cushion, and wipes his hands proudly. Next, a slotted board farther back in the cockpit is removed, and the socket for the gear-lever exposed. The gear-lever is supposed to pass through the slot into the socket, but, in short, it doesn't. All being ready, and the engine still going, the gear socket is pushed forward. To hold it in position, the slotted board is wedged in behind it against an empty calor-gas cylinder, which is itself supported against the after coaming of the cockpit. We are now under way.

But of course all this presupposes that conditions are perfect. I have not touched upon the complications which are liable to ensue when these operations have to be performed in a tumbling sea with frozen and fumbling fingers, nor have I so far suggested the infinite variations entailed by negative results in any of the processes. 'One more pull up, and the engine starts.' Ha, ha!

Let us examine some of the causes of this ironic laughter. First, the cranking arrangements. The starting handle rotates a shaft which is connected by a chain to the engine crankshaft.

There are ratchets engaging with the pinion of this crankshaft. These ratchets have a way of getting gummed up; then the starting handle rotates rapidly without anything happening. This usually occurs when one is quite certain the engine is going to start next pull-up; then one gets a long screw-driver and pushes down the offending ratchet. One also keeps a special oil-can filled with paraffin and oil and squirts it into the ratchets. Alternatively the handle is so stiff it will not turn at all. This is because the back bearing of the shaft is bolted down too tight and is binding the shaft. Very well, we will ease the bolt. But, by a laughable mischance, this bolt also does duty as a cylinder-head bolt, so that any easement causes gases to blow through the gasket of No. 4 cylinder. Well, compromise was always a strong point in the British make-up. A slight gasket leak and a slight stiffness of the handle, and we shall do nicely.

I have never seen the petrol tank. It is rumoured to be a cylinder of copper, and its filler projects up through the deck on the port side. When one is sailing on the port tack, any water collecting on deck banks up against the cockpit coaming. This brings the petrol filler under water for considerable periods. Although the filler cap seems perfectly water-tight, this water does in fact find its way into the petrol tank. So much for the petrol supply.

The ignition is by battery and coil. The battery is supposed to be charged by a dynamo, but the latter, though it does its duty well when the engine is accelerated in neutral, knocks off permanently when the gear is engaged. The battery therefore has to be taken out and charged at frequent intervals. This partly, but not wholly, explains why I do not make more use of the self-starter. To be quite honest, this device has been a source of some disappointment to me. After it has been over-hauled during the winter, and with the battery fully charged, it will produce just one resounding metallic clang, but for the rest of the season a thin fretful whine is all I am accustomed to expect from it.

The distributor has been bent at some time and consequently rotates slightly eccentrically. The rotor arm bites grooves of varying depths in the contacts. It will be seen therefore that this is a delicate piece of mechanism and needs a good deal of care and adjustment.

The engine itself is a good goer, if it goes. Nos. 3 and 4 cylinders, being ovoid in section, are rather too freely lubricated, and the plugs need taking out and cleaning a good deal. Otherwise no comments.

The gear-box once ran for months with bilge-water doing duty as oil. It survived, but is in poor shape. Pinions come adrift and fall off into the gear-box sump from time to time, and are very troublesome to get out.

I think that covers almost everything. As an exercise for the student, let us imagine that while under way—in a French waterway for example—the engine becomes very hot, pinks violently and conks out. To what would you attribute the cause? Dirty petrol, dirty oil, fault in water circulation, fault in ignition? Well, you could go on trying for a long time, as I did, and you would be wrong. The answer is autumn leaves wrapped round the propeller.

R G Mowat

TIDES

TIDES are, like Para Handy's herring, 'chust a mystery'. Oceanographers know all about 'moon's transit', 'age of the tide', 'vulgar establishment', 'local sidereal time' and 'Coefficient B', and with the aid of Tide Tables, log tables, a slide rule, and 'a piece of keelivine and a lump of paper', can tell the time of high water or low water, or, if they are very clever, both, at any port for any day of the year, but what they tell you is not necessarily true. The times they give are subject to this, that and the other qualification, which is another way of saying that it is the fault of the tides not of their calculations if things go wrong. But a ha'penny worth of experience is worth a tanner of theory any day of the week and, with no tidal education at all, every yachtsman knows that it will be dead high water (with the wind on-shore) when he comes to join his craft, giving him a maximum pull in his loaded dinghy. Similarly it will be dead low water when he comes to leave so that the dinghy will have to be hauled up miles and miles of keel-gripping beach. The tide will be so far out it will be quite impossible to get the dinghy in alongside the jetty and in trying to jump it the yachtsman will land in water which has miraculously deepened to about a foot while he was in mid-air. There you are—by experience the yachtsman knows. Nae bother, nae sums. 'High water joining, low water leaving', as Gillie's Law so concisely puts it.

Tides can be considered, as a rule, as 'bad things'. Principally because they are, practically invariably, contrary. This idiosyncrasy has, however, one good point as 'of course, old boy, the tide is against us and running pretty hard' is an ideal excuse when a visitor aboard begins to express some doubts about your contention that your boat is a flyer. It is a curious fact, too, that that other boat is always either in a stronger or a weaker running tide (according to whether you are going with or against it) than you are.

The wind is, of course, a close ally of the tides and the two conspire together to make a passage as uncomfortable as possible. They like to be going in opposite directions (the

stronger being against you) as this makes the nastiest mess of
the sea. Here, again, this little unpleasantness has its good side.
How, otherwise, could such as Francis B. Cooke have written
his chatty little articles on how to pick up a mooring with wind
against tide—and would not we all miss those cunning little
diagrams illustrating the text.

Talking about cunning. The fox has nothing on the tides.
Come into an anchorage you know really well and you will
find the tide is low and all the dangers are showing, but come
into one for the first time—dead high water for certain and all
the really bad bricks are covered by a depth of water sufficient
to hide them from any observation but insufficient to allow
you to pass over their tops and despite anything the experts
may tell you to the contrary after consulting their log books
and slide rules and subtracting two hours seventeen minutes,
the tide is always on the ebb when you go on a rock—this is
axiomatic.

The book of the words tells you that if going north from
Crinan you must leave with the first of the flood. A bold yachtsman does not like to show his ignorance by asking the lock-
keeper when that time is nor does he think it proper professional
etiquette to consult Murray's Timetable and Diary (with list
of shopkeeper's half-holidays) so he turns to the tide tables
he got as an advertisement from Blair and Binniee at the New
Year (Brown's at 12s. 6d. is now out with practical politics). To
work out the tides from these tables is not a very difficult
business—in theory—but in practice it is. The essence of yacht
cruising, as any cruising man will tell you, is its timelessness,
and though it is easy enough to know it is Wednesday by
counting back to the day when you were last refused milk
because it was 'The Sabbath', it is impossible to tell which
Wednesday with the result that you are probably a week late
or a week early in your calculations (there is, of course, the very
good chance that you have made a mistake in your subtractions
or your additions, and the two errors may cancel). A mistake
of a week lets the tides get you just where they want you as,
in that week, they complete practically exactly half their cycle
and you leave Crinan, not at low water, but at high water,
and you wonder why you can't get through the Dorus and why
Archie MacDermott looked at you so 'odd like'.

'The long and the short of it iss the tides iss chust a mystery.'

Hilaire Belloc

THE NEEDLES

BUT I will tell you one last thing about St Alban's Race. I have said that it is haunted. Well, what do you think of this? As I was passing there once, there came up to me, catching me up, at a pace far faster than the dear *Nona* could ever sail, such a fine, rich little boat, with canvas so new and so tight, and so white, and painted and enamelled, and gear well trammelled, and the brasswork shining like the sun, and the cordage new, and varnish upon all the combings, and on the tiller, and at her helm a man dressed as though for Cowes Week in *opéra bouffe*. She foamed, and was running past in a streak. The day was bright, well past its noon, and the shores of England stood clear all abeam. There was the Wight, with its brilliant chalk cliffs taking the sunlight, and there, very clear, the Hampshire coast, and right at hand, Purbeck: all as neat as a picture. But the man in the exhibition-shop-window boat hailed me, and shouted through a horn, pointing fiercely eastward, as he stood up and steered with his knee, 'Are those the Needles?'

Now what could such a portent mean? What was the explanation of that mystery? The sea brings all adventures, but what adventure was this? Whence did this man come? How could any man so lay a course from the Bill eastward without knowing what the Needles were, and without recognising them when he saw them? It is true we were end on; but they are the most conspicuous rocks, by their shape, in all the Channel, and they are as familiar as Piccadilly. Even a man who had never seen them must know by his chart where they lay, and by the obvious, unmistakable, glaring white point of the Island. To ask 'Are those the Needles?' was like asking 'Is that the Eddystone?' when one had been sailing with a good breeze southward from Plymouth, and perceived a tall tower standing up utterly alone in the midst of the seas, very far from land. This man could not have crossed the Atlantic (though men have done so in boats no larger), for she was spick and span. And even had he crossed the Atlantic, he would have a chart. Was he, perhaps, a western man, who had lived all his life as in Devon or Cornwall, and had set out thus in middle

age to explore the strange eastern people beyond Portland Bill?
There may be some few such remaining who wisely root
themselves in their native place, and such a man might for
so short a course take no chart—in which case he would have
only himself to blame for running through the Shambles, and
drowning if God so willed. At any rate, there he was, asking
poignantly whether, indeed, those were the Needles.

From 'The Cruise of the Nona' *1925*

TWE
DAWN AT CRINAN

IT was barely five o'clock when I awoke but even then I could see, through the portholes on the sides of the covered skylight, that it was a glorious summer's morning.

After allowing myself about a quarter of an hour's luxurious coming-to I turned out and, dressing quietly so as not to disturb the others, I crept on deck. The sun, just newly risen, shone from a cloudless sky, not a leaf stirred and it was already warm and I stood on deck awhile leaning over the boom drinking in the beauty of the scene. The unruffled waters of Loch Crinan reflected the brilliant sapphire blue of the sky, a haze born of the heat and heavy dew half obscured the further shore and Duntroon Castle appeared to be floating in air. Of sign of life there was none except up at the farm above the car park. There a curl of smoke from one of its chimneys was spiralling upwards into the air. Overall was a deep, deep silence only accentuated when a vagrant puff of wind sent the slack halliards of a bermudan ketch moored on the far side of the basin slap-slapping against the mast or when the fenders between the two yachts moored ahead of us creaked as one or other of them surged momentarily. One had to listen carefully to realise that, in the background of the stillness, there was a continuous sibilant whisper of falling water coming from No. 14 lock.

After a time I stepped ashore and wandered slowly round the basin. On one yacht I could see a young man sound asleep in a makeshift bunk in a miniature deckhouse, a long lock of hair falling over his eyes, one bare arm hanging limply over the edge of the bunk, his fingers touching the deck—it was he who till late the previous evening had been the life and soul of the younger set, up at the hotel, when his symbol of release from his schooldays was the freedom to order and drink 'a tankard of ale'. Seeing him lying there so peacefully asleep and so very young-looking, it was difficult to think of him as anything but still a schoolboy. In the cockpit of another yacht were the squalid remains of the noisy party that had kept us and many others awake till long after midnight—a tray with on it some dirty tumblers, one of them broken, an empty whisky bottle lying on its side, a half-emptied 'Sparklet' syphon, the lid of a biscuit tin full of stubbed-out cigarette ends and the torn remains of what had been a packet of biscuits.

Someone had left the water tap dripping freely and I had to jump to clear the muddy puddle which had formed, a puddle made iridescent with a scum from the diesel fuel pump.

I wandered on past the gates into the sea-lock over which a little water was flooding to splash into the dark waters below. An empty cigarette packet and a small branch of a tree were stranded on the top of the gate. As I went up the slope beyond the petrol pump, one from a row of gulls perched on the ridge of the hotel rose with a hoarse squawk and, sliding off and soon followed by two others, went to investigate a ruffle in the waters of the loch on the far side of the Black Rock.

Leaning over the embrasured wall beside the flagstaff I smoked a contemplative cigarette. Archie MacDermid appeared in his shirt sleeves at the door of his house and, shading his eyes, looked for a full minute out towards the Dorus Mor then, satisfied that nothing was on the way through, he walked slowly to the lighthouse and switched off all the lights. Back he came to the sea lock, crossed the seaward gate and let fall the chain across the canal entrance, the whirr of the winch sounding strangely loud that quiet morning. I waved a hand to him and he acknowledged the salute then slowly, stopping now and then to have a look at his flowers and once to stoop to remove a weed, he went back into his house.

A man with a small boy clutching at each of his hands came out of the front door of the hotel and, after walking to the wall and looking out to seaward for a couple of minutes, they went, the boys chattering excitedly, down to the jetty and from above I watched them launch a dinghy and set off for a row in the loch. Otherwise all was quiet and no one else stirred as yet.

For half an hour or more I stood dreaming, watching the changing lights on Jura and Scarba and on the hills around Craignish as the sun climbed higher above the Loch Fyne hills. Mull was still shrouded in the haze. The boat with the two boys had gone out of sight towards Crinan Harbour and again I had the world to myself. The gulls were all back on the hotel roof sitting silent and watchful as before.

After a while I strolled back to the basin and, sitting on the spar of the inner gate to the sea lock with my back to the sea, I watched Crinan come awake.

A puffer was lying in the basin in the berth between the old sea lock and No. 14 lock and the first sounds and sights of life came from her. A shovel clanged down in the stokehold and a wireless set suddenly blared only to be muted down immediately then, after a cloud of heavy smoke had belched from her funnel, her crew came on deck. One man came ashore and cast off the warps then, magnificently handled as these little ships always are, she was wriggled into the ready No. 14 lock just as Archie, still in his shirtsleeves, arrived at its wall. A yachtsman, accompanied by a wee brown dachshund appeared on the far side of the basin and he went up to join Archie and to help him to shut the gates and open the sluices and, when the puffer had been raised to the reach level and steamed off out of sight, these two remained on the near gate talking and, so still was the morning, I could almost hear what they were saying.

Next two lassies dressed in overalls came down the ladder from the hotel staff's dormitory above the lock-ups. One of them stopped suddenly then ran back the way she had come only to reappear a moment or two later tucking a highly coloured magazine into her pocket. The other had waited for her friend and, giggling, the pair of them disappeared up into the hotel. Archie came back to his house and, going in, shut the door. The yachtsman and his dog went strolling out of sight along the towpath.

A paid hand from one of the bigger yachts at the back of the basin was by this time on deck and I could hear the swish of water and the sound of scrubbing. Mrs Annie Campbell came out of her house and, after standing for a moment or two at the corner of the wall of her garden, she went up the hill a brush and a pail in her hands.

Things were moving now. Another yachtsman, still in his pyjamas but wearing an ancient yachting cap, came along and filled a kettle at the water pipe and another was on his deck hoisting his burgee. A lady poked her head out of the cabin of the yacht where the party has been held then, in pink silk pyjamas, she scrambled into the cockpit and hurriedly took the evidence down below out of sight.

On my feet again and, going the long way round via the P.O. wharf and No. 14 lock, I set off to go back to my boat as I reckoned that, by that time, breakfast must soon be getting under way. As I passed the end of the road leading to the pier I met the dachshund I had seen earlier, trotting home, probably tired of waiting for his master whom I could see leaning over the bridge over the canal overflow a hundred yards up the towpath.

A man was on the deck of the ketch trying to silence the flapping halliards and in another boat the shipping forecast was switched on as I approached and I stopped to listen — 'a large anti-cyclone is stationary over the northern half of the British Isles and is intensifying'. Calms or light variable winds force 1 or 2 were promised for both Malin and Hebrides.

Contented, I moved on to my own boat and coming from the fore-hatch as I stepped on board came the delectable aromas of frying bacon and brewing coffee. I threw back all the skylights and went below just as two little girls exploded out of the fore-hatch of a boat lying three out astern of us and, shouting with laughter and calling to each other (one was Eileen and the other Ann), they had a race to get ashore then went scampering off round the basin towards the sea lock.

The quiet of the dawn was ended. Crinan was awake.

L Francis Herreschoff

SHIP CARPENTER

In my youth and before, the boat builder's trade or profession was looked on as a craft quite apart from that of the ship carpenter. This difference was perhaps as great as that between the work of the house carpenter and the cabinetmaker. While the ship carpenter always has looked down on the house carpenter as a wood butcher, still both of their trades have several branches requiring various degrees of skill, for the stair builder who does a fine job on a spiral stairway deals with as many curves and bevels as the ship carpenter. However the framer, the roofer, the floorer and the lather at the present time require no other credentials than a union card, while the planker, caulker, outboard joiner and the spar maker need, besides the union card, several special tools and considerable skill, in fact so much that I rather look askance on those who lack a few grey hairs. While a recent incumbent as president has suggested that all workers should be retired before they reached the age of skill. I must say that the best ship carpenters I have known were nearing four score.

I remember one of these old fellows who used to work at the George Lawley Company who could get out an irregularly shaped piece, like the corner of a deckhouse, from very few measurements. He would scribe on a piece of pine the crown of the deck, the slope of the sheer and a few other bevels, and then retire to the bench where presently, with the aid of a draw knife, a chisel and a jack plane, he had shaped a piece of mahogany that fitted perfectly. In fact after it was driven in place and anchored with a key, it would be hard to slide a piece of paper into any of its several seams. Some of these old boys lacked two or three fingers, for during their apprenticeship of some fifty or sixty years they had lost one perhaps every twenty years or so, but it seemed to have no effect on their skill. I remember one very well who only had the thumb and middle finger on his right hand and these digits had grown to unusual proportions so that the hand resembled a great lobster claw, but it could connect with a plane or saw as well as any other hand; in fact generally when it made contact with any of the ship building tools it sounded rather like the coupling of two freight cars coming together, for some of these men had grown as hard all over as the oak they had been working for three score years. They had acquired the colour of oak and gave off about the same pungent acid smell. Yes, some of them were tough all right. The temperature and weather made little difference to them. They would stand a surprising amount of abuse also from anyone they respected, but let someone try to boss them who did not know a cant frame from a knighthead and they would soon kick over the traces. They were then about as docile and easy to handle as wild bulls.

When my father was in his old age and had been running a yacht yard for some seventy-five years he told me once that if he could get together a handful of good ship carpenters (he called them 'old fashion mechanics') he could build yachts better and cheaper without any power tools than with a whole shop filled with moulding machines, cutting off saws, buzz planers and mortisers, for, as he said, 'The old fashion mechanic could get out a piece of work right on the job with his adze and jack plane without walking to the buzz planer, the band saw and the moulder. Nine chances out of ten the old fashion mechanic will have his part all fitted in place before the modern mechanic has adjusted the cutters in the moulding machine, and what's more, it will be a wood to wood fit which the young men can't do any more since they have lost the use of their hands.'

From 'The Common Sense of Yacht Design' 1948

J D Sleightholme

IT'S THE SENSIBLE THING TO DO

'I t's the logical and sensible thing to do,' you say.

'The kids have grown up and we need a smaller boat,' the wife adds.

'Every time we slipped that mooring last year,' you argue statistically, 'it cost us ten quid and, based on that, it cost me two pounds ten for every time I woke up in a wet canvas bag at two a.m. to go stand and shiver in the rain.'

You can't afford that boat. She's too big, you're getting a bit stiff in the crooks. You don't like washing, shaving, changing clothes and completing every aspect of your toilet in a 'cupboard under the stairs', any more than your wife enjoys cooking with her head in a hole like a tea-chest, or eating tinned stewed steak on a big dipper.

That boat handles like a bathing machine in a weather-going ebb. She sails like a wet haystack, her transom is so big that billstickers have to be kept at bay with an axe. An hour under power costs as much as an evening out.

'We need a small, fast, plastic day-boat which is easy to sail, labour-saving, cheap to run and needs no upkeep,' you quote.

'Like a Bendix,' the wife says.

Seriously, you have to be logical about it. You don't really enjoy those worrying, windy nights at anchor when you're up and down like a fiddler's elbow looking at things or even those deathly quiet ones with a Brasso tin alongside going 'Poink, ponk, poink' all night long. It isn't as if you could get far in the slow, old heap. Not when you have to bumble along dragging six feet four of decaying oak through the water with your great, round, fulsome sails looking like a Christmas card galleon and your wake like a biscuit tin's. It's all right looking like a country cottage down below, but to hell with sailing like one as well.

. . . think of the agonizing slowness of a passage down

Channel. The long slow curtsey of her venerable bulk, no fiercely hissing bow-wave but the regular splash and gurgle. Long, slow nights, gear creaking like an old wicker chair, the column of smoke from the starboard side-light . . . fine for meditation but the landfall in the morning is scarcely altered.

Advertise her, that's the thing. 'Gaff cutter, comfortable sea-boat, ideal large family, mainsail new 1930, full inv., recent survey, etc.'

And then, later, when the last of the 'pretty certain' buyers has shaken his head out on the saltings in the rain and said that 'he would let you know', then you can go home to the wife to break the news.

'So we're stuck with her,' she'll say.

'How did you guess?' you'll ask.

She'll grin. 'Why else should you be looking so bloody pleased with yourself on such a miserable day?'

Ann Davison

FELICITY ANN IN NEW YORK

Felicity Ann moved from the Coastguard station to a shipyard at City Island on Long Island Sound, which, although within the environs of New York City, is really an island and surprisingly rural, and there the little ship was hauled ashore by a great crane and laid up for the winter. Two months later the annual Boat Show was held in New York, and *Felicity Ann* was invited to come out of temporary retirement to appear as a guest artist at the show.

Interest in pleasure boats had grown so much that the exhibition was moved to a new site that year, and was held in the gigantic Armoury in the Bronx, which, none the less, proved only just big enough to hold all the exhibits and the crowds. There was no room for *Felicity Ann* to be shown in the building, which was just as well, for she was in a very rough state at the end of the voyage, and she would have been sadly out of place amongst the sparkling show vessels. But outside the building, just by the front entrance, was an enclosure, and here she was put on solitary display, behind iron railings and floodlit, with a notice telling of her voyage.

I had no part in this, it was *Felicity Ann*'s own private party; but I used to go there in the evenings and stand by the railings to look at her and wonder a little. Forgetting all the discomforts, the terrors, and the weariness, I wished I was back aboard, preparing to set out for some other far-off magic land. . . .

On their way to the Boat Show entrance the crowd jostled, saw the rugged, dirty little ship illuminated by floodlights and stopped to read the notice.

'Say, how d'ya like that—some dame sails this thing across the Atlantic by herself!'

'Not for me, brother. Christ, I wouldn't cross the river in it.'

'Nor me. What'd be the matter with someone they'd do a crazy thing like that?'

What, indeed?

One man turned to me and grinned, nodding in the direction of *Felicity Ann*. 'Don't get ideas, honey,' he said.

J B Kirkpatrick

THE RIDDLE WITHOUT AN ANSWER

WE do not make much progress by saying that yacht-sailing is a sport. It is in a sense, just as hunting or climbing mountains or even walking across country are sports, that is to say they are activities which in past ages any man might be forced to undertake as part of the struggle for existence. As civilisation advanced these activities became no longer indispensable, and by reviving them voluntarily men have turned them into sports. . . . 'Small yacht sailing is more than a sport,' wrote a man who has loved and practised it in many parts of the world. 'It is a way of life. It is not a game which can be gauged by the multitude, written up by the Press and paid for in an afternoon.' That is nearer the mark. Can we say what it is in this way of life that holds so firmly those who have once ventured on it?

In some men, certainly, not love of the sea but love of the little ships in which they sail the sea is the spring of action. They will find their keenest delight either in racing (especially in a one-design class, where pure skill in helmsmanship and sail-trimming finds its best expression), or more often in the work of fitting out their boat with their own hands. In the latter the craftsman instinct is supreme, and they are never so happy as when they have paint-brush or scraper or marline-spike in hand for the performance of some task that will add to the beauty or the efficiency of the beloved. But beware lest the end be forgotten in the glorification of the means. I have known men who hesitated to put to sea lest salt water should spoil their new varnish.

To others again the sea offers a way of escape from the tyranny, the monotony and the over-regimentation of life on land. They love the sea as a manifestation of nature as far removed as possible from the artificialities of civilisation. It is a relief to escape to a sphere where the tides are more important than the clock and the vagaries of the wind mock at cast-iron plans. From these men the ranks of cruisers are recruited. They may be content to potter round the coast, sailing from one secluded creek to another, caring little where they come to anchor each evening provided that they find peace and contentment to allow them to forget. Or they may find the truest relief from the routine of the land in the routine of a ship on a long passage, where the day's work does not come to an end with sunset, but the succession of watches follows without pause through the day and night, and the changing sea and sky and the hour-to-hour handling of the ship provide variety enough to occupy the thoughts.

To a man of yet another type the sea affords a means of expressing himself. He feels that at last he is really doing something when, relying solely on his own cunning and tenacity, he takes a little boat about the seas, defending himself against the assaults of sea and wind and fog, outwitting the attempts of the tide to puzzle and delay him, avoiding the traps which are set in his path by shoals and rocks. Of this type is the single-hander made, of all who take their pleasure on the sea the most incomprehensible—to those who have never sailed single-handed. It gives an illusion of independence, of power and of accomplishment, but one thing it cannot give, the sense of comradeship that for most men, whether they realise it or not, is one of the best things in the life of the little ship. For nowhere can you test the worth of a man so surely as at sea. Meanness, conceit, hypocrisy cannot be concealed in the face of the winds and waters, but the man whom you have learned to trust in dirty weather or in anxious night watches, him you can trust anywhere.

A certain few will find in ocean racing the supreme expression of their love for the sea. To pit skill and endurance and foresight against the elements, to drive a yacht at its highest possible speed for days on end, accepting open-eyed the certainty of discomfort and the risk of disaster, has for them an inexplicable fascination. Ocean racing demands stout ships and stout-hearted crews, the best of equipment and painstaking preparation. It is not a game for every man, but every man who loves the sea and ships should try it once if he can. He may return thankfully to his harbour racing, his single-handed pottering or his leisurely cruising, but the experience will have broadened his vision. Few men know the full capabilities of themselves or the ships they sail.

These then are some of the desires, conscious or unconscious, which impel men to the sailing of the sea in little ships. Are these desires, you ask, fulfilled? Why, no, I must confess, they are probably very seldom fulfilled with any completeness. For, as I have said, the sea is a way of life, and like any other way of life it is often confused, inconsequent, full of meaningless repetitions, of moments of doubt and discomfort and dismay.

But for all that it is alive and moving, and in retrospect full of coloured memories that enable us to endure until we can pick up its thread again and follow the clue that shall lead us at last to a solution of the sea's enigma.

The memories alone are worth having; memories of good days reaching down channel with a fair tide and a whole-sail breeze; of the first landfall on the glorious Devon coast after a night at sea; of twilights in Essex creeks where nothing broke the silence but the sob and gurgle of the ebb running off mud that gleamed purple under the sunset; of blue days in the Gulf Stream and days of pearly haze in the Rays'n and of wind and white foam in the Bay of Biscay. Memories of Portuguese men-o'-war and leaping dolphins and little landbirds resting on the deck in the middle of the North Sea, of shoals of mackerel frazzling the water under the Dodman and of herons fishing in the pools of Goldhanger Creek. Of Thames barges and Brixham trawlers and the sardine fleet of Belle Ile with red and yellow and green and blue sails against the blue of the Bay, of apple-cheeked *schuyts* bustling through the popple of the Roompot, of six-metres slashing gunwale under past Calshot, of a tall square-rigged training ship clewing up her sails as she entered Plymouth Sound, all the masts together, a dozen boys on every yard. Of night watches when the phosphorescence of the wake raced away into the darkness like a reflection of the Milky Way in the sky above, of morning watches when the deck was black with dew and the spars gleamed like amber in the low sun, of dog-watches in easy weather and their songs and stories. Memories, too, though these are not so clear, of endless beating over foul tides against a rising gusty wind, of nights when halyards fouled and reef-tackles jammed and the cry of 'On deck' roused one from uneasy sleep with hands stiff and smarting from hauling on wet ropes; of hours of humiliation, stuck on mud-banks, and of apprehension when fog veiled the crowded fairway. Hours, too, of sea-sickness. . . .

Acknowledgements

Acknowledgements and thanks are due to the following authors, publishers and agents:

Mr Gordon Rowbottom and William Blackwood and Sons Ltd for 'The *Elaine*' from *Blackwood's Magazine*

William Collins Sons and Co Ltd for 'The Wreck' from 'The *Mary Deare*' and 'Out of Bond' from *Harvest of Journeys*, both by Hammond Innes

Jonathan Cape Ltd for 'Out to Sea' by Arthur Ransome from *We Didn't Mean to go to Sea*

Mr Alfred F Loomis for 'Professional Aid' from *Atlantic Monthly*

The Executors of the E Arnot Robinson Estate and Jonathan Cape Ltd for 'The Regatta' from *Ordinary Families* by E Arnot Robinson

Mr Charles Rawlings for 'Blue Duster' published in *Saturday Evening Post*

Sidgwick and Jackson Ltd and the author's representatives for the extract from *The Riddle of the Sands* by Erskine Childers

John Murray (Publishers) Ltd for 'Initiation' and 'The Engine' by E E Nott-Bower from *Ten Ton Travel* and 'No One to See' by Carleton Mitchell from *Passage East*

Edward Arnold (Publishers) Ltd for 'A Chilly Introduction' by Maurice Griffiths from *Magic of the Swatchways*, 'The Ostend Race' by D R Collins from *Sailing in* Helen and 'The Riddle Without an Answer' by J B Kirkpatrick from *Little Ship Wanderings*

Mr Claud Worth for '*Ianthe*', 'Seaworthiness' and '*Tern* in the Gale of 1896' from *Yacht Cruising*

The Editor of *Yachting World* for 'A Short Cut to London' by A W Roberts and for 'The Cruising Spirit' by Sir Alker Tripp, from *Under the Cabin Lamp*

Mr Weston Martyr for 'Sailor in Search of Smooth Water' from *Yachting*

Mr Robert Hunter and William Blackwood and Sons Ltd for 'A Ship is Launched' from *Blackwood's Magazine*

Mr George Millar and William Heinemann Ltd for '*Serica* Crosses the Channel' and '*Neon* and *Smew*' from *A White Boat from England*

A D Peters and Co for 'The North Sea' from *Hills and the Sea*, published by Methuen and Co Ltd, and 'The Needles' from *The Cruise of the Nona*, published by Constable and Co Ltd, both by Hilaire Belloc

Acknowledgements

The Editor of *Yachts and Yachting* for 'She's Yours Chum', 'Slurrup Clonk' and 'It's the Sensible Thing to Do' by J D Sleightholme

Mr Eric Hiscock for 'Savage Force Eleven' from *Yachting World*

Mr Gilbert Wheat for 'Nowhere and Beyond' published in *Sports Illustrated*

Miss Grizel Hartley and William Blackwood and Sons Ltd for 'The Laurel and the Snow' published in *Blackwood's Magazine*

Mr John Seymour for 'By Sail and Oar Again' published in *Yachts and Yachting* and in book form in Willynilly *to the Baltic* by William Blackwood and Sons Ltd

Mr Iain Rutherford for '*Suilven*'s Hardest Fight' from *At the Tiller*

Mr Peter Scott for 'The Trapeze' from *The Eye of the Wind* published by Hodder and Stoughton Ltd

Mr Iain Rutherford and *The Yachtsman* for 'Running back to the Finish'

Mr Erroll Bruce and Hutchinson and Co (Publishers) Ltd for 'Storm near Rockall' from *When the Crew Matter Most*

The D Van Nostrand Company Inc for '*The Panic*' by William F Buckley, Jr, from *Racing at Sea*

Lutterworth Press for '*Whisper*' from *Wake* by Keith Shackleton

Mr Peter Combe for 'The Last Hours of *Windstar*' published in *The Little Ship Club Journal*

Mr Aubrey de Selincourt and David Higham Associates Ltd for 'Fitting Out' from *A Capful of Wind* published by Methuen and Co Ltd

Mr Peter Haward and Rupert Hart-Davies Ltd for 'Tragedy' from *All Seasons' Yachtsman*

Putnam and Co Ltd for 'Marathon Run' by Edward Allcard from Temptress *Returns*

Brigadier Miles Smeeton for 'Survival Training' published in *The Royal Cruising Club Journal*

A P Watt and Son and the owner of the copyright for 'Voyaging on the Canals' by Arnold Bennet from *The Log of the* Velsa

Mr R G Mowat for 'Tides', from *Clyde Cruising Club Journal*

The Editor of *Rudder* for 'Ship-Carpenter' by L Francis Herreschoff from *The Common Sense of Yacht Design*

Miss Ann Davison and A M Heath and Co Ltd for '*Felicity Ann* in New York' from *My Ship is So Small*

Index